REALLY USEFUL
WEB SITES
VERSION 3.0
CW00339850

HELEN SMITH AND KEVIN O'DRISCOLL

foulsham

LONDON • NEW YORK • TORONTO • SYDNEY

foulsham
The Publishing House
Bennetts Close, Cippenham, Berkshire, SL1 5AP, England

ISBN 0-572-02739-7

Cover illustration by Terry Pastor

Typeset by Grafica, Bournemouth
Printed in Great Britain by The Bath Press, Bath

Contents

Introduction

We are all aware of the vast potential of the *world-wide web*, now available to many of us in our own homes or offices. It is the most up-to-date source of information possible; it's direct; it's personal; it's international and it's at our fingertips. It offers an infinite amount of information that can be immensely useful and stimulating for us in our daily lives, whether that involves research for work or school, cheap holidays, *online* shopping opportunities, catching the latest stock prices, searching for an elusive item, or almost anything else you can think of.

However, those of us who've used the web already *also* know that in order to find what we want, we often have to wade through a mountain of stuff that is of no interest to us at all – it might be useful to someone else, or it might be just plain garbage, but it's all getting in our way, hindering our ability to go straight to what we *really* want. Add to that the fact that those who know a lot about the web often assume that we are all equally familiar with the jargon and know how to manoeuvre through those sticky snares without getting hopelessly entangled, and you have a recipe for wasted potential – in a big way!

This book will be your guide through the web, helping you to find exactly what you want quickly and easily, while avoiding the pitfalls along the way.

IS THIS BOOK RIGHT FOR ME?

The answer is yes, if:

- You have – or are considering – access to the *internet* and want to use it for your personal benefit – in whatever way that may be.

- You are interested in making the web work for you to find what you want, not in understanding what actually goes on behind the scenes in getting the information to and from your computer.

- You have no intention of wasting time – and you certainly don't want to waste money running up phone bills while you track down the information you are after.

- You either know nothing, but want to get started, or you know a little, and want to know more. If you have tried before and failed, you want a solution to your problems. You want to be a net 'user' – you don't want the web to use you!

That's what this book will give you.

We assume you are starting from scratch, and explain how to get connected to the internet and start feeling your way around, before introducing you to different ways of finding what you want and offering some recommendations on how to avoid what you *don't* want. We even suggest how to *download* items from the web quicker, to save on telephone costs and frustration!

The web is peppered with jargon, most of which is unnecessary for day-to-day use, but there are certain terms that you do need to know to get on. We explain exactly what these are, and show you how they can benefit you. Nothing is included for its own sake – it's all aimed at getting something done or teaching you something important – and that's the only time we'll use jargon. As you're likely to encounter it in your travels around the web, however, we've provided a full glossary of internet and computer terms at the back of the book, and included details of sites at which you can look up such terms and get sensible definitions.

Once you are familiar with the basics, you'll want some good sites to look at, so we provide a selection of over 1,000 really useful *web sites*, so that you can go direct to the best sources of information currently available on the net. These sites have all been personally vetted by the authors, mostly as a result of personal recommendations, and no payment has been received for including any site in our list – unlike many of the 'best of the web' directories that are printed in newspapers and magazines, many of which are simply classified ads. If a site is not useful, it doesn't get in our book, no matter how prestigious the owner.

TELL US MORE!

By its very nature, the web is in a constant state of change, so as you find your way around and discover new and fascinating sites you would like to share, let us know about them by giving us the addresses and a few words about the sites' content. Leave your comments on our web site at:

www.foulsham.com

or e-mail them to us at: reception@foulsham.com

Now for a little legal stuff. We have to print this, but you can skip it if you like.

TRADEMARKS AND ACKNOWLEDGEMENTS

Several product names mentioned in this book are trademarks of other companies:

- Microsoft, Internet Explorer, Outlook Express, MSN and Hotmail are either registered trademarks or trademarks of the Microsoft Corporation in the United States and most other countries.

- Netscape, Netscape Navigator and the Netscape N logo are registered trademarks of Netscape Communications Corporation in the United States and other countries. Netscape® Communicator and Netscape® Messenger are also trademarks of Netscape Communications Corporation, which may be registered in other countries.

- Eudora is a registered trademark of the University of Illinois Board of Trustees, licensed to QUALCOMM Incorporated. QUALCOMM is a registered trademark of QUALCOMM Incorporated.

- CompuServe is a registered trademark of America Online, Inc.

- Lotus and Lotus Notes are registered trademarks of Lotus Development Corporation.

All other trademarks are the property of their respective owners, and this ownership is acknowledged. References to and screen shots of internet web sites and services are also provided: the author and publisher acknowledge all trademarks appearing in these, and trademarks of any other products and services described or pictured in this book, and stress that responsibility for the content of these web sites, products and services rests with their respective owners.

So now that's over with, let's start with some basics.

A beginner's guide to the internet

In this section, we answer the most basic questions about the internet, such as what it is, what you can do with it and what equipment you need to access it. If you already have the internet set up and ready to go, you probably don't need to read this chapter or the next two – although even experienced surfers may find some useful and enlightening information in these pages – but can instead go straight to chapter four, starting on page 36.

WHAT IS THE INTERNET?

The internet is basically an international network of computers, connected together via cables and satellite links to provide a seamless hoard of information. These computers are switched on 24 hours a day, 365 days a year, so when you are connecting to the internet you are just linking your computer into this world-wide, constant network. You can't plug directly into that network from your own home, so you link to it through high-capacity computers provided by another company known as an *internet service provider* or *ISP*. This company literally provides the *link* from your computer to another computer which holds the information you need, whether that be in the next street or on the other side of the world. Distance has no meaning on the internet.

Once that link has been established, what can you do with it? There are six main areas of the internet which you can access, to communicate and find information world-wide in seconds rather than in days or weeks. This can save you time, effort and money, and it can all be done without having to leave your home or office.

The world-wide web: www

This area is like a constantly changing and expanding digital library, full of *web pages* which make up web sites. All web sites have an address which is prefixed with *http://* and many, although not all, follow this with www. This address is called a *URL* (which means Uniform Resource Locator, not that that tells you very much) and tells your computer where to look for that web site in the vast network of computers that makes up the internet.

File transfer: ftp

This facility allows you to receive (download) *software* on to your computer from the internet – for example a new version of a *browser* – and also to send (*upload*) files to internet *servers* – for example, if you are creating your own web site. *FTP* means file transfer protocol – a protocol is a computer 'language' – and all FTP sites have an address which is prefixed with ftp://. The remaining facilities are all to do with communicating with other internet users:

E-mail

This is your electronic postal system through which you can send a letter, memo, picture or any other type of computer file anywhere in the world. It is cheap, effective and quick. If you are sending or receiving *e-mail*, you need an e-mail address, which you can obtain from your internet service provider. Most people use a specific e-mail program, such as Outlook Express, to send and receive e-mail, but you can also often e-mail from web sites. We look at e-mail in more detail in chapter seven.

Newsgroups

Newsgroups are like club *bulletin boards*. They contain e-mail messages that people have sent to a particular *discussion group* and which are then available to everyone. Those messages can contain text, pictures, video clips or anything you can put into an e-mail, although most newsgroups prefer you to stick with plain text. We look at newsgroups in more detail in chapter eight.

Internet chat

Like digital meeting rooms, here you can hold conversations – sometimes even with a video picture – or just type messages on the screen for other people to read. As most of these are run via web sites, all the information you need should be on the web. Some chat sites are listed in chapter 10. Security considerations are discussed in chapter nine.

Private fora

These are similar to newsgroups, but access is more limited, usually by subscription only. The subjects of *fora* (sometimes called *forums*) are often technical in nature, rather than of general interest.

The diagram opposite shows a representation of the internet and how it works. As you can see there are several routes into the internet, depending on whether you are accessing it from within a company that runs its own internet-based network (*intranet*), from a internet-enabled (*wireless application protocol or WAP*) device such as a mobile phone, from a dual function device such as digital TV, or from your own computer. This book concentrates on the last of these.

WHAT CAN YOU DO ON THE INTERNET?

Almost anything that can be done in real life! Say you want to book a holiday, read today's newspaper, contact a local maintenance company, check your bank balance or the latest sports results, make a bet on tomorrow's big race, purchase software, contact friends and family world-wide, research your school or college homework, buy your weekly groceries – all this and a lot more can now be done electronically on the internet through the www or e-mail, both of which are very easy to use. Despite the hype, it has been found that buying goods or paying for services on the internet is pretty much as safe as making a purchase in a store with a credit card. The added advantage with the net is that the shops or services are available 24 hours a day, 365 days a week, so you really can shop 'til you drop!

Using the internet is simple, straightforward and fun. It is all done by pointing and clicking your mouse, with the occasional bit of typing. It will open up a world of information resources that you never knew existed and which is growing all the time. After a few hours you'll feel as though you have been using the net for years.

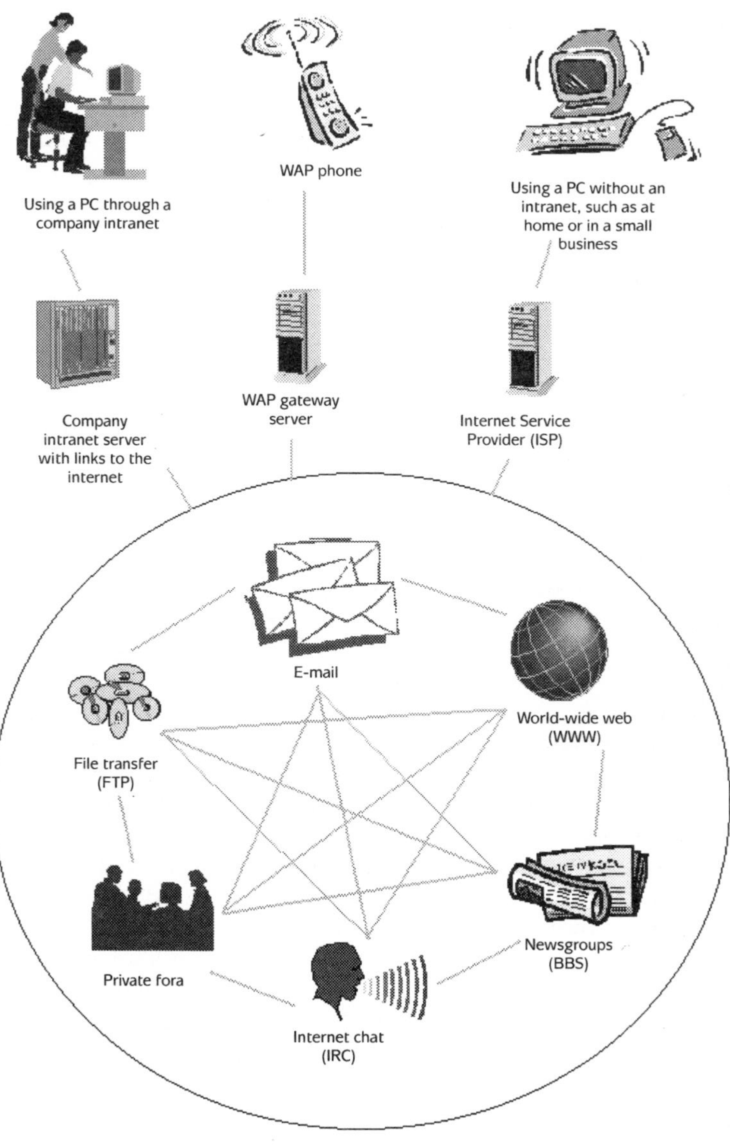

Using a PC through a company intranet
WAP phone
Using a PC without an intranet, such as at home or in a small business
WAP gateway server
Company intranet server with links to the internet
Internet Service Provider (ISP)
E-mail
World-wide web (WWW)
File transfer (FTP)
Newsgroups (BBS)
Private fora
Internet chat (IRC)

THE INTERNET AND THE LAW

Before you start, remember that the laws of the land apply to the internet as to everything else. If you break the law, you are liable for prosecution. If you are viewing information that is legal in the country that is hosting the documents but not in your own country, you cannot download that information on to your hard drive. That is illegal. So is sending e-mail containing inflammatory or offensive material. Ignorance is no defence. Similarly, beware of making rash promises in an e-mail that may be legally enforceable in the recipient's home country.

Be aware that there are some unscrupulous individuals who have harnessed the power of the net to make money from innocent users. Most web sites selling goods and services are perfectly genuine, and you can expect your payment details to be handled securely, but others are not so conscientious or have fraudulent intent. Remember, you cannot necessarily believe everything you read and you really have no idea where a web site is based or who is running it, so be careful: you may not always be able to get your money back easily if needed. We take a further look at these issues in chapter nine.

WHAT DO I NEED?

To access the internet, you generally need a computer. I say *generally* because these days you can also access internet information from certain mobile phones, through digital television and with various other forms of technology that don't resemble the usual white box and screen of the humble PC. Even if using a computer – still the most widely used and comprehensive source of internet information – it doesn't have to be your own, as many public libraries, cafés, community centres and schools are now internet-equipped and you can usually surf there for a small fee. (This is a great way to find out whether the internet is really for you, and to try out different software and different types of computer to see which you like best.)

In this book, we go with the majority and assume that you are using a computer, rather than another method to access the internet, but most of the information is relevant whichever way you choose. If you are using one of the other methods, you may find that some web sites are not available to you, or that you have limited access to facilities such as newsgroups, fora or FTP, and you will probably not be using a mouse or *modem* so some of the described methods of accessing information may be different. Details of the alternative ways to access information and functions will be provided in the user manual for your particular system.

Getting connected

Connecting to the internet is easy. All you need is the right hardware (the basic equipment) and some free software (the programs which run on the computer). If you have purchased a complete computer package from a computer retailer, the software will be pre-installed, so if that applies to you, you can skip this chapter. You can also skip it if you are using a WAP device, digital TV or another, non-computer based method of accessing the internet. If you are starting from scratch with an older computer, or with no computer, read on.

COMPUTERS

If you are buying a new computer to access the internet, then these are the things you need to consider.

PC or MAC?

Home computers basically fall into two categories: the personal computer (PC) and the AppleMacintosh (Mac). Each has its own advantages but programs that work on one don't necessarily work on the other.

Mac computers are traditionally supposed to be more user-friendly then PCs, so if you are a complete novice then a Mac could be a good choice, particularly if you work in graphic art, publishing or the media, as Macs excel at image handling. There are some drawbacks, however. Mac hardware (computers, printers, scanners and so on) tends to be more expensive than the equivalent equipment for a PC, and is less readily available in the major stores, with less brands to choose from. Software designed for a PC will usually not work on a Mac, so you will need software specifically designed for the Mac, and there's a lot less of that available than for PCs. In addition, if your friends and family use PCs, you may find that some of the things they send you are unreadable on a Mac, and vice versa.

If you choose a PC rather than a Mac, there's more choice of both software and hardware when you start, and more choice when you want to upgrade your computer. Prices are therefore more competitive and you should be able to find a good package which contains everything you need. Most businesses outside publishing, communication and the media use PCs, as do almost all 'shared facilities' such as internet cafés and libraries. These days, with so many people using computers, PC software is becoming more logical and intuitive to use, and less dependent on lists of commands: in many ways the image-based software used on most PCs these days, such as the Microsoft Windows operating system, is more like that of the Mac. As far as brands are concerned, there is little to choose between them; the cheaper models are less likely to be upgradable later, but the low cost of PC hardware these days means it's rarely worth upgrading an older model anyway – often it's cheaper just to buy a whole new machine.

Processor

Whether Mac or PC, choose a computer with the most powerful processor you can afford (that's the bit that does the work, the calculator, if you like). Processors have names like Pentium, followed by a number – the latest, Pentium 4, has just been made commercially available at the time of writing – while older processors were numbered, for example 386 or 486, or, back in the dark ages of computing, XT. The immediate advantage of an up-to-date processor is that the more powerful the processor, the faster your computer will be able to process the data it receives, so you will be able to access information more quickly, and will therefore save time and money. Systems technology improves at a terrifying rate, so the more power you have, the more likely you are to be able to use new software and communications options well into the future. As a minimum, you require a computer with a Pentium processor: while an older computer will work, it will be slower and more prone to *crashing*, and it is likely that the hard drive will have limited capacity, so you will be unable to download and install larger files, such as *MP3 files* and games software.

Hard drive

Go for the largest-capacity hard drive possible (this is the part of the computer that stores all the programs it uses) and as large a memory (*RAM*) as is available (this stores information temporarily while the computer is switched on). It's the same principle as when you buy a freezer: you think you'll never fill all the space but you have it crammed to overflowing within a month and then it doesn't operate as well! If you have an older PC with a meagre hard drive, find out whether you can fit a larger drive or even a second drive: your local computer retailer should be able to tell you. You may need to bring the computer in to the shop for them to check it over: if so, get them to fit the new drive while you're there – it doesn't cost much and it'll save you a lot of head-scratching as the instructions for installing such items are rarely easy to follow.

After-sales service

After-sales service is also an important consideration, especially if you don't know a lot about computers. Make sure that suitable service is provided with whatever computer you buy: most well-known manufacturers and retailers offer various levels of after-sales agreement – some even offer same-day replacement for your PC or faulty parts – so the name on the box is not the most important thing on which to base your purchasing decision. Check what is on offer as after-sales support. For example, the retailer might provide extended warranties, software help and support or hardware support. If something does go wrong, do they come to you or do you have to take the computer to them? How quick is their response time? Be particularly careful if you are considering buying a laptop or portable computer: often these cannot be repaired in-store and are excluded from several clauses of such service agreements, meaning that you have to send the computer away in the case of a fault, and may not receive it back for some weeks.

INTERNET SERVICE PROVIDERS

Your service provider (ISP) is your doorway to the internet, the company that provides you – individual or company – with internet access. Different providers have different pricing structures and offer different services, so it is important to choose your provider carefully, depending on your individual needs. We'll talk about how to do this later on (see page 22).

MODEMS

Computers store and use data in a digital format but most telephone lines use an analogue representation of sound (although digital lines are becoming more widespread for high-volume business use, at least). Computers communicate with each other down a telephone line, so a device is required that can convert the computer's digital data to analogue to transmit it down the phone line and back to digital so that it can be read by the receiving computer. This is what a modem does – the word 'modem' describes the conversion process: **mo**dulate and **dem**odulate.

Most new computers come with a modem already installed, and you need only plug in the appropriate lead to the telephone socket. Older computers may not have a modem at all. If your machine is modemless, you can either take it to a specialist, who will install a new modem into the shell of the computer, or buy a plug-in modem off the shelf. Either way, always go for the fastest modem you can afford (for the same reasons as buying the computer with the fastest processor), and make sure you read the instructions carefully before you try to install or use it.

Different types of modem

Modems are rated by their data transfer speed, which is expressed in Kilobits per second, or Kbps. Currently, most modems are able to receive data (download) at 56Kbps, although they can only send data (upload) at a maximum of 33Kbps. If your computer is a few years old, you may find that it will download no faster than 28 or 33Kbps. This is fine, but you will find that web sites containing lots of pictures will take longer to load, and it will take a very long time to download software and samples to disk. Modems are not expensive, so we would suggest that in this case you upgrade your modem to a more powerful one as soon as you can. You will then be able to access information much more quickly, which will save you waiting time, online costs (which really means telephone bills) and a lot of frustration.

If you have just bought or are considering buying a PC, it will probably already have a modem connected. Depending on the type of computer, this could be external, internal or PCMCIA. Older computers will have either an internal or an external modem. There is no major advantage of one over the other, although an internal modem tends to be slightly cheaper and saves desk space. An external modem plugs into the back of your computer via a cable, as well as to the telephone socket and power supply.

External Modem

Internal Modem

PCMCIA Modem

Three main types of home user modems

If your computer is a laptop or portable, you most likely need a PCMCIA card: this is basically a credit card-sized modem that plugs into the appropriate slot on your machine and directly to the telephone socket. It can easily be removed if the slot is needed for another kind of card. Again, there are various speeds available, but you should always go for the fastest that you can afford. Some manufacturers now fit internal modems to laptops, and it is perfectly possible to use an external modem, although it will be rather bulky for a portable machine.

Installing a modem

Each modem is different, as is each computer, so it is not feasible to give detailed instructions here. If you are unfamiliar with computer hardware (i.e. the machine and its various wires, buttons and circuit boards) it is probably best either to purchase an external modem, which you simply plug in and install using basic software, or to ask your retailer to install an internal modem for you. In all cases, don't be afraid to ask your retailer for advice: you may be required to bring your computer into the store so that they can check which modems will be compatible, particularly if you use an older machine. While this may seem a nuisance, it is far less bother than trying to return a modem you've purchased and found to be unsuitable.

Other types of connection

ISDN stands for Integrated Services Digital Network and this provides another way to connect to the internet, instead of using a modem. It is very fast, quick to connect and rarely has faults, so if you are online for long periods, ISDN is a great idea. However, an ISDN line has to be specially installed by your telecommunications provider (i.e. the phone company) as a separate line, and installation and connection are still fairly expensive. If speed is important to you, however, it is worth checking out the latest deals from a variety of providers. You may be offered a single-*channel* connection (up to 64Kbps – not much faster than the average modem), or a dual-channel connection, which will give you super-fast connections of up to 128Kbps.

A recent development, not yet generally available, which is destined to revolutionise the way we access the web, is known as *broadband* access. This provides its users with a high-speed connection (often in excess of 500Kbps, sometimes up to 10 times this, rather than the current 56Kbps with a modem) that is always 'on' – no dialling in is required – and is ideal for instant web access and, most especially, for online gaming. It is available primarily through cable operators and in some cases through the telephone network where ISDN lines are unavailable, and the cost is slightly above that of a standard ISP connection. Cable is the preferred route as it doesn't tie up your phone line – so you can still make and receive calls – but you may need to purchase certain new equipment, such as a *cable modem* and network adapter, to access it. Certain cable operators now offer broadband service and the relevant equipment as part of their internet package, so if you have cable TV contact your provider for details.

As ISDN and broadband are not widespread – most of us still use the modem, no matter how slow – the next chapter will assume that you are using a modem and connecting to the internet via an ISP. If not, skip this chapter and talk to your ISDN or broadband supplier for details of how to get connected.

Internet service providers

Once you have your modem installed, you need only one further thing before connecting to the internet: a connection from an internet service provider (ISP). This is the company whose number the computer dials in order to connect to the internet via its server (basically, another, high-volume computer), and through whose servers your e-mail is sent and received.

There are many ISPs available these days and it is worth spending time making the choice that is best for you, as services and costs vary. Select one that is well established, offers good back-up support, easy access at local rates – or toll-free if possible – a reasonable monthly charge, and free, frequently upgraded and useful software. There are some lousy packages on the market, with poor and slow access once you are online; obviously these are the ones to avoid, so you do need to shop around before you choose.

Before settling on a particular ISP, ask friends who already use the internet, consult computer stores and check out computer/internet magazines. Not only do these give you information on ISPs, but they also sometimes carry disks on the cover offering free trial *accounts* with some of the most reputable providers. Avoid taking up such a trial if it requires you to enter credit card details: often it can take several attempts to cancel such an agreement.

To many people, a major concern is the monthly charge, which varies between suppliers. Some ISPs offer a 'free' service, and if you are going to use the internet a lot, this can be a good idea. The downside is that because of their popularity, the connection can be slow, or even impossible to achieve in some cases. Don't believe all advertising claims: many ISPs that seem to offer unlimited free access for a low monthly fee simply don't have the capacity to deal with a large volume of new customers. You might end up paying a set fee and being unable to connect other than at strange hours, or finally getting connected at low speed after 20 attempts, only to be disconnected a few minutes later. Often such ISPs lure you to try out their service with such offers, only to recommend one of their higher-priced tariffs when you complain about inadequate service! They know that few people will change to another ISP once their friends, family and business contacts know their e-mail address (which usually includes the name of the ISP and so cannot be transferred to another ISP). In fact, a change of e-mail address is a small price to pay to improve your service: just think of the savings in telephone charges!

You are likely to find that both local and national ISPs serve your area. One way of finding out what is available is to use a browser to check some of the sites listing such companies (see page 45). You will need to be able to connect to the internet in order to view this information, so maybe try this out at an internet café or library.

CHOOSING A GOOD ISP

These are the things you need to consider when selecting your ISP.

Reliability

You should expect the same sort of reliability with an internet connection as you do with an ordinary phone line. If you are paying a company a monthly amount for unlimited connection time, then you should be able to connect whenever you want and not expect to experience a lot of busy signals or sudden disconnections. Most of the bigger ISPs have realised that this is a primary function of their service so you shouldn't have to wait for a connection. Unfortunately there are others who are less concerned with their customers' satisfaction than with raking in their monthly fees.

Connection type and speed

You want to be able to use the fastest possible connection so that you spend your time doing what you want on the internet and not simply waiting. Check that the ISP you are considering offers a standard service that will support your modem and the connection service you are using.

If you are using a normal phone line connection, all ISPs provide dial-up numbers for connections with 33.6 and 56Kbps modems (see the section 'Modems' on page 19). If you are using an older modem with one of the earlier standards – X2 or K56flex – you will need to make sure that your ISP will support your modem.

Most ISPs will support a connection via an ISDN line (see the section 'Other types of connection' on page 20) but often your ISDN provider acts as your ISP instead.

Local access

If you are paying per month for access to your ISP and the internet, you do not want to pay for a national or long-distance call to reach your ISP, so one of the first things to look for in your choice of ISP is the cost of the initial call that connects you. Most national ISPs have local dial-up points of presence (POPs) for cities and towns across the country, which means that you pay local call rates for the duration of your connection to the internet. Some international ISPs may even offer you local POPs no matter which country you are in. Some (mostly national) ISPs offer toll-free (freephone) numbers, meaning that you incur no charge however long you are connected, but these are usually counterbalanced by a higher monthly fee.

Support

Good technical support is essential for many people who use the internet at home. Many ISPs offer a choice of support options, with talking to a person on the phone as a last resort. An ISP with a good support structure will offer you some or all of the following support options.

Newsgroup: Some ISPs have special newsgroups set aside for people to ask support questions and obtain advice. This is useful, but can prove a slow approach to fixing your problems.

Chat support: Some ISPs will provide a chat room, which produces the opportunity to discuss problems with the ISP's staff or willing volunteers.

FAQ: A Frequently Asked Question document may be provided by the ISP, answering the most common questions from subscribers.

E-mail: Most ISPs will have an e-mail address to which you can send any questions and from which you can expect an answer quickly, although not immediately.

Phone support: This will be a telephone number that you can dial and get help straight away to fix your problem. Most ISPs will offer this as a premium rate number (so you pay through the nose for the phone call) to make up for a low-cost connection charge. If you are familiar with computers and can fix most issues yourself, you should rarely need to use this: if you know little and think you will need a lot of hand-holding, try to find an ISP with cheaper telephone support.

Cost

You can connect to the internet for free; it can cost you a few pounds per month; or it can cost several hundred a month for a permanent ISDN connection. Costs can vary according to how often you expect to use the service, at what hours (some ISPs offer an off-peak tariff) and for how long at a time. Many ISPs will offer you different ways to pay – by direct debit, in advance, by credit card, and so on – and there should be discounts available for some payment options.

Internet services

Many ISPs offer a range of internet services. Although using the world-wide web is the main reason people use the internet, with e-mail running a close second, there are more services available to you (see the diagram on page 13) and a good ISP will give you access to all or at least most of them. Check what is on offer, as certain services may be available from one ISP but not another.

Services include the thousands of different newsgroups (although not usually those in foreign languages or on controversial topics), online gaming (online game servers which host online versions of the most popular multi-player games available) and *web hosting* (if you want to design and create your own web site). ISPs offer differing amounts of web space, but you can usually add the cost of additional space to your monthly fee.

Free stuff

One way that ISPs try to persuade you to sign up with them is to offer you free software, discounts on goods and services, and other gifts once you have subscribed to them. Many will offer you free connections for a specified period (often for one month) or cheaper connection charges for a longer term. Another popular inducement is to include free software on the installation disk and this will always include at least one browser (see page 36).

ONLINE SERVICE PROVIDERS

As an alternative to ISPs, you can choose to connect to an *online service provider* (OSP). The difference is that instead of just giving you an entry point into the internet – where information is stored on a fairly random basis – an OSP takes in the internet information and organises it for you into logical sections. You simply choose your subject, make one click and you will see a listing of all the information on your selected subject in front of you. As an OSP subscriber, you will therefore have access to an exclusive network separate from the internet and a range of additional services. OSPs are more expensive than ISPs but they can be worth it as they are very well organised, easy to use, secure and regulated for use with children. Also these accounts will give you world-wide access, which is useful if you travel around. The only downside is that they are more expensive, so make sure you need the services they offer before you decide to sign up.

WHAT YOU NEED TO KNOW ABOUT YOUR ISP OR OSP

Here are some questions you should ask your ISP or OSP before you sign up.

What to ask	Why you need to know
Do you have free/local call access?	The time you are connected to your ISP is charged on your telephone bill, so you want to be paying local call rates for your connection, at the maximum, and preferably no call charge at all.
What is your user to modem ratio?	Look for an ISP that will allow as many users as possible to connect to the internet at the same time so that you do not experience delays. Avoid any that have a ratio higher than 10:1.
Do you use POP3 e-mail?	POP3 really is a must as it will allow you to download your e-mail no matter where you are as long as you know the server connections and can alter the e-mail program being used. Unfortunately AOL does not support this but it does have access numbers for you to use world-wide.
Do you have startup costs?	Most service providers have no startup costs, and that is what you should look for when choosing.
How much are your monthly fees?	Most service providers have various price plans based on how you want to use your internet connection. You can pay a monthly fee for a set number of hours, or a higher fee for unlimited hours, or can select a package that is only usable during certain times for cheaper charges.

What modem speed do you support?	Modems vary in speed and you need to make sure that your service provider will support your modem, especially if you have old equipment. Older modems are known as X2 or V90 and are slower than 56k modems.
What are your support hours?	Some providers offer support only at certain times of day from Monday to Friday, which is not much use if you surf the internet from home mostly at weekends. Make sure your provider will be able to offer support when you need it.

SETTING UP THE CONNECTION TO YOUR ISP

No matter what operating system you have, you need to use the agreed way of 'talking' to the other computer. This is known as the protocol. The protocol needed for connection to the internet is *TCP/IP*. If the operating system you are using is either Windows (95/98/NT or ME) or MacOS (system 7.5 or later) the TCP/IP software you need will be installed already. If you are using another operating system, you need to install the TCP/IP software first before carrying on: refer to your operating system manuals for details of how to do this, and skip to the end of this section.

Windows software includes a dialler program for connecting to the modem installed with the operating system (if it was installed as part of the original package). For the Mac operating system, you will need to install a separate program to enable dialling. The two most popular ones are FreePPP (available from http://www.rockstar.com) and ConfigPPP/MacPPP (which is part of the Apple Internet Connection Kit).

The following sequence shows you how to configure the Dial-up Networking software that comes with Windows. Note that this may vary slightly according to which version of the Windows software you have installed: if you get lost, consult the Windows online help.

1. First, double-click the My Computer icon to open up the window and select the Dial-up Networking *folder*.

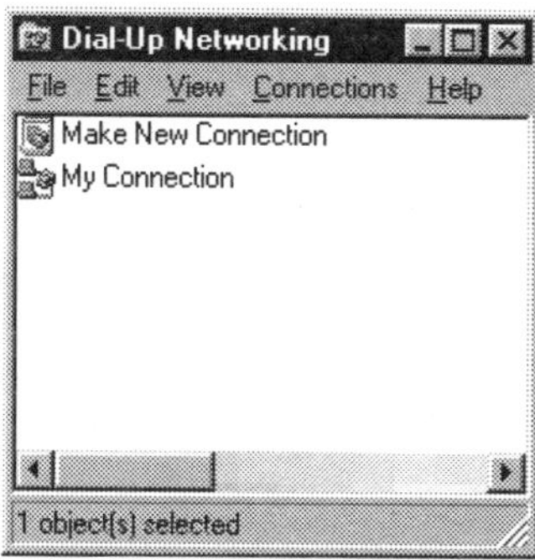

2. Double-click the Make New Connection icon and this will open the New Connection wizard with the first page of information needed to set up your dialling.

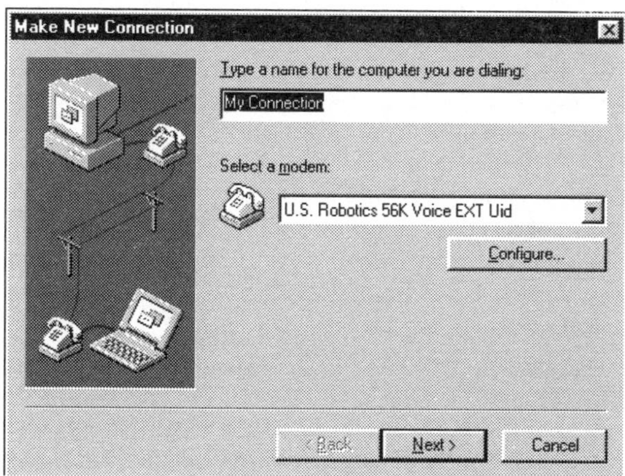

3. In this window, type a name for the connection you are about to make. It's a good idea to name it after the ISP you are using to connect to the internet, especially if you are likely to be using more than one.

4. In the Select a Modem field, you should see the name of the modem that is installed on your computer. If you do not, click the drop-down arrow to the right of this field and select your modem from the list.

5. Click the Next button to display the next page of the New Connection wizard.

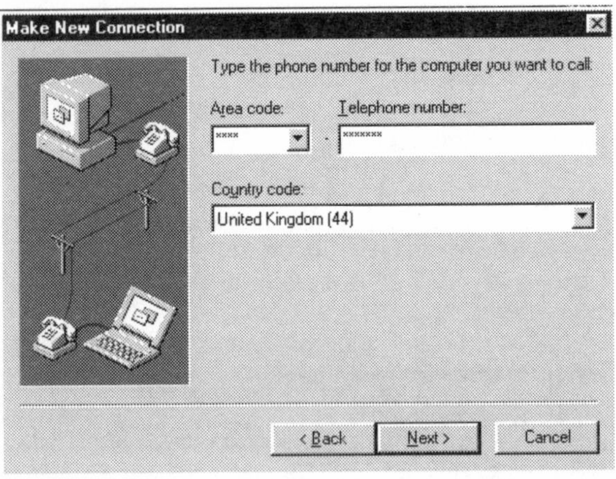

6. Enter the details of your ISP's *dial-up connection* numbers in the Area code and Telephone number fields. Enter the country you will be dialling in the Country code field (this is usually correct already), and click Next to continue.

7. The final page of the wizard tells you that you have set up the dial-up connection and that it will be saved in the Dial-up Networking folder. To view the connection details, double-click the icon in the folder. If you prefer, you can create a shortcut by copying it on to your desktop.

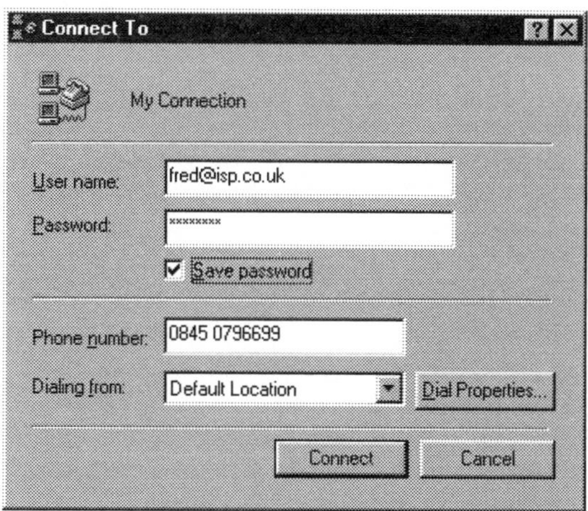

Now you *might* need to configure the connection. This sounds very complicated but in fact you rarely need to do anything at all; most of the settings should have been automatically detected for you by the Windows software. To find out whether you need to configure, try to connect (see next step): if it fails, you need to follow the configuration sequence shown in the next section. (If it works, you can ignore this section.)

8. Now you are ready to connect to your ISP. Double-click the icon for your connection to open up the Connect to window.

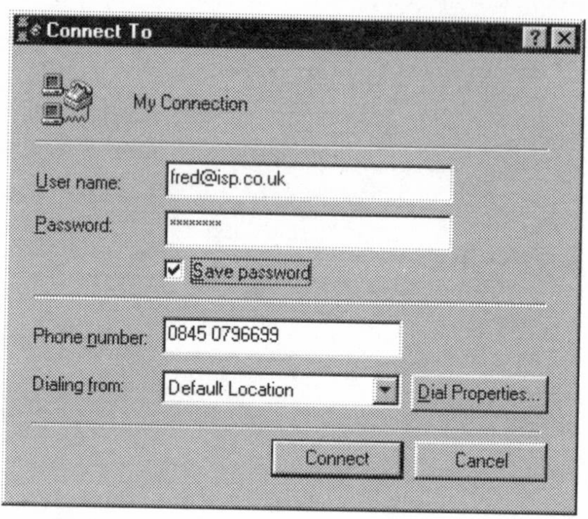

Enter the user name and password allocated by your ISP. When you first enter your password, you have the option to save it, so that you don't have to retype it each time. If you are the only user of this connection and computer this is fine, although you should remember that this means that anyone encountering your computer can use the service and thus run up your telephone bill! For this reason you may not want to do this if different people use your computer, unless your computer is password-protected (i.e. you have to type a password to be able to get past the screen saver). See page 85 for details of how to password-protect your computer.

While your connection is being made, you will see the window change and it will tell you what the modem is currently doing. Once you have connected to your ISP, it will tell you at what speed you are connected and for how long you have been connected. When you see this you can open your e-mail software or your internet browser to begin *surfing* the net. When you are ready to disconnect, display the Connect window and click the Disconnect button.

If you have any problems connecting, follow the sequence below to check the configuration of your connection. Refer to the Windows online help for details of what you need to provide in each configuration window, as this varies from one system and connection to another.

You can also connect directly from your e-mail software or browser: normally when you open such software it prompts you to connect automatically. The same Connection dialogue box is used.

CONFIGURING YOUR CONNECTION

If your connection fails, right-click the icon for the connection you just created and select Properties from the pop-up menu. This displays the General information about your connection, which you entered in previous steps.

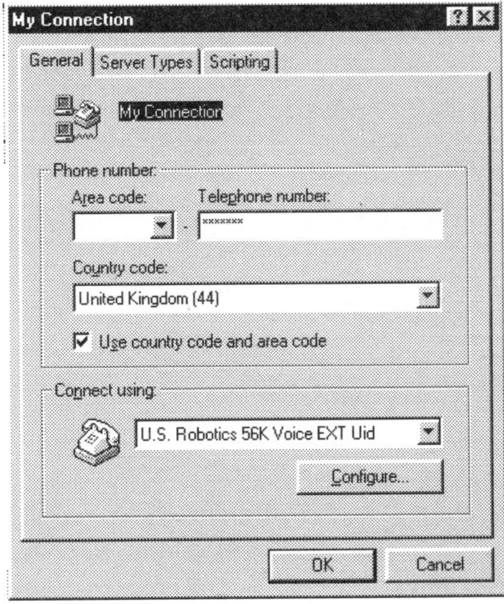

(The window looks slightly different in the various versions of Windows. You may have the choice of two buttons underneath the Modem selection field instead of two tabs. Use these buttons or tabs to configure the selected modem and to configure your connection to your ISP's internet server.)

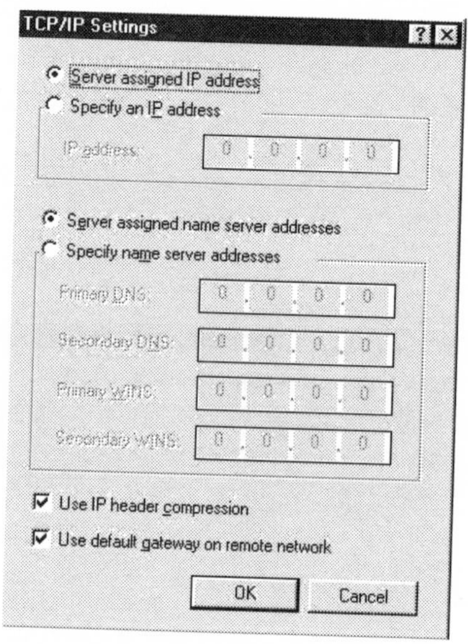

You may need to supply the TCP/IP address of your computer and the address of the name server, information that will have been provided by your ISP. If you do not have it for any reason, you will need to ring them to obtain it. Select the Server Types tab or button to display the Server Types window, then the TCP/IP button to display the TCP/IP Properties window, shown opposite.

If your ISP tells you to let their server handle your TCP/IP addressing, make sure that the Server Assigned options are selected. If you need to supply your own addresses, select Specify an IP address and enter the details in any of the list of numbers, then press the spacebar to move on to the next number. Repeat the same process for the name server address. Once you have done this, click the OK button to save the information and return to the Dial-up Network folder.

Web browsers

Internet browsers are the software you need to be able to view the information on the world-wide web. Once you are connected to an ISP you can connect to web sites using your web browser. Several browsers are available but we will concentrate on the two most popular – Internet Explorer and Netscape Navigator. The latter is sometimes referred to as Netscape Communicator, but really this name actually refers to a whole suite of Netscape programs for internet use, of which Navigator is just one.

INTERNET EXPLORER AND NETSCAPE NAVIGATOR

These products – the first produced by Microsoft, the second by Netscape – are both easily available and free to use. Many ISPs provide a version of one of them with their setup disks and many computer magazines contain free CDs that contain either or both of these browsers. For the average user, the latest versions are both excellent pieces of software that will fulfil all your surfing requirements. You can usually obtain updates free of charge from the Microsoft and Netscape web sites. Each comes in several numbered versions, to suit various operating systems (for example, at the time of writing, Netscape 6 is available for most Windows systems, but only Netscape 4.5 will run on MacOS). The web sites usually tell you which best suits your existing software.

Although there are some differences between the two browsers, there are many common features. For example, both automatically try to match the URL you are typing to one you have used previously, using the list of accessed pages in the web history file. (If the address is not the one you want, carry on typing and it will type over the suggestion.) Similarly, both browsers automatically fill in the address prefix when you enter a URL, for example, if you type in www.microsoft.com the browser automatically places the http:// in front of it, which is essential to make it a valid web address.

OTHER BROWSERS

There are many other browsers out there, and you may prefer to use another with which you are familiar from previous internet use. Most of them have similar features, although these may operate in different ways or have different names (for example, Favourites may be called Bookmarks, or something else). For consistency, examples in this book use the two main browsers discussed above, but that does not mean those examples are invalid for another browser. Use the browser's help facility if you can't find the feature you require.

The web sites for some other browsers are listed in chapter 10 of this book, under 'Internet software'.

CHOOSING YOUR BROWSER

Since browsers are free, the best thing to do is to try several and see which you find easiest to use, then delete the ones you do not wish to keep. If you do this, though, remember to copy over your *bookmarks* or favourites from one browser to the other so you don't lose any of your favourite places. Bookmarks are the web page addresses of popular places you visit on the web that you store on your browser (see page 47).

INSTALLING YOUR BROWSER

Install your browser following the instructions supplied. Some installation programs will offer you a choice of installation types, for example, minimal, normal, full and customised. The latter is most appropriate for experienced users who know which features they require and which they can do without. The minimal installation is good for those who require only basic facilities and have limited space on their hard drive (for example on a laptop or an older computer): it installs only those components that are required for basic surfing. You can always re-install to add other features later if you need to.

Once you have installed the program, an icon will appear on the screen. You double-click on this to start the browser. Depending on which software you are using, there are often several other ways to start up your browser, but this is usually the easiest.

Once you have opened your browser, it will normally try to set up or open the connection to your ISP (depending on settings you specify during installation). You can then select Options or Preferences to change the display of your browser to suit your own needs.

Most browsers come with online help, which explains the various features and functions. Some may also have an interactive tutorial (a step-by-step run through the features) that guides you through the common processes. It is recommended that you try these out before you start using the program, especially if you are new to computers in general: they will save a lot of head-scratching and frustration later on. If your selected browser does not have online help, you're probably using an inferior browser – switch to a better one!

THE FEATURES OF A BROWSER

Now let's look at what a typical browser looks like, and explain some of the major points. The screen below is from Internet Explorer version 5.0 as it appears on a Windows PC (it looks a little different on a Mac), as this is one of the most commonly used: although newer versions are available in some languages and for some operating

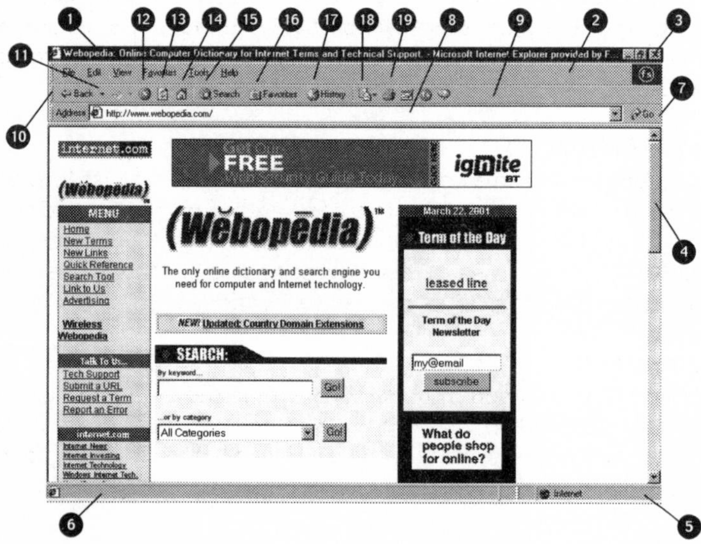

systems they are not suitable for all, as this version is. Other browsers may have less, more, or simply different features, although the basic window layout of menus, toolbars and display area is usually the same. Use the online help to find out how the various features work in your browser, and how to best use them to fulfil your internet needs.

As you can see, the browser has a wide selection of buttons, bars and menus. There are also many options open to you to change and configure your browser. Let's look at each in turn.

Title bar (1)
Most browsers display the browser name of the program you are currently using, plus the title of the web page you are currently viewing. This very often differs from the web page address, or may be blank. The bar usually also contains the standard Minimise, Maximise and Close buttons (3) in the right-hand corner.

Menu bar (2)
This displays all the internet drop-down menu options, in a similar way to other Windows or Mac programs. Using these options you can change your browser settings, save or print web files, access the Help files and your Favourites/History folders. The exact contents of each menu vary according to the browser and the type of installation you selected. (For example, there will probably be more choices available if you selected a full installation than if you installed minimal features.)

Title bar buttons (3)
These standard buttons appear in most software, not just browsers. Each has its own function. The left-hand button minimises (hides) the window, placing it on the toolbar at the bottom of the screen. The middle button maximises the window so that it fills the entire screen. The right-hand button closes the window entirely.

Scroll bars (4)
These are also common in most software. If the web page contains more information than will fit on one screen, you use these to move up and down the page. You can either click on the bar and drag it up and down or click on the arrows to move the page up and down.

Indicator bar (5)

This is where the browser will display the status of your internet connection – whether you are online (connected through your telephone line) or *offline* (not connected). In some browsers this is a small area to the left of the status bar.

Status bar (6)

This bar shows the status of the internet activity. When you access a site, it may take some time to download the page to your computer. Once you connect to the site and are downloading, this bar displays a message such as 'Web site found – waiting for reply'. Once the page has finished downloading, the message changes, for example to 'Done' or 'Complete'. The status line may also provide information as to the security of the site you are viewing. If you see an open padlock or broken key, then the site is not secure for credit card transactions. If the padlock is closed or the key whole, the site is secure and safe.

Links button (7)

This allows you to visit web sites with just one mouse click. Most browsers come pre-loaded with several links to recommended sites, to which you can add further links as required. Clicking a link with the right mouse button will enable you to change the details. If you drag a URL from the Address bar on to this button, that will make a new link for you. In Explorer 5.0, the Links button contains a pop-up menu where you can store up to ten addresses.

Address/Location bar (8)

This is where you type in the web site address (or URL) of the site you wish to view, then press Enter to go to that address. To return to an address you have typed in earlier, click on the down-arrow for a list of those most recently visited.

Standard button bar (9)

This houses the one-click shortcut buttons for all the most commonly used tasks. It is therefore quicker and easier than the menu. This bar is sometimes called the Navigation bar (for example, in earlier versions of Netscape Navigator). Some of the buttons most frequently found on this bar include:

Back button (10)

Pressing this button once will take you to the previous page you were previously viewing. If the page you wish to view is further back, click the small down-arrow for a list of previous pages. You will only be able to return to pages that you have visited during your current connection.

Forward button (11)

This works in exactly the same way as the Back button but this time it takes you forward to pages that you have viewed since the currently displayed page (to which you must have returned in order for this button to be accessible).

Stop button (12)

This button will stop the current page from loading, which is useful if the page is taking a long time to load and you do not need the rest of the data.

Refresh/Reload button (13)

This will reload the page you are viewing. This is especially useful if the page you are viewing loads incorrectly, or if it is taking a very long time to load.

Home button (14)

Using this button will take you to what you have assigned as your home page (usually you set this from an Options or Preferences menu-choice, depending on which browser you are using).

Search button (15)

This button will take you to a defined *search engine*, allowing you to search for information on the internet. You can set the search engine you prefer to use, usually from an Options or Preferences menu-choice, depending on which browser you are using.

Favourites or Bookmarks button (16)

This will open your Favourites folder (or Bookmarks – same function, different name), from which you can add, organise or visit your favourite web pages.

History button (17)

This button opens your History folder so you can return to sites you have already visited without needing to remember or retype the addresses. This function works slightly differently from one browser to another, so check the online help for further details.

Mail button (18)

This will open your e-mail software program. The default program installed with Internet Explorer is Outlook Express; with Netscape Navigator it is Netscape Mail (sometimes called Netscape Messenger). If your browser does not have a dedicated e-mail program this button may not exist.

Print button (19)

This will print the currently displayed web page.

CUSTOMISING THE BROWSER

Some browsers allow you to create a personal, or customised toolbar in addition to those described above, or to customise the appearance of the browser and its contents in other ways such as setting a specific home page or preferred search engine. Usually you do this from an Options or Preferences menu choice, but we recommend you refer to your browser's online help for details, as this varies widely from one browser to another.

WORKING OFFLINE

Working offline means that you download web pages on to your hard disk, to be read at your leisure, thus saving you both time and money on your phone bill. If you have a lot of information to read, this is definitely worthwhile. Refer to your browser's online help for information on how to do this.

USING PLUG-INS

Your web browser is the piece of software that allows you to view web pages but for true interaction with the web you need *plug-ins*. Available to download from the internet, a plug-in is a small program that runs in conjunction with your browser, enabling you to view multimedia files – such as animations, sound and movies – over the web. If the relevant software is already incorporated in your browser, you will not even need to know they exist. However, if you access a web page but do not have the relevant plug-ins to view the page properly, you will have a problem.

Before you download any additional plug-ins, check those that come as standard with your browser. If you are using Internet Explorer on a Windows PC, type C:\Windows\downloaded program files into the address line. If you are using Netscape Navigator, type about: plug-ins. This will display the contents of the plug-ins folder in your browser.

These are three of the most popular and widely used plug-ins:

Shockwave (www.shockwave.com)
Many web sites use animated graphics and many of these are produced using a program called Shockwave from Macromedia. You will need to load the Shockwave player before you can view these animations.

QuickTime (www.quicktime.com)
Many sites offers videos which you can download and view offline. Many off the videos have .mov file extensions, which means they were encoded using QuickTime, so you'll need the plug-in to be able to view them.

RealPlayer (www.real.com)
Instead of downloading videos to watch offline, you can now use RealPlayer to watch them as your browser window loads. You can also listen live on the web to many radio stations using the RealAudio plug-in which is part of RealPlayer.

Note that if you use plug-ins frequently, your hard drive may become quite full with the various sound, image and animation files. It is recommended that you remove unwanted files on a regular basis to help your computer to keep running efficiently. Software specifically designed for this purpose is available: it monitors items that you download from the web and allows you to later select items you wish to delete, without the risk of removing anything essential to the system. One of the best ranges of such products is provided by Norton Utilities (part of the Symantec Corporation), a long-established firm that provides a lot of computer maintenance tools. You can visit their web site at www.symantec.com or purchase the software from your computer retailer.

How to browse

This chapter uses an example – finding and downloading the Shockwave plug-in – to show you how to connect to the internet, locate and use a web site and then bookmark the site so you can go back to it later. The project is applicable for both Internet Explorer and Netscape Navigator, and may work for other browsers too, although certain functions may have different names.

LOCATING A SITE

1. First, open your browser window to display your home page. Wait for the connection to be made to your ISP.

2. In the Address box, type www.macromedia.com/shockwave – the URL for the Shockwave web site, then press Enter to try it

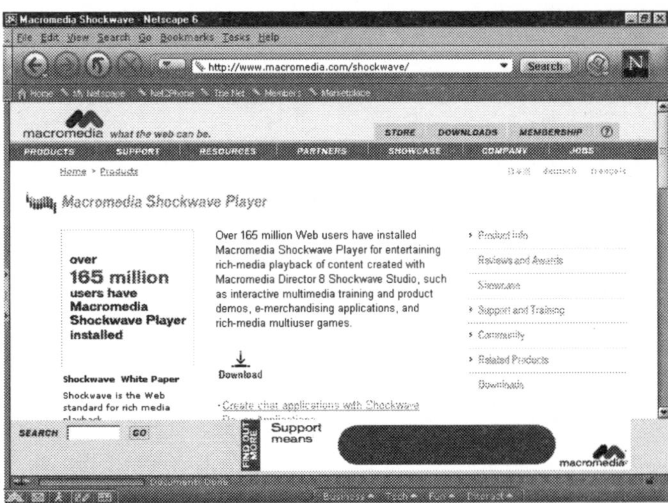

without the http:// prefix and see that your browser will begin to find the web page. Although this plug-in comes with a lot of browsers, you may find that it is not the most current version. This is what you should see in your browser window (this example uses the Netscape 6 browser).

The right-hand side of this page lists the site's many *hyperlinks:* those items on a web page that you click on to jump to another page. The most common form of hyperlink is a word or sentence that is underlined, although they can also be images. If you place your mouse pointer over a word or image and it changes to a small hand, then that is a hyperlink or link. Clicking your mouse button while the hand is showing causes it to 'grab' the link and jump to the web page to which it points.

Now you have found the site, you can proceed to downloading the plug-in software.

DOWNLOADING A PLUG-IN

1. Click on the link to download the software and your browser will try to connect to that page. You will see one of the pages shown below, depending on your browser. Internet Explorer allows you automatically to install software direct from the web. With Netscape, you will have to download the file, then run it to install the software. Let's look at each of these in turn.

Explorer users

a) Click on the button that will install the software for you and choose a country from which to download. The time it will take will depend on your connection and the speed of the modem.

b) Click the Next button. Now the Shockwave software will begin to download on to your hard drive and the image on the screen will change.

c) The Security warning window will appear because the software has a *digital certificate* attached to it that your browser has read. If you click the Always trust content from Macromedia box, any other piece of self-installing software from the same source would download without a security warning. Click the OK button and the software will start to download.

d) The window that now appears allows you to fill in the registration details of the software.

Once the software has been successfully downloaded you can move on to a different page if you wish.

The software is automatically installed for you by your browser. To make sure that the installation has completed correctly, click on the link that will take you to the test page where you will see some Shockwave multimedia playing. If you cannot see the Shockwave animations working properly, click on the link that will take you to the installation support page. If everything is okay, you have the choice of either closing down your browser and connection or continuing to look around the internet. Now you can proceed to the next stage.

Netscape users

a) Click the button to indicate from where you wish to download the software: this will be the USA, Europe or Japan. The download is faster if the data is stored on a server close to you. You will then be asked to specify where you wish to save the file. You must remember this location as you will need to run this in order to load the software.

b) The site will show you the speed at which it is transferring the data to your computer, how much has already been completed and the amount of time remaining for the download to be complete.

Once the software has finished downloading, this will be confirmed in another message. You can then either shut down your browser and run the downloaded file or continue looking around the internet.

BOOKMARKING A SITE

Now you have downloaded your plug-in, it is a good idea to bookmark the web page so that you can return to it at a later date to see whether an updated version of the plug-in is available. To do this, you select either Bookmarks (Netscape) or Favourites (Internet Explorer), and select the option to Add. Both these browsers allow you to create a 'hierarchy' of bookmarks, placing them into folders, which can be very useful if several people use your computer. To place this bookmark into a particular folder, just click on the folder name first before you select Add.

USING YOUR PLUG-IN

Now that you have a browser plug-in installed, you can try to find some Shockwave sites to view. You can bookmark these, too, if you wish.

To go back to the site listings on the previous Shockwave page, click on the small down-arrow next to the Back button and keep the mouse button pressed. This will show a selection of previously viewed pages. Keeping the mouse button pressed, highlight the page you wish to go back to, then let go of your mouse button. Your browser will open the selected page.

Now it is time for you to step out by yourself! Either click on the link to a specific site to display it, or enter the web address (or URL) of a search engine (a site that searches available web sites and will give you lists of what is available on a specific topic; see the next chapter for details of how to use them, and page 43 for a list of some of the most popular) and look for something that takes your interest or visit one of the other sites listed in this book.

One important point to remember is that not all the software you download will be plug-ins; most of it will run outside your browser. These files must to be saved to your hard drive and then run to install the software. While you are downloading the software, you can carrying on viewing different web pages.

6

Searching for information

One of the biggest grumbles about the web is that people find it hard to locate the information they want. 'Why is it,' they ask, 'that when I ask Yahoo to find me information on one subject, it points me towards 2,846,792 sites that have nothing to do with it at all, and maybe 25 that actually mention the subject in passing, but it completely fails to mention these three really obvious sites?' The simple answer to this is that these people are not being specific enough in their search to find only the information they require. This usually stems from not understanding the way in which search engines and search directories work. Don't forget, there are around a billion web pages out there already, and this figure is growing all the time, so finding what you want can be the equivalent of searching for that needle in a haystack unless you know how to zoom in on what you really need.

WHAT IS A SEARCH ENGINE?

A search engine is just a collection of programs that run on a server and can read documents on that and other servers to which it has access. You tell the engine to search for one or more words or phrases (by typing them into that search engine's web site), and it locates each occurrence of the items you specified within any number of files and web pages based on its linked servers dotted around the world. When it has searched the lot, it lists the information it's found on your screen (usually this includes the site title, page URL and maybe the first line of the text on the page): this information is called the search results.

So how does the search engine know where to look for these files? Well, the owners of those sites and/or files have to register with the search engine beforehand, so that it knows they exist. This is often organised by the server owners. (If you create your own web site at any time, you will need to register it to search engines so that others can find your site. Many web hosting organisations provide such a registration service for free, registering your site details with all the main search engines when you first load your web pages.)

There are several different types of search engine and search directory, each providing a different 'level' of search. Which you use will depend primarily on the type of information you require: whether you need to find every mention of a particularly unusual word, or just sites that contain a substantial amount of information on a topic.

- Most *general search engines* search meticulously through every server to which they have access, picking out every document (e.g. a web page, or a file stored on an FTP server) containing the word you specify – whatever its context. So you can see that if you asked it to find 'black cat' there would be an awful lot of pages that contained these words but that did not necessarily give much information on black cats. In fact, most search engines will treat the two words separately, so documents containing just 'black' or just 'cat' would also be selected unless you tell it to only find the two words together (more on this later).

- A *meta-search engine* goes one step further: as well as searching all the servers to which it has access, it also searches other search engines and their servers – thus giving you wider coverage. This is particularly useful if you are looking for something unusual that might only appear on a couple of sites; say if you were researching your family tree or looking for a particular breed of black cat.

- A *search directory* is a simplified search facility that works on a directory structure similar to the file structure on most computers. It provides a list of categories of information; when you select the category you require (say, Animals) it displays a further list of items within that category from which you can select again (say, Pets), and so on until you find the level of information you require.

This is fine if you want generalised information, but remember that in order for a site to appear in such a directory, it has to have been selected for inclusion, so you are unlikely to be offered all the sites containing information on your specified topic – it's just too much work for the people running these searchers to categorise every single site. They do provide a good starting point for information though, particularly when you are looking for items relevant to a particular market (e.g. you might get more specific information on a particular plant from a search directory dedicated to gardening than you would from a general search engine).

The term 'search engine' is often used to cover all three, so don't be surprised if you've not heard of the other types before.

NARROWING YOUR SEARCH

It's worth taking a little time to work out exactly what you are looking for before you try and search. It'll save a lot of looking around at totally irrelevant web sites, for a start. You can limit what the search engine shows you by telling it exactly what you want.

Most search engines allow you to narrow your search in one or more of the following ways:

- By searching only sites based in one country or region (e.g. UK only or all the web)
- By searching only documents in a particular language (e.g. sites written in English, or sites based in English-speaking countries)
- By searching for a particular type of file (e.g. audio file, images)
- By searching only for documents written before or after a specific date or within a specified range of dates
- By searching for words in a particular order in a document, or excluding documents containing particular words (more on this in the next section)

The more of these options you use to zoom in on the information you want, the fewer spurious listings you will receive. Remember that not all search engines have access to all servers, so if your specific search returns nothing useful, try another search engine – or several if necessary – to try to pinpoint what you need.

I WANT THIS...BUT NOT THIS

Here is where searching gets clever. Most search engines use something called *'Boolean logic'*. This sounds very complex but actually it is quite simple. If you want two particular words to appear within a document, say 'black' and 'cat', you type AND between them in the search engine (so, black AND cat). This helps to exclude from the search results web pages that contain only one word or the other, thus cutting down the number of irrelevant matches. To be really specific, you can use 'black NEAR cat', which will only show details of those pages on which the words 'black' and 'cat' appear within the same sentence, thus eliminating those pages that contain a sentence about black rats at the top of the page and a brief mention of cats at the bottom. Or you can simply put the words 'black cat' inside parentheses like this: (black cat) to ensure that only pages containing the two words next to each other are listed.

You can take this further: if you don't want to see anything about black dogs, you add 'NOT dog' and the search engine will exclude from its results any page that contains the word 'dog', but be careful here; some useful matches might be excluded in this way – it's not uncommon for pet store sites to have both dog and cat items listed on the same page!

Unfortunately not all search engines use the same logic, so what is allowed on one may be disregarded by another: typing 'black AND cat' on some may actually return all documents containing the words black, and, or cat. Some search engines prefer you to use quotation marks rather than parentheses; some prefer you to use + in place of AND and – in place of NOT. Some will search only for words written using the same mixture of upper and lower case as you typed; most will search for any mix of case (e.g. typing CAT would find cat, Cat, CAT and any other combination). When you first use a particular search engine, therefore, it is a good idea to look at their search rules (often on a page called 'Search Tips' or 'Advanced Search'). For example, the search tips page for the Alta Vista search engine can be found at: http://doc.altavista.com/adv_search/syntax.shtml

SEARCH EXAMPLE

Let's look at an example by going back to our black cats. Maybe what you really want is a present for a friend who is mad about black cats: preferably a small sculpture or figure of a black cat. So you don't really want lots of listings to sites owned by other feline-friendly people; nor do you want a potted history of black cats; nor do you want the Black Cat Casino or Black Cat Coffee House. You want sites that sell sculptures of black cats; not museums containing priceless Egyptian cats or books about cat sculpture.

We'll use Alta Vista for this example, so if you have not already done so, read up on their search rules at the address given above. However, any search engine would do, as long as you follow their particular search logic – it is often worth using several to check that you're not missing anything that's not listed by your favourite searcher.

1. Open your browser and type the address for Alta Vista (http://www.altavista.com) in the address bar. This will display the main search window, as shown below.

2. In the search field, type the following:

   "black cat" AND sculpture AND NOT museum AND domain:uk (because we want 'black cat' to appear as a phrase, not separate words; we want to look for sculptures of black cats; we aren't interested in museum pieces; and we only want to shop in the UK) and click on Search.

3. After a few minutes, a list of results will be returned. Click on any URL in the list to display that page; to return to the results, click on the browser's Back button.

The results you achieve when you try this may well be different from the ones we received, as sites will have moved and new sites will have been added since this book was published. But the principle remains the same. All the pages listed should contain the word 'sculpture' and the phrase 'black cat'; they should not contain the word 'museum' and should be based in the UK. Of course, this doesn't necessarily make them relevant: sites may be listed that describe products with the brand name Black Cat that actually have nothing to do with cats at all; or links to poems and personal odes to black cats. This is inevitable, but at least you should have less to sift through than if you had just typed 'black cat'. You can play around with different combinations until you find the results you require. Many search engines also allow you to refine the results of your search, for example, if you decide you really want to buy your friend a black cat mug, you can search all the sites you've already found for the word 'mug' (sometimes you will get better results by running a new search, with 'AND mug' specified in place of 'AND sculpture').

HOW DO I KNOW WHICH SEARCH ENGINE TO USE?

It's a matter of trial and error. After some practice you will find certain engines better at locating certain types of information; you'll find one or two become your favourites while others you swear never to use again. It's all a matter of personal taste. However, we have listed some of the most common and most useful in the section *Internet: Search Engines* starting on page 295 of this book. Also listed under this section are some search engine reviews, which might help to guide you towards those of particular relevance for your search.

E-mail

One of the biggest advantages of the internet is e-mail. No more waiting for days for mail to be delivered, no more postal charges. All it takes to send a letter to the other side of the world is a local call to your ISP and seconds later the recipient has the message: even better, you can send the same message to many people simultaneously. Not only this, but you can also send pictures, sounds, videos and even whole web pages just as easily as text.

There are many different e-mail programs (sometimes called *clients* by the techies) and your choice will depend on whether you want something simple or something with all the bells and whistles. Both major internet browsers come with e-mail software: Internet Explorer uses Outlook Express and Netscape Navigator uses Netscape Messenger. Both of these are easy to use. There are many other programs available with similar features.

Most e-mail programs are supplied either free of charge or at low cost: the companies producing them have to be competitive or no one would use their software. Many of these products can be downloaded from the web: addresses for some of these sites are given in the section *Computers and Software: Software Suppliers and Download Sites* starting on page 148. Note that many of the free products contain advertisements to cover the cost of their free service. This can be very irritating at first as they constantly flash and distract your attention, but you soon get used to it: if not there is usually an option to switch the ads off, although you may then have to pay to continue to use the software.

You can also access many basic e-mail services on the web, from sites such as Hotmail, Yahoo and Rocketmail. These allow you to create an account and *log in* to it from anywhere in the world (you require an ISP connection), so they are ideal when travelling, or for use at shared facilities such as libraries and internet cafés, as well as at home.

THE FEATURES OF AN E-MAIL PROGRAM

The screen below is taken from Outlook Express version 5. It may appear differently on different operating systems (e.g., the Mac version of Outlook Express looks a little different from this Windows version), but the basic features of this and other e-mail programs will be the same, although their names may be different and the buttons may appear in a different order. A list of alternative names for functions is given at the end of this section.

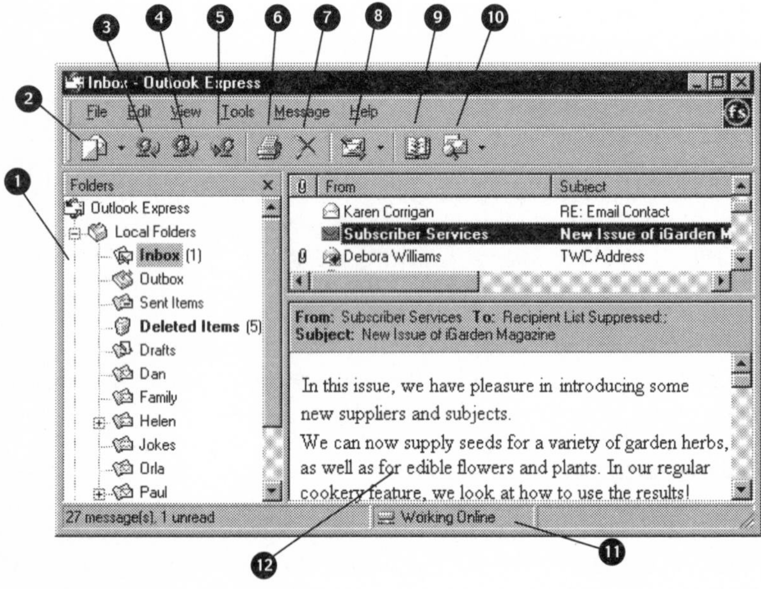

Message folders (1)

The Inbox stores messages and files you have received.

The Outbox stores outgoing e-mail you have not yet sent (called Unsent Messages in some products).

The Sent Items folder stores the messages you have already sent.

The Deleted Items or Trash folder stores e-mail you have deleted.

The Drafts folder stores unfinished e-mail.

The Samples or Templates folder stores standard e-mail layouts.

The News folder, if provided, is used to access newsgroups (see later).

Compose Message/New Mail button (2)
Click this to begin writing a new e-mail. If you want a snazzy background to your e-mail, you can provide this in Outlook Express (but not in many other programs) by clicking the down-arrow next to this button and selecting one of the 'stationery' options. This will only show up if your recipient receives mail in HTML.

Reply button (3)
If you highlight an e-mail to read, and then click this button, it will then open a new window for you to write your message, but will automatically fill the Address box with the details of the person who sent the highlighted message and the Subject box with the same subject, prefixed with Re:.

Reply to All button (4)
This works in the same way as the Reply button but addresses your e-mail to everyone who received the original e-mail.

Forward button (5)
If you highlight an e-mail message, then click this button, a new window will open containing the highlighted message, so you can forward it to someone else. The Subject box will show the original subject, prefixed with Fwd:.

Print button (6)
Highlight and click this button to print a message without opening it.

Delete button (7)
If you highlight a message and then press this button, the message will be removed from its current folder to the Deleted Items folder. You can then empty the Deleted Items folder at your convenience (rather like the Recycle Bin in Windows, or Trash Can on a Mac).

Send and Receive button (8)

Click this to check for any new mail and send any items in the Outbox. There is a down-arrow beside it, which you can use to select the e-mail account you want, if you have more than one, or to select to send only or receive only if you do not want to do both at once.

Address Book button (9)

This button will open the Address Book (sometimes called Contacts Book) where you can store or access e-mail addresses of friends and contacts. The level of information that you can store varies from one e-mail program to another: some allow you to include only basic name and address information, while others include entries for phone and fax numbers, even personal details such as birthdays and children's names!

Find (10)

If provided, a Find function usually allows you to search the folder or section you are in for items such as the message sender, the message subject or even a word or phrase contained within a message.

Indicator (11)

This shows whether you are online or offline and whether any errors have occurred in transmitting or receiving mail. The exact contents of this area vary from one program to another.

Message area (12)

This shows you the content of the highlighted e-mail message.

Each e-mail product has a variety of ways in which you can adjust the display to suit your own needs. Each version is different, so I recommend you investigate the possibilities for your own e-mail product by visiting the online help, or running the product's tutorial, if one is supplied.

If you want more information on e-mail and the various features supported by the major e-mail products, read *The Beginner's E-mail Book*, also published by Foulsham, which covers this subject in far more detail than space here permits, and provides helpful hints for getting the most from your e-mail.

The table below shows alternative names for features in the most commonly-used e-mail products. A dash indicates that this feature does not appear in the tested version of the software although it may appear in other versions of the same product. Further details of the features listed here can be found in *The Beginner's E-mail Book*.

Microsoft Outlook Express	**Netscape Messenger**	**Qualcomm Eudora**	**MSN Hotmail**
Inbox	Inbox	In mailbox	Inbox
Outbox	Unsent messages	Out mailbox	–
Sent items	Sent	Sent items	Sent messages
Deleted items	Trash	Trash	Trashcan
New mail	To: mail/New msg	New message	Compose
Receive all	Get mail/Get msg	Check mail	–
Send all	Send messages in outbox	Send queued messages	–
Message rules	–	Filters	Filters
Folder	Folder	Mailbox	Folder
Options	Preferences	Options	Options
Show header	Show headers	Blah Blah Blah	Message Headers*
Group by conversation	Thread messages	Group by subject	Sort by subject†
Move to folder	Move	Transfer	Move to
User name	Name	Personality	Sign-in name
Word wrap	Wrap long lines	Word wrap	Line width*
Text settings (for replies and forwards)	Automatically quote...	Replying options	Replying to messages*

* All these Hotmail options are found in the Preferences section of the Options page.
† This sorts by the message subject only: it does not provide collapsible threads.

SENDING AN E-MAIL

This example is based on Outlook Express version 5. The procedure is similar for most e-mail programs, although the button names may be different (see the table above).

1. First, open your e-mail software. Depending on how you have set up your software, it may try to connect to the internet straight away. You need to be online to download messages but not to create an e-mail, so click Cancel if it does try to connect.

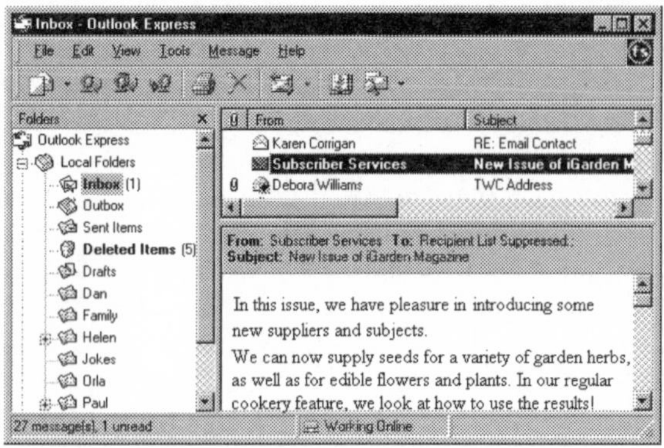

2. Outlook Express will load its main page, allowing you to select different options. To create a new e-mail, open a blank message by clicking on the Compose Message/New Mail button.

   A new message window appears on the screen with its own toolbar, a header section and a blank area for you to type the message you wish to send. (Note that if you have more than one e-mail account, there will be an extra box marked From: as shown below. Use the drop-down menu to select the account you wish to use.)

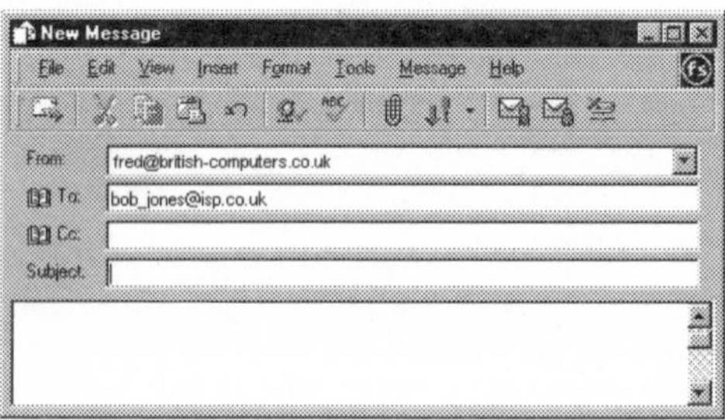

3. Click in the box marked To: and type the e-mail address of the recipient. Type accurately otherwise the mail will not get to the right person.

Alternatively, if the person's details are listed in your address book, click on the book icon to the left of the line marked To: and select their name from the list, or double-click on their name in the Contacts pane if it is displayed.

To send the mail to more than one person, repeat this process. You can put the remaining addresses in either the To: or the Cc: box, separating the addresses with a semi-colon (;).

4. Next, type a title in the Subject box. This is the first thing the person receiving the mail will see, as it appears in the message list, so make it something appropriate and not too long.

5. Now click in the large empty box in the bottom half of the screen and start typing your message. If you want to change the appearance of your text, use the Format menu to compose your message in HTML. Note that your recipient will only be able to view the changed format if he or she uses e-mail software that recognises HTML coding: some of the more basic products, such as the internet-based e-mail services, do not. If this is the case, they will still be able to read your message, but all the effort you made in styling it nicely will be wasted. Never use HTML coding when writing e-mail to newsgroups.

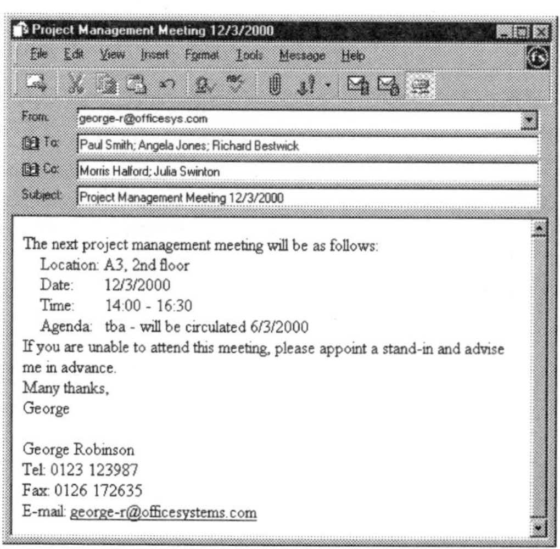

6. To send your message, click the Send button on the toolbar to send it immediately, or select the File menu if you want the choice of sending it later.

   If you decide to send immediately, you will be prompted to connect to the internet. While you are connecting, the message will be placed in the Outbox.

   If you decide to send later, your message will be placed in the Outbox until you next connect to the internet and select Send/Receive. A number in brackets after the Outbox folder will tell you how many messages you have waiting to be sent.
   To confirm that your e-mail has been sent, open your Sent Items folder and you will see a copy of the mail you sent. The number next to the Outbox folder will have disappeared.

RECEIVING AN E-MAIL

This example is also based on Outlook Express version 5 but, as above, is applicable to most other browsers.

When you connect to the internet while your e-mail program is running, the messages sent to your e-mail address, which have been stored on your ISP's server waiting for you to log in, will be delivered to your Inbox (or to a different folder if you have set up rules to redirect your mail). When this new mail arrives, the name of the message folder in which it is contained will be shown in bold and followed by a number in brackets representing the number of new messages waiting to be opened.

1. Double-click on the folder to open it and display the list of messages. The titles of new or unread messages will be highlighted in bold. As you click on a message title, the content of the message is displayed or 'previewed' in the lower part of the screen (note: this may depend on how your software is set up). You can either view the message here or double-click on it to open it in a new window.

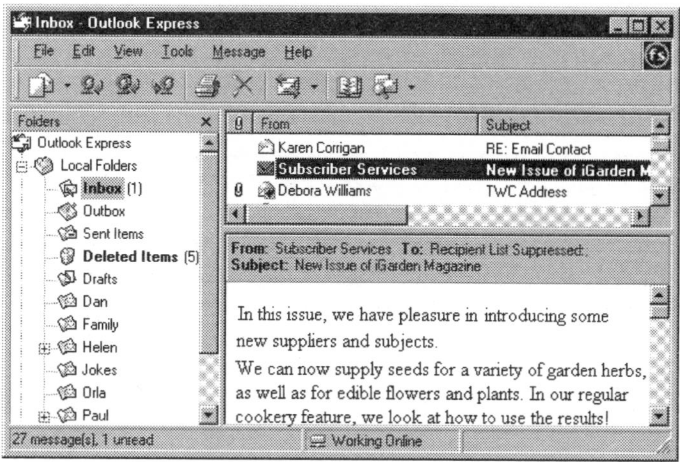

2. If there is a paperclip icon next to the message title or in the right-hand corner of the preview, this means that the e-mail contains an *attachment*, a file that has been sent with it. This could be anything from a text file to a video clip, photograph, sound file or program. As unsolicited attachments often contain *viruses*, it is recommended you only open attachments you are expecting or that have been sent by people you know and trust. It is wise to run a virus scan before opening any such file.

   Many e-mail programs offer a facility for viewing certain types of attachment (not programs) inline. This means the attachment is automatically opened and shown within the message window (for example, an inline graphic will appear within the text of the message).

   To open the attachment, double-click on the paperclip on the preview and it will display a window asking what you want to do with it. You can either save it to your hard disk or open it.

3. If you have been logged on to the internet for a while and you wish to see if you have received any new mail, click on the Send/Receive button in the toolbar and any new mail will be delivered to your inbox.

NETIQUETTE

Although e-mail is supposed to be fairly informal, the medium has built up a form of etiquette or code of conduct to ensure that the writers of e-mail do not irritate or offend their readers. This is often referred to as *netiquette*, and is particularly applicable when sending e-mail messages to a newsgroup, *BBS* or forum (see chapter eight for more details on how to use these facilities). The most important points of netiquette for everyday e-mail are described below. Further details can be found on the internet by searching for the word 'netiquette'.

If you are accused of breaking netiquette, it is best to apologise as soon as possible, and if you are not sure what you have done wrong, ask.

Shouting

Using block capital letters is considered to be the equivalent of shouting and should be avoided. It's acceptable to use block capitals if you are sending a short e-mail to proclaim an achievement and express excitement, for example 'WE'VE GOT THE CONTRACT!', but in general, capital letters are difficult to read *en bloc* and thus cause irritation to the reader. Many recipients will simply delete a message written solely in capitals, so it is best to avoid them wherever possible. Be sensible: would you read a book or a newspaper article written entirely in capitals? You'd be hard-pressed to find one.

This applies only to block capitals – you should still use single capitals where needed at the start of sentences and proper nouns. Some people use no capitals in e-mail at all, but this can be confusing and almost as difficult to read as block capitals.

Flaming

Flaming is the electronic equivalent of losing your temper or being overly aggressive, and usually results from someone reading a controversial comment and sending a hasty and ill-considered reply. Always read through your message before you send it, and remove any angry or rude comments. If you wish to make a comment that you think may provoke an angry response, try to take the sting out of it by preceding it with a statement like this:

//Flameproof suit on...//

as this shows you realise the nature of the statement and are open to reasoned argument. This is not carte blanche to be rude, insulting or abusive, and should only ever be used in personal messages or in *postings* to newsgroups/lists where such an approach – and the provocative comment it precedes – would be appreciated for what it is.

Humour

Don't try to be funny or sarcastic. E-mail does not translate humour very well because the person cannot see your face. Sarcasm in particular can come across as sincere: and remember, once a message has been sent, you cannot retrieve it. It is possible to use humour in personal e-mail to friends, especially if you indicate it with an appropriate *emoticon*, but only if they will understand it.

State your subject

Always give the message a title by filling in the Subject line. It helps to tell the recipient what your e-mail is about before they open it, and it also helps you to file it correctly. If you are responding to a message, use the Reply function to automatically copy the subject from that message, preceding it with Re:. If you are sending a received message on to someone else, use the Forward function to do the same but precede it with Fwd:.

Make sure the subject of the message reflects its content. This is particularly important for users of newsgroups and fora who may be involved in exchanges of e-mail on various topics. It is very annoying to those who sort their mail by thread to find an unrelated item in an existing thread. (A thread is a message topic, a term much used in newsgroups but rarely in personal exchanges.) For example, in a cookery newsgroup you would not expect to find a query on how to boil potatoes with a subject line of 'My mother's raspberry soufflé'. This error normally results from someone using the reply function to write an unrelated message to the same list, rather than starting a new message.

Remember, unless you are replying to a specific message on a specific topic with more information on that topic, start a new message instead. Even if there is an element of commonality, it is best to start afresh: if you want to write about raspberry jam or cheese soufflé, start a new message with an appropriate subject line. This also works in reverse: don't start another thread about raspberry soufflé, reply to one of the previous postings on this topic to add your thoughts, so that anyone interested in raspberry soufflé has all the information in one place.

Check the address

Always check an e-mail address is correct before sending your message. It is all too easy to mistype an address: many addresses are very similar, especially those used by companies, and it is not possible to cancel an e-mail once sent. Don't assume, for example, that John Brown who works at StarTools plc has an e-mail address of john_brown@startools.com – there may be another John Brown there and it could be someone in a senior position who will not welcome your intrusion into his mailbox, particularly if your message is of a personal nature. Such an error could backfire on you and your intended recipient.

If you are not 100% certain of an address, check it! This is particularly the case if you have located an address via a directory listing on the internet; you may think you know the only Sandra Chase in Cape Town, but you could be wrong. If writing on spec to see whether you have the right person, be polite; ask a pertinent question in the subject line, prefixing it with a question mark (e.g. ?Are you Sandra Chase previously of EdCo?); offer an apology in case you have contacted the wrong person, and leave it at that. Never follow such an approach with another message if you receive no response: it could be that you have located the wrong person or that the person does not wish to communicate with you further.

Most e-mail software these days allows you to save e-mail addresses in an address book. This is recommended for people with whom you regularly correspond as it saves a lot of typing and the potential for mistyping.

Security

Don't send anything confidential by e-mail. Remember that e-mail can be easily read by other people. Anything private should be sent in a conventional sealed letter, not over the internet.

Legal

Using e-mail to hire or fire people is not only very bad manners, it's also not a legally recognisable form of correspondence on such issues. Although many internet *portal* sites advertise jobs and allow you to tender for work via e-mail, for your own protection this should only ever be used for initial contact to exchange names, addresses and informal bids.

Rules for replies

When replying to someone, you can quote parts of their original message. Insert a chevron (>) before a line containing a quotation. Most e-mail software does this automatically when you select the Reply function; it copies the original e-mail and places > in front of each line. You may then delete lines as you wish: insert <snip> to indicate where you have cut information out. Never take quotes out of context in order to change their meaning, and always acknowledge the origin of the text: this is particularly important when writing to newsgroups or lists where recipients of your message may not have read the original from which you are quoting.

Style

Many e-mail applications now offer a variety of 'stationery' on which to type your e-mail. This is fine for personal messages but do not use it for business, or for postings to lists and newsgroups. For these purposes, write plain text on a plain background. Similarly, do not use HTML (sometimes called Rich Text) formatting for postings to lists and newsgroups, as not every e-mail user is able to read HTML: it depends on which software they are using.

If you are sending attachments such as images, sound or video clips, establish beforehand whether your recipient knows how to deal with them. Make sure they have the correct level of software and if not, where they can find it. Software to display or play common file formats is often available free on the manufacturer's web site; if not there is usually a trial version available for download that allows a recipient simply to view or listen to the attachment without providing the full functions of the product.

Newsgroups

Newsgroups offer a vast resource for information, based on e-mail messages. You need software called a *newsreader* (sometimes called a news client) to access a newsgroup: these are often supplied as part of a browser or e-mail product. Microsoft's newsreader is part of the Outlook Express package, while Netscape provides a newsgroup reader called Collabra as part of its Communicator suite. If you are going to use newsgroups a great deal, you may want a few extra facilities, in which case you could investigate a dedicated news client such as Newsmonger or Forte Agent, both of which can be downloaded from the web.

One drawback with newsgroups is that because they are public, they open the way to a new problem in the form of unwanted advertisements (junk mail or *spam*), mainly for 'get-rich-quick' schemes or adult sites. They will often have nothing to do with the topic of the site, and may take up a vast bulk of the newsgroup files. This is because it is impossible to control what gets sent into a newsgroup and because it is easy for someone to hide their true identity when posting.

That said, newsgroups are a very useful way of communicating on the internet.

HOW NEWSGROUPS WORK

Newsgroups are based on e-mail. Groups are arranged by topic and anyone can put a message in the group or download a message from the group in the same way as sending or receiving an ordinary e-mail. Just as with e-mail, you can forward messages to someone, reply to the author or reply to the group. You can also add attachments, which can be either pictures, sound, video clips and other files, although most newsgroups discourage this as it takes up valuable space on the server. Most newsgroups also insist that messages are written in plain text, rather than HTML.

Most newsgroups concentrate their discussions on a particular subject. Discussions are formed from individual notes written by e-mail users, which are sent to a specific e-mail address representing a news server. On receipt at the server, the message is copied to news servers world-wide using a technology called *Usenet*, and subscribers to that newsgroup receive a copy of the message in their inbox when they next check their e-mail. If you don't want to be swamped by messages in your inbox, you can usually read and post to a newsgroup without subscribing: you then need to connect to a particular server to view the postings in a list format.

JOINING A NEWSGROUP

To join a newsgroup, you need to connect to a news server. All the major ISPs have servers dedicated to newsgroups. The number of groups carried will depend on the ISP but is likely to be up to 30,000. You will need to ask your ISP for details of the news server address (which is likely to be something like news.isp.co.uk) and supply this information to your newsreader, browser or e-mail software in the appropriate place – read your online help to find out how and where to do this.

When you have supplied the relevant information, connect to the internet in the usual way, access the news server by selecting the newsreader (or the News folder in the case of Outlook Express) and download the list of newsgroups available. As this is likely to be quite extensive, it is recommended that you disconnect to save telephone costs while you search this list for the names of any groups you wish to join and make a note of them. You can then connect again and join up without delay.

An example of a list of newsgroups as viewed in Outlook Express is shown on page 70.

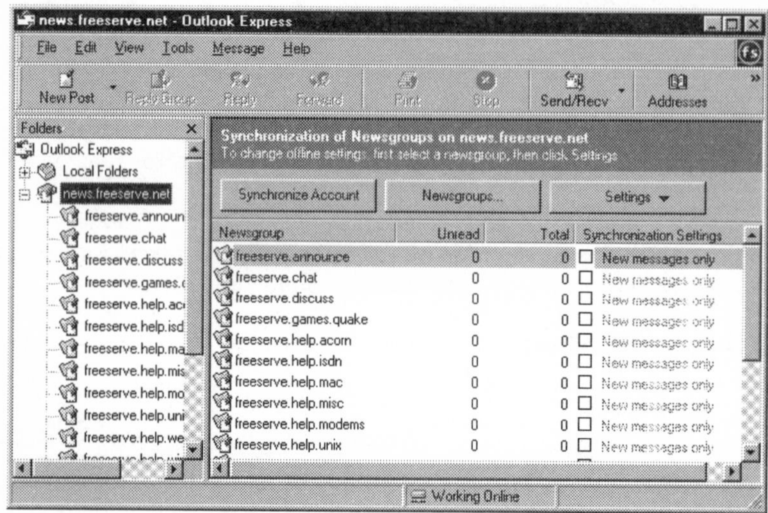

FINDING A NEWSGROUP: A GUIDE TO NEWSGROUP NAMES

The first part of a newsgroup's name indicates the major subject category and the rest indicates subcategories: rather like some web addresses. A newsgroup might be called, for example, news.isp.net (notice there are no @ signs in newsgroup names). For example, some of the major subject categories are:

alt	alternative
bus	business
comp	computers
news	news
rec	recreational
sci	science
soc	social/society

Some newsgroup names start with a country code (for example, uk, za) if their content is specific to one country. Others start with the name of the newsgroup provider, for example zetnet, claranet, or telnet.

Here are some examples of newsgroup names:

news.freeserve.net	A 'news' newsgroup provided by the ISP Freeserve (in the UK).
alt.fan.nicole.kidman	Provides news and gossip for fans of this actress.
fr.sci.psychologie	A French newsgroup on psychology (with discussions conducted in French).
japan.pets.dogs.breed	Provides information for Japanese dog breeders.
sci.optics.fiber	A forum for discussion on fibreoptic technology.
sdnet.sports	Provides details of sports in the San Diego area.
soc.men	Discusses issues related to men and their problems (soc.women does the same for women).
uk.rec.motorcycles	A UK-based newsgroup for those interested in recreational motor cycling.
za.org.cssa	The newsgroup for the Computer Society of South Africa.

Some companies provide support for their products via newsgroups, and in this case the company name is usually the first part of the newsgroup name, for example:

novell.netware3.installupgrades
symantec.support.win95
usa-today.money
zippo.announce

SUBSCRIBE OR NOT?

Subscribing to a newsgroup does not cost anything. Once you have subscribed and are connected to the newsgroup, message headers will download on to your PC. Once this is done, you will be able to view them either offline or online. You can then mark messages for download to your PC and see the complete message. If you mark messages when you are offline, they will download automatically when you go back online. Once downloaded, the messages can be viewed either online or offline.

To view the postings of a newsgroup since you last viewed it, you use the synchronisation feature. Read the documentation that came with your e-mail software to find out how to do this, as it varies from one product to another.

SENDING MESSAGES TO NEWSGROUPS

Before sending a message to a newsgroup (known as *posting* a message: the messages themselves are also called postings), you should learn basic netiquette, some of which is described in chapter seven starting on page 56, and become familiar with the content of the newsgroup and the style of its postings. Most newsgroups have specific sets of rules relating to the format and content of messages, and provide a list of frequently asked questions (*FAQs*) to prevent the same questions being asked repeatedly. Most expect postings in fairly informal language, but it is wise to read first and adapt your style to suit.

Some newsgroups are moderated by a designated person who decides which postings to allow or to remove: these often show 'moderated' or 'mod' as part of the name. Most newsgroups are unmoderated.

Posting your own message to a newsgroup is as easy as sending an e-mail. Highlight the group to which you would like to send a message, and then click the button to create a new message in the usual way. This will automatically add the correct address into the To: box. Add the subject, message and any other information you want to send, then simply use the Send button to send your message to the news server and distribute it to the rest of the members of the newsgroup.

One thing you may notice is that there are some messages which all have the same title. These are called threads, which are replies to an original message. Some (but not all) newsreader and e-mail software allows you to group such messages together into conversations, with only the first message in the conversation showing by default: you can then click to show the rest of the conversation if you wish. This is a good way to minimise the number of listed messages, while making sure you don't miss anything.

RESPONDING TO A POSTED MESSAGE

How you respond to a message will depend on which software you are using. Most products provide a 'Reply to group' option, which posts your reply to the server and on to the entire group; and a 'reply to author' option, which sends your reply directly to the person who posted the original message. Take care with this latter option: sometimes posters will hide their own e-mail address for security reasons, so your message may be returned to the list instead. Some software provides a third option, to reply to author and recipients, which forwards the mail to those people who downloaded the original message, without posting it to the newsgroup itself.

Generally netiquette dictates that if you are sending a reply that others in the group may be interested in (i.e. answering a technical query), you should send to the list: if it is likely to be relevant to the original poster only (e.g. your bid for an item he or she is offering for sale) send it directly to that person.

9

Protect yourself from internet problems

Though the vast majority of information on the net is useful and positive, there can be problems regarding both what you can view and download, and what others can find out about you. Anyone can set up a web site, so it is up to you to ensure that the sites you visit and from which you make purchases are reputable, and that if children have access to your computer they are protected from information which is inappropriate; also that you are protected from possible attack by internet-launched computer viruses. In this section we look at the various problems that can occur, and how to protect your children, your computer and your wallet while continuing to enjoy the benefits of the internet in relative safety.

PROTECTING YOUR CHILDREN

It is a sad fact that the internet is not totally safe for children. While it may seem that communication by computer eliminates the 'stranger danger' that seems to permeate everyday life, this is not so: many of the people about whom we should be most concerned ply their trade via the web as much as in the playground. The web can be both educational and fun for children of all ages, but you do need to take some precautions.

Inappropriate behaviour: the seedy side of the web

The 'freedom of information' philosophy of the internet is generally laudable, but unfortunately this means that it has its seedy side just as real life does. Anyone using the net can access pornographic material and information about drugs, crime or other related issues: and those so minded can easily put such information up there for anyone to see. Though it can be difficult and time-consuming to find these sites, it is also possible to stumble across them while looking for something quite different: unappealing to most of us, and particularly dangerous for children.

Chat rooms in particular have been described as 'unhealthy' places for children to visit. While they may seem a lot of fun, and in most cases such fun is totally innocent, there have been cases of child abduction and abuse resulting from a chance 'meeting' between a child and paedophile on such sites. Such sick individuals have no qualms about posing as another child to obtain the trust and personal details of others, and will often engage a youngster in 'conversation' on seemingly innocent topics before trying to arrange a real-life meeting or obtain scanned photographs. While many chat room operators promise to monitor conversations to reduce the likelihood of such contact, this is not always effective against the most devious of characters. Of course such problems are not restricted merely to children; there have been similar cases of adults being attacked after arranging to meet someone they have been 'talking to' on the internet for some time, especially those who frequent the 'lonely hearts' sites.

Simple protection measures

There are several ways to help protect your children from dubious material on the internet.

- Firstly and most importantly, explain to all children who have access to the internet – whether at home, school or elsewhere – that they should never talk 'privately' to strangers online or give out personal details such as their full name, age, address, telephone number, or, of course, the user name and password of their account. Explain why this is not a good idea, and ask them to tell you immediately if anyone asks them for such information, even if they think that person is another child.

- Next, make sure that children are not allowed completely free, unmonitored access to the net but employ an appropriate level of supervision so that they are guided towards the useful and interesting. Having the computer sited in a communal area of the house, rather than the child's bedroom, is often a good idea. Show interest in what they are doing (be careful – teenagers in particular can be very protective of their privacy!) and ask about the type of topic they research and 'chat' about, and who they have 'met' online recently.

- Become familiar with rating systems. Many browsers 'rate' particular sites so that you can stop children from accessing sites with specific ratings. Thousands of different web sites have enrolled with reputable rating systems, which you can investigate on your browser's help pages or by searching on 'security' or 'rating'. In Outlook Express, you can use the Content Advisor to restrict access to sites with certain ratings: in most versions this is accessible from the Internet Options notebook – which you can find in the Control Panel or from the Tools menu of your browser – on the Content page.

- It is a good idea to learn about the various organisations that offer guidance to parents on helping their children to surf the internet safely. These are listed in the section *Internet: Security and Protection*, starting on page 292.

- You can also buy software that will allow you to block access to unsuitable sites, or check whether your internet service provider offers facilities to block unwanted sites.

Blocking software

Blocking software or internet filters are available to prevent children gaining access to adult material. Some of these will block out sites that contain offensive material – often allowing you to specify different categories such as sexually explicit, violent, hate speech, gambling, drugs and alcohol – and prevent you from giving out private information in chat rooms, or even from using chat rooms at all. Different profiles can be created for different members of your family, so that you can each gain appropriate access. Most such software allows you to add specific URLs in case you find any offensive sites that it does not currently list, and provides a facility to unblock sites if you do want to view them. Some software also allows you to limit the vocabulary used in sites and chat messages – such as by blocking specific words in addresses and telephone numbers.

Some web sites for blocking software are listed in the section *Internet: Security and Protection*, starting on page 292.

The following questions should help you select appropriate blocking software.

- Do you want software that blocks out entire web sites or only pages that are of dubious content?
- Is it possible to fine-tune the software in different profiles for different members of the family, to screen vocabulary, for instance?
- Is it possible to configure the software to different members of your family so that the older members can view a broader range of sites?
- Is it possible to prevent your children from giving out personal and private information to strangers?
- Is it possible to block e-mail from certain sources on the internet?

PROTECTING YOUR WALLET FROM INTERNET FRAUD

Unfortunately the internet has attracted its fair share of fraudsters, who trade on the popularity and convenience of online shopping to capture credit and debit card details and use them to raid your accounts. Such fraud has had a lot of media exposure, which has led to a welcome crackdown on security by many of the major internet traders, but the problem has not entirely gone away although it is reported to be decreasing. Most reputable sites now *encrypt* all transaction details, which supposedly renders them impervious to *hackers* and other forms of fraud, but errors still occur. People with internet bank accounts have logged in to their supposedly secure personal account only to find they are viewing someone else's financial details; orders for goods have been mistakenly repeated so that the card owner is charged multiple times for the same order; third parties have illegally obtained and used information on a site's customers for their own ends. Even employees working within a legitimate organisation have been known to record customers' credit card details and use them later for fraudulent purposes.

Remember that anyone can set up an internet site, complete with a product list and order form. Once they have your credit/debit card and address details, they can make repeated use of your card to purchase goods for themselves – you have already given them all they need to make internet or telephone purchases. The first you know about it could be when your bank calls you to see why you have been spending so much – and remember that until you report a problem, you are liable for charges to your account. (Don't panic immediately if you do get a call from your bank though; many banks are now running routine checks on cards used for internet purchases, to reduce fraud, so you may get a call even if all your recent purchases have been totally legitimate.)

The best advice in all cases is to be wary. Stick to recognised store names and internet traders. If you are unsure of a particular site, order by another means – most sites provide a telephone helpline – or if you simply must have that item from a bargain site which insists on credit card payment, use a card that is covered by purchase insurance (most banks include this) so that you can cancel the transaction if the goods fail to turn up without losing any money. Check credit card statements carefully for any unknown transactions, and report any to your bank immediately so they can arrange for a new card to be issued. Avoid giving details of your bank account – it should not be necessary – and never send financial details in an e-mail as this is highly insecure. If you bank online, report any anomalies immediately by telephone and follow this up in writing: do not use the online service again until your query has been resolved.

PROTECTING YOUR COMPUTER AND FILES

If you use the internet from home for purely personal purposes, you can probably see no reason why a hacker should invade your computer or your e-mail messages, but you would be wrong. Use of the internet often involves the exchange of information, some of which can be extremely useful to others who wish to use it for fraudulent purposes, so beware of what you store and particularly of what you send in e-mail messages. And no matter how infrequently you use the internet and how selective you are about the sites you visit, you do need to protect yourself against viruses.

E-mail interception

You may wonder why anyone would bother reading your personal messages; the answer is that, as with other forms of mail interception, they are probably not specifically looking for a chatty letter to your brother but for something more useful, and open everything in the hope of finding it. If you were sending a message to a company requesting goods, for example, they would immediately have your name and address, e-mail address, and possibly banking or credit card details or delivery information if you have provided them. For corporate e-mail, industrial espionage is big business, and hackers have been known to operate on behalf of one company, political party or pressure group against another to procure sensitive information for their employer.

To call any e-mail exchange 'private' is a misnomer, although this term is frequently used online; you can almost guarantee that if you send something confidential, risqué, potentially offensive or newsworthy to another person via e-mail, someone else will read it, and not only hackers – either the original recipient will forward it to someone else (and they to someone else, and so on, ad infinitum) or it will be read by a system administrator or over the recipient's shoulder by a colleague. Remember also that most systems automatically scan e-mail for certain key words or word combinations, such as abusive retorts or obscenities, and messages containing these items are automatically rejected.

Even if you only send e-mail 'letters' to family and friends, be aware that anyone can tap into your communication and copy it, including any photographs: it is not unknown for people to find their snaps on another web site, perhaps having been tinkered with along the way. Usually such adaptations are intended to be funny rather than malicious, but it is still an invasion of privacy and in some cases can have distasteful intent. Be particularly wary of sending photographs of anyone – especially children – less than fully clothed, such as on the beach or in the bath.

Protection against viruses

Computer viruses are programs that hide inside other computer files, mainly program executable (.exe) files and *macros*. They are not normally contained within pictures or sound files but are often hidden in files sent as e-mail attachments as this is the easiest way for their creators to spread them around the world. Generally they are contained within files that need a run command, but it is possible that such a command can be issued automatically and innocently by your software – for example, to display the content of an e-mail attachment as part of the message. The way viruses work varies, but most lie dormant on your computer until they are activated by a particular trigger: pressing a particular key a certain number of times, or using the computer at a certain time or on a certain date, for example. As long as you have adequate protection in the form of anti-virus software (see opposite), few viruses will cause major damage as any that do will be easily detected and destroyed before they are passed on. However, some can make your life very difficult – destroying the contents of files, for example – and need to be avoided. In any case, you should minimise the possible damage by backing up the data on your computer regularly, to a tape drive, CD-ROM or diskette.

Computer viruses come in many different forms and have many different effects. They can just be annoying – for example displaying a message on the screen every time you press a certain key combination – or they can be downright destructive – deleting all the data on your hard drive. The more you use the internet, the more chance you will have of contracting a virus and the more careful you should be. The first way to protect your computer is to make sure that you download files, especially programs, only from reputable and well-known sources. However, this is not foolproof and it is strongly recommended that you also install anti-virus software (often called a virus protector or virus scanner). Such software is cheap and easy to install, and if it detects even one virus during its lifetime it will have paid for itself many times over, as it will alert you before the problem occurs. Once loaded, every time you display a web page or download a file from the internet, the software will check it for known viruses and alert you if there is any problem. You will need to update your protection frequently to ensure that the most recent viruses are recognised by your software, as new viruses are being created and distributed every day (these updates are usually available free from the manufacturer's web site, and some will even advise you when a new version is available). Anti-virus software can also be used on non-internet files, such as items supplied on diskettes and CD-ROM, as well as all files sent by e-mail, and it is recommended that you run the software against all files on your computer regularly.

There are many ways to tell if you have a virus on your system. The most common one is that if you begin to notice that programs take longer to start up or in some cases do not start at all. If this happens, then you should run a check on all drives using the latest version of your anti-virus software. The programs that are causing the problem should be removed and reinstalled if a virus is found: many anti-virus packages will do this automatically.

Anti-virus software

There are two different types of anti-virus protection available:

Sentries: This type of program stands guard whenever your computer is powered on, operating in the background as you work. Every time you open a file, it automatically scans that file for viruses. Every time you power on or off, it scans your memory and system files for viruses. The only drawback is that occasionally when you install new software, the anti-virus sentry may check with you first as each file is loaded, as it will recognise these as unknown executable files.

Search & kill: This type is popular and quite adequate for many home users. It scans the complete hard drive at regular intervals and deletes or repairs any infected files. You can schedule the scan to run as frequently as you wish, usually specifying a time, day and the extent of the check (for example, just one drive or the entire machine) and nothing is run in the background that could conflict with other programs running at the same time.

There are several reputable and easy-to-use programs readily available for purchase over the internet or at your computer retailer. Some of the best ones, and the web sites from which you can obtain them, are listed in the section *Computers: Security and Protection* in the latter part of this book. It is also worth checking through computer magazines (such as *What PC?* or *PC User*) and their web sites for more information, as they often run comparisons of different types of software, including virus scanners, and there may be new or more advanced products available since this book was published.

Protection from junk

As if we didn't all complain enough about junk mail, unwanted telesales calls and unsolicited faxes, now you are online you will probably receive even more junk, in the form of e-mail. This is known as spam, and can be extremely irritating, especially if you have a slow modem that takes a long time to download mail only for you to find that half the items are adverts for things you don't want or sites you have no interest in visiting.

Those not-so-sweet cookies

So how do spammers obtain your e-mail address? The answer generally lies in *cookies*, little files of information that are created when you visit a web site and leave your details. These are stored on your hard drive and are intended to give you more personalised information when you access a site – for example, if you have visited a bookstore and shown interest in Australian fiction, the next time you visit they may show recommended books in this category. In theory only the web site that created a cookie can access and use it.

Most browsers allow the creation of cookies but also allow you to choose whether to accept them. Only the information that you specifically provide and the choices you make while visiting a site can be stored in a cookie. For example, the site cannot determine your e-mail address unless you choose to type it. Allowing site to create a cookie should not give that or any other site access to the rest of your computer, but that assumes that every site owner is reliable and responsible, and we already know that they are not. In fact, it is easy for a web server to which you are connected (even via your ISP) to poll your computer for information, receiving your e-mail address and details of your bookmarked sites and the sites you have visited most recently. They can use this information to target people who have visited or bookmarked sites on a similar topic. It is rather like using a credit card or loyalty card in a shop: these days they can find out an awful lot about you from that little magnetic strip! Certain sites also sell on such information: by law you should be given the option to refuse to allow your details to be passed to third parties but of course many sites are based in countries with inadequate laws on data protection.

Mailing list spam

Spam has received such a bad press that most reputable sites and site providers don't misuse customer information or issue unsolicited mail any longer – unless you frequently visit their site, that is, in which case many seem to think they have carte blanche to bombard you with special offers, updates and all manner of junk on an almost daily basis (just like non-internet organisations do with through-the-door catalogues and so on). Usually you can stop these mailings by 'unsubscribing' from the *mailing list* of which you have unwittingly become a part: look at the bottom of the e-mail message, where you will normally find instructions on how to do so. It is not always sufficient to reply to the e-mail asking to be removed, as many such messages are issued not by a human operator but by a program, which can't read your pleas for it to cease. However, if you can't find any unsubscribe details, this is worth a try.

Blocking junk mail

If you regularly receive spam from a particular sender, use the blocking feature of your e-mail program to get rid of it automatically. In Outlook Express, for example, you can do this using the Blocked Senders function. When you receive a junk message, highlight it in the list and select Block Sender from the Message menu. A message pops up to tell you that this e-mail address has been added to your Blocked Senders list. That's it – an easy solution to an annoying problem.

One important thing to note about blocking: it relies on a single address being used to send the junk mail. Many persistent junk mailers propagate numerous e-mail addresses from which to bombard you with information, so you may still receive some messages from the most persistent of offenders. Some e-mail programs, such as Hotmail, now offer inbox protection that works in reverse: it allows you to specify those people from whom you *do* want to receive mail, and all other incoming mail is placed in a single folder, kept for up to 30 days and then deleted. This is a good way to sort the important from the trivial, but remember to scan the non-specified mail regularly or you may miss messages that could be of interest, such as those from a contact with a new e-mail address, or a query from an old friend or potential client.

GENERAL SECURITY ADVICE

If all this has rather put you off using the internet, there is no need to let it. There are several simple ways to protect yourself and your computer from these problems so that, while you need to remain aware, nothing need spoil your enjoyment of surfing.

- The first is to use your common sense. Use the available features of your browser to restrict access to unsuitable sites and, if necessary, to allow you to access only sites with secure servers. (You can find out how to do this for your particular browser by reading its online help, which should describe all the security options in detail.)

- Investigate the virus-checkers readily available in all computer stores, and also the additional software that is available to block information of a sensitive nature from any children who may have access to your computer. Equip yourself with virus protection right from the start, even if it's only one of the free trial versions.

- If you arrange a meeting with someone you have 'met' online, make sure other people know where you are going and when, and make the meeting point a neutral and highly public place, preferably somewhere with CCTV surveillance in case of any problems. Try to encourage your date to bring a friend, and do the same yourself, to eliminate the chance of being alone with someone you'd rather be away from.

- Be sensible about giving out other details as well. If you are going on holiday, don't send an e-mail to all your friends telling them the dates you will be gone – it could be intercepted. Don't provide personal information to sites other than the absolutely necessary, and never write down passwords that you use to access a site.

- Most browsers will store information that you type in certain fields, and pop it up for you when you next complete a field of the same type (for example, your postcode): while this is useful as it saves typing, it can also be insecure, especially if it includes passwords and financial details. Clear such items regularly using your browser's option to Clear History (which removes details pertaining to sites you've recently visited) and Clear Cache (which clears all stored entries: it's sometimes called Clear Forms and Passwords). You can usually switch off the automatic storage of such information: in Outlook Express you do this from the Personal Information section of the Internet Options notebook (accessible from the Tools menu in most versions). If you visit a lot of web sites, you'll find that switching this option off saves you a lot of hard disk space – all those little bits of information take up a lot of bytes.

- Remember that if you have connection to the internet, nothing on your PC is secure or inaccessible to a hacker, and to be doubly safe from intrusion, always disconnect from the internet and switch off the power when you finish using your computer, even if you do not have to pay for internet usage. Unplugging the phone socket is probably unnecessary, but do it if it gives you extra piece of mind.

KEEPING OTHERS OFF YOUR EQUIPMENT

Finally, spend a few minutes protecting your computer and its information from other people's fingers. If there is a chance someone else could use your machine when you are away from the screen – and that includes people working in your home such as cleaners, builders and babysitters – use a passworded screen saver so that no one else can gain access to your e-mail and internet accounts. You can do this in most versions of Windows as follows:

1. Open the Control Panel (usually accessible from the Settings option of the Start menu, and often also from the My Computer icon)

2. Select Display to show the Display Properties notebook.

3. Go to the Screen Saver page and select the pattern you want. Select Settings if you want to change any of the details.

4. Click the Password Protected box and select Change to specify your password. Make it something easy for you to remember, but

not easily guessable by others (don't, for example, use your name: instead use that of your favourite brand of crisps or your favourite actor: even your mother's birthdate). You need to type it twice so the computer knows you haven't made a mistake. Click OK.

5. Back on the Screen Saver page, select the number of minutes you want the computer to wait before displaying the screen saver. You don't want it appearing every time you pause to look up a web site name, but you would expect it to appear while you boiled the kettle, so somewhere between three and ten minutes would be best. If you work in a shared area where people pass your computer regularly, you might want it set lower than this if you think they might dive in to raid your computer in the intervening moments.

Now you are forewarned, go ahead and surf! The rest of this book offers you a selection of high-quality, personally recommended sites from which you can start exploring the web.

1000 Really useful web sites

Here is a selection of some really useful web sites so that you can go directly to the information you need without wasting time trying to find that essential gem of knowledge for your household finances, hobby or school project. As the web is growing all the time, we need your input so that we can expand and update the list, so if you have come across other valuable sites in your travels around the net, e-mail the details of your favourites to us at:

reception@foulsham.com

Happy surfing!

ANIMALS

These sites cover everything from household pets to zoo favourites, and even a few extinct species! Many also have links to other sites of similar interest. If the animal you seek is not covered here, try running a search on the species name and the type of information you require (for example, giraffe gestation).

PETS

About Gerbils

This site provides a basic guide to looking after gerbils. There are many sections in the web pages that should broaden the foundation of information in this basic guide. Regardless of whether you want information about breeding, general care, naming your gerbils or even funny and serious stories featuring gerbils, you will find it somewhere on this comprehensive web site.

www.gerbils.org.uk

Acme Pet

This site is a huge directory listing of pet sites on the web, and has its own newspaper, club, marketplace and multimedia gallery. You can send pet and e-cards and lots more.

acmepet.petsmart.com

Allpets.com

This is an online magazine and encyclopedia which provides practical information about caring for all sorts of pet.

www.allpets.com

The Bug Club

Do you have any pet insects? If so, this fan club for owners of creepy-crawlies will help you to look after them properly and keep them alive! The Bug Club with its e-pal page, newsletters and pet care sheets has everything you need to know.

www.ex.ac.uk/bugclub

Dogs On Line

This site describes itself as a 'magazine and marketplace for dog-lovers' and provides lots of useful information, including lists of kennels, breeders, dog sitters and dog-friendly hotels. It advertises puppies for sale, lost or found, and has links to sites offering doggie goods, insurance and books.

www.dogs-online.co.uk

Feline Advisory Bureau

This charity is based in Wiltshire and supports research into the health and welfare of cats by making the latest information available to vets, cat breeders and owners. FAB members receive a quarterly colour journal outlining the latest information and treatments in the feline world. Over 50 information sheets are also available on feline diseases, behaviour and breeding for you to download and read on your own computer.

www.fabcats.org

Fish Information Service

Free information service about topics of interest to the aquarium hobbyist. FINS is constantly changing as new information is added and old information is updated. All that you need to know about aquariums is included. There's also a glossary, a catalogue of fish and invertebrates, plus information on diseases, diagnosis and treatment.

www.actwin.com/fish/index.cgi

Hamster Site

This site is packed with information about these popular pets. The site includes an in-depth guide to the various species, health and care advice, plus links to breeders, clubs and shows.

www.hamsters.co.uk

The Horse Interactive

This site is concerned with all aspects of equine health, and it is written for hands-on horse owners, trainers, riders, breeders, and barn managers who want to know more about taking the best care of their horses. There is extensive information on topics of concern, supplemented by timely features on horse health and news from researchers, veterinarians in the field and other equine professionals.

www.thehorse.com

If you like horses, whether ponies or thoroughbred racers, the following sites are also worth a look:

www.equine-world.co.uk

www.ponyclub.org.uk

The Kennel Club

If you like dogs, this is the site for you. The Kennel Club is not just the organiser of Crufts, but also runs all sorts of dog clubs, training and obedience classes, issues pedigree registrations, and advises on purchasing, keeping and breeding dogs of all breeds. The site also includes a good selection of links to other doggie sites.

www.the-kennel-club.org.uk

Pet of the Day

This is a free site on which one pet is selected to be honoured each day, plus sister sites Dog of the Day and Cat of the Day. If your pet is selected, they will let you know in advance which day will be your pet's special day.

www.petoftheday.com

www.dogoftheday.com

www.catoftheday.com

Pets Park

Pets Park has been created as a place where pet and animal-lovers can meet and share their experiences as well as shop for all their pet-care needs. There's information and advice provided by their vet Gina and animal behaviourist Laila to help you understand, care for and cherish your pet. You'll also be able to buy all you need for your pet at the Pets Park superstore. It will soon be the largest internet pet shop in Europe.

www.petspark.com

Pets Pyjamas

Pets Pyjamas is a major European site catering for the needs of pet owners by offering shopping, information, services and entertainment. In addition to the web site, a Pets Pyjamas catalogue is also available in which you will find the full range of products and services offered on the internet.

www.pets-pyjamas.co.uk

Planet Koi

This site is dedicated entirely to Japanese koi carp, or Nishikigoi. Here you can find information about koi varieties, koi health, koi breeding, feeding koi, buying koi, and koi clubs. Also a great links page and the opportunity to buy koi and accessories online.

www.koicarp.demon.co.uk

OTHER ANIMALS

Animal Information Database

SeaWorld, the major theme park in Orlando, switches on its webcams at meal times, but in between the shows it provides games, quizzes and guides on the animals to give you an insight into their behaviour.

www.seaworld.org

Animal Omnibus

The Animal Omnibus is a reference list of animal web sources, indexed by the name of the animal, so provides links to information and booklists on any specific animal.

www.birminghamzoo.com/ao

Bird Box Company

A unique site selling wildlife boxes into which you can fit a camera to connect to your TV or PC so you can watch and hear the birds or mammals from your armchair without disturbing them. They are in the process of establishing an eco-network so you can also view other people's images.

www.thebirdbox.com

British Aquatic Resource Centre

This site aims to provide interesting and informative articles both on a general level and from specialist societies. Information is included about clubs and societies in Britain that you can join, including local clubs and national specialist societies for people with particular interests in this field. There's also information on interesting books and CDs, shops for you to browse and information on where to buy what you need.

www.cfkc.demon.co.uk

The Dinosauria

What does modern science tell us about the dinosaurs? How did they live? Are they really obsolete, long-extinct relics of a more primitive stage in the history of life, or is there more to them than meets the eye? Find out the facts and theories here. The Dinosauria includes a section on myths and contains links to numerous other dinosaur sites.

www.ucmp.berkeley.edu/diapsids/dinosaur.html

The Electronic Zoo

This is a directory of fauna information which is guaranteed to have what you are looking for. It just takes a while to find it!

netvet.wustl.edu/e-zoo.htm

Net Vet

Whatever queries you have about any animal, you are bound to find the answers here. The site contains an electronic zoo, the Net Vet gopher, many specialist directories and the veterinary medicine page of the web's virtual library.

netvet.wustl.edu/vet.htm

Panda Camera

A live panda to watch as it sleeps, plus facts and information.

www.sandiegozoo.org/special/pandacam/index.html

Royal Society for the Protection of Birds

For all bird-lovers, you can find out about the society and read interesting articles on nature reserves, conservation issues and generally looking after our feathered friends. Also contains information on membership of the society.

www.rspb.com

Royal Society for the Prevention of Cruelty to Animals

This is the official site of the Royal Society for the Prevention of Cruelty to Animals. It is full of information about the work done by the RSPCA and also how the public can help them. You can also download a foxy screensaver, adopt a cyber pet, and receive online advice on how to deal with common pet ailments. Enter into the kids' zone and you can read the zany zodiac and meet the mystic monkey.

www.rspca.org.uk

ZooNet

ZooNet has useful information on various zoos and contains all kinds of picture sections. Visit the animal galleries, where the pictures can be viewed in two different sizes: a small thumbnail size and a larger versions to help you get a better look at the contents of this interesting site.

www.zoonet.org/gallery.htm

ANTIQUES AND COLLECTIBLES

There are many thousands of antiques sites out there, many being owned by small antiques shops or trading organisations. Some are merely an online one-page advertisement (not very 'useful', so we haven't listed them); those below offer a wide selection of goods. Collectibles sites are often run by enthusiasts so are less 'commercial'. If you are looking for a particular piece, try the sites listed under *Auctions*, as well as running a search using the name of the item you require (for example, Clarice Cliff teapot).

Antique Desks

This truly is a specialist: every type of desk imaginable, all original. Stock changes regularly but there is always a good selection and all goods are delivered free within the mainland UK.

www.antique-desks.co.uk

AntiqueStall

This simple, mostly text-based site is basically an antiques marketplace, with lists of items available for purchase from individual sellers. There is a wide variety of items, organised into easy-select categories, mostly with full descriptions and photographs (although this is the responsibility of the individual seller). If you have something to sell, the site will charge you 6% of the price achieved on completion: there is no charge to the buyer. A great place to find that one item that you really want, or to find a buyer for that hideous lamp left to you by a maiden aunt.

www.antiquestall.com

Antiques Web

This site claims to have the best selection of art, antiques and collectibles in the UK. It is a very well-designed site with extensive lists of dealers and showrooms, as well as forthcoming festivals and auctions.

www.antiquesweb.co.uk

Artizania

Not art, but clothing and costumes from a bygone age. This site offers antique and vintage clothing, accessories and memorabilia from Victorian times to the present day, so whether you want an Edwardian wedding gown or a Sixties minidress and matching Mary Quant tights, you'll probably find it here. Stock changes regularly, as it's all original and unique, and if you can't find what you want you can e-mail the site owners to ask them to look out for it. Well worth a look!

www.artizania.co.uk

Chelsea Clocks

Antique clocks and other similar objects with online ordering and e-mail for further information.

www.chelseaclocks.co.uk

China Matching

Are you missing a vital part of Granny's best dinner service? Are your tea plates chipped, or has the dishwasher destroyed the pattern? The sites below offer help: they deal in new and discontinued tableware, including antique sets from Wedgwood, Denby, Worcester and many others. Each has an e-mail enquiries service for you to track down exactly what you need, and some also provide useful information on various collectible ranges.

www.chinasearch.uk.com

www.platemates.co.uk

www.perfectmatchchina.com

www.chinamatchuk.co.uk

www.tablewhere.co.uk

Collectibles Today

This American site covers anything you could possible think of collecting, with links to related organisations and collectors' groups, online shopping (with gift suggestions) and many useful articles. It also has its own auction site.

www.collectiblestoday.com

Cyber Antique Mall

The purpose of this page is to provide a web directory that categorises quality antique dealers and antiques-related sites on the web. Most of these links have been checked out for quality and usefulness. Cyber Antique Mall guarantees that all antiques posted on their site are authentic, although they will not be responsible for authentication of antiques from other web sites.

www.cyberantiquemall.com

Enamels

This site is operated by a Florida antiques company, Cameron Smith, that specialises in English enamels. It is the world's largest dealer in the retired issues of Halcyon Days Enamels, with an inventory of over 900 retired and current issues. The site shows many of the available designs, with prices (in dollars, of course), and you are able to order online – although note that the shipping cost for overseas orders is not stated.

www.cameronsmith.com

The Internet Antiques Shop

This site contains a unique group of antique and collectible cybershops that can't be found anywhere else on the web. Tens of thousands of antiques and collectibles are available online from antique shops around the United States, Europe, Canada and South America. Pictures, text and complete online catalogues. If you like to browse antique shops you will love this. The Tias Bookshop is one of the largest of its kind on the web, with almost 1,000 new books about antiques and collectibles.

www.tias.com

National Shelley China Club

If you collect or admire Shelley pottery and fine bone china, check out this site, run by the American club but with members world-wide. It aims to 'give people a chance to share their love of Shelley China with others who also love and collect Shelley China', and to provide a forum for education and information about their shared passion.

www.sweetpea.net/shelleyclub

Reel Poster Gallery

If you are a lover of old films and film memorabilia, this is a must. This gallery supplies vintage film posters and its site contains historical information about posters and poster collecting, as well as a list of their current stock. You can e-mail them with your personal requests, and browse or purchase their various catalogues and books.

www.reelposter.com

Rocking Horses

There are many companies offering rocking horses, mostly replicas, but this site, from Windmill Antiques, outshines them all. It offers both originals and modern replicas, plus a full restoration service, and the site contains a lot of useful information including details of construction methods, traditional designs and even photos of some of their satisfied customers! Worth checking out if you yearn for a horse of your own.

www.classicrockinghorses.co.uk

Totally Teapots

The creator of this site is nuts about teapots and runs the Totally Teapots Collectors Club. Club members can advertise free on the site for teapots they want to buy or sell.

www.totallyteapots.com

Portobello Market

Portobello Road in London is famous for its stalls and shops, which offer an unending source of reasonably priced antiques. The web site gives you information on which stalls are on the market and the range of goods available. There is also a map of the market area and travel directions, which you can download to print out.

www.portobelloroad.co.uk

ART AND DESIGN

Most art galleries and museums have their own web sites (see *Museums, Galleries and Historical Sites*); these are more generic sites covering art and design in general, or a particular period (often useful for homework!). For books on art and design, see the sites listed under *Books: Bookshops and Catalogues*.

About Design

Good for the creative and design world, which seems to be becoming more pervasive. Glossary, chat, links, etc.

www.aboutdesign.co.uk

Art4Deco

This catalogue features hundreds of original artworks from around the world so you can now effortlessly view them at unbeatable prices, and even see how they fit in with your own room's colour scheme, with or without a frame! Once you have selected your piece, you can order it online, and it will be delivered to your door. All prices include delivery to UK, Europe and the US.

www.art4deco.com

ArtAIDS Link

The AIDS patchwork quilt consists of thousands of personal tributes made by family and friends of those who have died of AIDS. You can now add your own tributes by connecting up to this site. ArtAIDS Link is the internet equivalent of this incredible quilt.

www.illumin.co.uk/artaids

Artchive – Theory and Criticism

This is a museum-style site where they say, 'At the Artchive, the only constant will be change.' Each gallery will include new material so that each visit offers variety, taken from new scans in the Recent Acquisitions gallery, to additional art criticism excerpts and new installations of feature exhibits. The museum is divided into several galleries: The Artchive, Art Reviews, Theory and Criticism, Juxtapositions, CD-ROM reviews and Art links.

www.artchive.com

The Art Connection

If you are interested in seeing what artwork is for sale in some of London's top commercial galleries, then this is the site for you.

www.art-connection.com

Art Guide – The Art Lovers' Guide to Britain and Ireland

There are hundreds of magnificent public art collections in Great Britain and Ireland, and each year they are enjoyed by millions of visitors from all over the world. Art Guide is for anyone who has ever enjoyed a trip to one of these collections, or for people who are planning a visit to one of them. Art Guide is organised by artist, by museum and geographically. The database currently contains more than 1,900 named artists, more than 650 museums, over 4,500 individual listings and comprehensive exhibitions listings. For each artist there is a list of their works and where they can be found; for each museum a list of outstanding works in the collection, an address, telephone number and links to other museums in the same region.

www.artguide.org

ArtLex

ArtLex is a dictionary of definitions of all 'artistic words', containing the explanations of more than 2,800 terms along with illustrations, pronunciation notes, quotations and links to other resources.

www.artlex.com

Design Council

Find out all about the many people around today who have helped to add substance to the arts in the UK, whether or not you agree that they have made such a contribution! Find out about the latest movements and exhibitions here at the Design Council's web site.

www.design-council.org.uk

The Fray

On the site it is stated that 'the Fray is a place for people who believe the web is about personal expression and a new kind of art'. If you choose to visit this site, you will definitely find it is provocative, perhaps disturbing, too. You have been warned!

www.fray.com

Grove Art

The Grove Dictionary of Art is the most comprehensive online reference resource for all aspects of the visual arts from prehistory to the 1990s. You will also find links to further information in museum and other art-related web sites. You will need version 4.0 or above of Internet Explorer or Netscape to view the site and either one can be downloaded free from here. It is a subscription site.

www.groveart.com

Pre-Raphaelite Art

This web site, operated by Duxton Ltd, offers a wide selection of Pre-Raphaelite and Victorian art prints, wall hangings and greetings cards. Each is displayed online with details of its artist and history, dimensions and price. You can browse the catalogues and purchase online. Unusually, delivery is free world-wide.

www.pre-raphaelites.co.uk

World Wide Arts Resources

This site is an enormous interactive guide to art and culture on the internet. It has information on over 7,800 artists and over 100,000 further arts resources on top of that. The site covers visual and performing arts too, so you can find out about dance, antiques, opera, theatre, architecture, film and literature here as well. Finally, when you have completed your research you can then use the site to send artistic e-postcards to all your friends.

www.wwar.com

ASTROLOGY

There are many spoof sites out there, and many that ask for a fee to provide you with a 'personalised' horoscope, which are rarely as described. Those sites listed below are well-established, seemingly genuine sites, with links to other areas of interest. For related subjects, see *New Age*.

Astrocenter

You can get free personalised horoscopes on this site, plus an astrological forecast for the year, in-depth readings, natal charts, career reports, numerology reports and much more. Nice, easy to use site – highly recommended!

www.astrocenter.com

Astronet

This astrology magazine consists of a wide selection of regularly updated articles and different types of horoscope. Astronet also includes advice columns and offers interactive features including personalised horoscopes, relationship compatibility and instant readings that can be obtained by various methods using only a birth date. You can also join a workshop and have a basic astrology lesson. There are message boards and a chat room for you to use, together with links to other related sites.

www.astronet.com

Astrology.com

This extensive site offers free horoscopes by e-mail, a chart shop, celebrity sign information and even a 'past life generator'!

www.astrology.com

Astrology et al

A great site for finding astrology books and gifts, including many rare or out-of-print titles. It also features many astrology articles written by the site owners (who also own the bookshop), an introduction to astrology by the resident astrologer Laura Gerking, and even natal charts for US Presidents. Computer-generated charts are available, but you have to pay for them.

www.astrologyetal.com

Astrology on the Web

This is a huge astrology resource with detailed horoscope information, topical astrology features and horoscope readings. The site can be viewed in English, French, German, Italian, Portuguese and Spanish.

www.astrologycom.com

Astrology Portal

This site is basically a list of links, but what a list! Here you can find links to all flavours of astrology and its related sciences, and an enviable selection of horoscopes.

www.webarium.com/altent/astrology

HumorScope

Have you found that your horoscopes are getting too boring or too cynical for you? Check your stars out at HumorScope. The readings are changed daily and, according to the author, are scientifically worked out by spinning a carrot. The author also sends out the daily humorscope to you by e-mail, if you would rather receive it there than on the web.

www.humorscope.com

Indian Astrology

This site is offered by *Express StarTeller*, the biggest-selling astrology magazine in India. It centres on Vedic astrology, which is fully described, and offers a range of free and paid services, together with a wide selection of articles on astrology and mysticism. You can even advertise your 'matrimonial needs' in their column!

www.starteller.com

ASTRONOMY AND SPACE

This fascinating subject is covered on a wide range of sites: these are the best we have found, giving not only stunning pictures from space but also excellent research information and background. Most are fairly graphics-intensive so may take time to load on an older computer or one with a lower-speed modem.

Aboriginal Star Knowledge: Native American Astronomy

Stone medicine wheels were in use about 2,200 years ago on the northern plains of Alberta and Saskatchewan and you can discover how they work at this interesting site. Study Native American legends and folklore behind the stars at this site, too.

www.kstrom.net/isk/stars/starmenu.html

Bradford Robotic Telescope Observatory Site

Anyone can access this telescope and ask it to look at anything in the northern night sky. This is a real 'hands-on' site and is a must for all astronomy enthusiasts.

www.eia.brad.ac.uk/btl

Center for Mars Exploration

This site presents historical references to Mars, together with previous Mars mission information and current Mars news. It also gives you the tools to analyse Mars and take your studies further.

cmex-www.arc.nasa.gov

Constellations

Do you need information on the stars, how they are grouped into constellations, and the Milky Way? The first thing that might surprise you is how far apart the different stars in a constellation actually are! A source of all sorts of fascinating information about the stars is to be found at this site.

www.astro.wisc.edu/~dolan/constellations

Earth and Moon Viewer

This site 'presents an earth map – you can see where it is day, or night, right now'. View either a map of the earth showing the day and night regions at this moment, or view the earth from the sun, the moon, or the night-side of the earth. You can view it above any location on the planet that has been specified by latitude, longitude and altitude, from a satellite in earth orbit, or above various cities around the globe.

www.fourmilab.ch/earthview/vplanet.html

Hubble Space Telescope Site

The Hubble space telescope evokes a new sense of awe and wonder about the infinite richness of our universe in dramatic, unprecedented pictures of celestial objects. This site presents a selection of Hubble's most spectacular images, plus news, history and background of the Hubble project, and video of new views of our universe.

hubble.stsci.edu

NASA

This official site is full of information on NASA science and technology. If you are interested in the latest news on the space programme, then this site is a must. It is updated daily and always features a lead article on the latest space discovery. It contains links to other interesting NASA sites, such as future shuttle launch dates and details of the space station. You can also experience further sights and sounds by stepping into the NASA multimedia gallery.

www.nasa.gov

Students for the Exploration and Development of Space

This extensive, 90+ page site includes everything you need to know about space, and a lot more besides! Browse the entire Messier Catalogue, which provides images of the brightest and most beautiful diffuse objects in the sky, including nebulae, galaxies and star clusters, or learn more about the nine planets in our solar system. This site is intended for a general audience, so all technical and astronomical terms and names are defined in the glossary. Planetary scientists and astronomers will find much of it familiar, plus a few new items of interest. There is one page for each major body in the solar system, each with a large picture of its object plus additional thumbnail images (all linked to their full-size originals); scientific and historical facts; tables of data on the object's satellites (if any) and links to their pages; links to more images and information about the object elsewhere on the web; and a list of open issues for which we as yet have no answers.

www.seds.org

Northern Lights Planetarium

The northern lights, or aurora borealis, have been called 'nature's own gigantic light show'. This special light phenomenon can be seen within the northern and southern hemispheres, only when the circumstances are right. Basically, the northern lights occur when particles from the sun are thrown against the earth by the solar wind. When the particles collide with the earth's atmosphere, the energy of the particles is turned into light. Go on a ride in the universe at this Norwegian planetarium and see it all for yourself.

www.uit.no/npt/homepage-npt.en.html

Saturn Watch

Cassini Mission to Saturn allows you to follow along with the spacecraft as it makes its 6.7-year journey to the planet. Launched in October 1997, every step of the project can be found on this site. You can find out about the mission design, watch movies of the launch to navigation, or look at photos taken along the way.

www.jpl.nasa.gov/cassini

Space Online

Space Online's web site content is divided into five categories and covers all aspects of space information. The site's categories are: Next Launch targets (when the next major rocket launch is scheduled to depart the planet with a complete launch manifest); Space Today (up-to-the-minute news and top space stories from Florida plus NASA status reports, industry news releases and other timely information); Visit the Space Coast (an electronic journey to Florida's space coast to check out the best places to see a launch and learn more about the space programme in Brevard County; Explore the Archives (recent history of the space programme told in stories, photos, sounds and video culled from *Florida Today*'s library and other sources); United in Space (a complete report on the international space station which is now taking shape in orbit).

www.flatoday.com/space

Star Child

Attention all budding young astronomers – look up this site before you next look up at the stars. StarChild is a fun-filled site on all aspects of astronomy that is easy to use, entertaining and extremely educational.

starchild.gsfc.nasa.gov

Star Wars

The official Star Wars site with free club for kids to join, inside news, pictures to print and colour, regular newsletters and interactive scenes. A very classy site.

www.starwars.com

UFOs – Fact or Fiction

This site will help you make up your mind as to what is really going on in space with the UFO stories. This site is mainly based upon UFO information but there is a lot of content you would see on the TV series *The X-Files*. Here you can post your views on conspiracies, UFOs and paranormal phenomena; swap information; buy from their online source for alternative media and paranormal paraphernalia (books, magazines, aliens in a jar and lots more); browse ParaScope's image gallery, read hundreds of declassified documents on covert operations, abuses of government power and UFOs, and find everything you need to use the Freedom of Information Act successfully to obtain government information.

www.parascope.com

Views of the Solar System

Go on a vivid multimedia adventure of the solar system from the comfort of your own home! This site shows the splendour of the sun, planets, moons, comets, asteroids and more. Discover the latest scientific information, or study the history of space exploration, rocketry, early astronauts, space missions and spacecraft through a vast archive of photographs, scientific facts, text, graphics and videos. The site is available in English, Spanish, Portuguese and French.

www.solarviews.com

Windows to the Universe

Windows to the Universe is a user-friendly site helping people to learn about the earth and space-related sciences. It uses the web to allow easy access to numerous sources of space information. The project is aimed at people using publicly available platforms with high-speed internet connections at libraries, hands-on museums and classrooms. It is highly graphics-intensive so may take a long time to load if you use an older computer with a low-speed modem.

www.windows.ucar.edu

AUCTIONS

Online auctions can be a great way to find that collectible item you've been looking for, or to sell something you no longer need. As with all online transactions involving money, use reputable and secure sites only, and remember that if you are bidding for items for sale outside your own country, there may be legal implications plus hefty carriage and excise costs on some items. Here are some of the most established and wide-ranging sites, most of which offer advice on such matters as well as a wide range of auction categories.

NOTE: For details of some security issues when using an online auction, check out www.because-we-can.com/ebayla/index.htm. For further information on the Because-we-can site, see *Internet: Security and Protection*.

Children who have items to sell or who are looking for a particular item may be interested in the many 'swap-it' or exchange sites that are springing up. See *Children* for some examples.

The Auction Channel

The Auction Channel is 'the first interactive themed television and internet channel offering live coverage of auctions and related programming, broadcasting via satellite and cable to television and internet users'. However the live auctions are accessed, viewers can take part in the bidding using the unique interactive bidding system. Fine and contemporary art, antiques, memorabilia, classic cars, country estates, jewellery, collectable toys and posters are all on offer.

www.theauctionchannel.com

Bullnet Auctions

This UK-based free auction site sells items from the normal to the bizarre! Here you can bid for anything from surveillance equipment to toys and novelties, once you have supplied your credit card details. This site may be of particular use to subscribers interested in electronics and computers. If you are selling goods you can add more information about yourself, if you wish.

www.bullnet.co.uk/auctions

eBay

eBay is 'the world's largest personal online trading community', with subsidiaries in various countries. It sells everything from pottery to pianos. Browse and shop at eBay by category, location or availability. Enter your own goods for online auction and sell here, too. Prices can be viewed in pounds or dollars. Auction times are given in GMT or BST.

www.ebay.com

eBid

eBid has been carefully designed and is good to use because it has an extensive and well-organised list of categories. It is a person-to-person auction site that offers items for sale in the UK. Prices are in sterling, and the site requires no credit card registration.

www.ebid.co.uk

Icollector Online Auctions

At Icollector Online Auctions, lots are put up for sale by a wide range of auction houses from around the world. It has a glossary of terminology and the facility to enable bidding directly from the site. It gives details of how to use the site and how to pay for lots, but it does not arrange shipping. You can get advice about this in the Terms and Conditions section or you can ask at the Customer Help desk.

www.icollector.com

Invaluable

This is not just an online auction site but also posts information on auctions through the UK and has a search facility so you can track down specific items from auction catalogues.

www.thesaurus.co.uk

QXL

QXL is an online auction for Europe only and it lets you buy quality goods at great prices. Auctions are opened and closed each day and they offer a variety of computer goods, electronic goods, jewellery, gifts, household items and travel. The site is also available in a number of European languages.

www.qxl.com

Sotheby's

One of the world's most famous auction houses is now on the net, and allows you to buy in one of two ways; online-only sales, similar to those held on eBay and other auctions sites, and absentee bidding at the more traditional sales. Some fabulous items for sale, at a wide range of prices.

www.sothebys.com

BANKING

We can't list every bank here, but these are some sites that we found particularly useful or well-designed. If your bank is not listed, it doesn't mean that it doesn't have a web site or conduct online banking – refer to your branch for details.
See also *Finance and Insurance*.

Barclaycard

Pretty much everything you can do at a bank, you can do from your PC with this site dedicated to Barclaycard customers.

www.barclaycard.co.uk

Barclays

Online banking, business park, stockbrokers, newsroom and recruiting from one of Britain's biggest banks. You'll also find investor information on this site.

www.barclays.com

Cahoot

Part of the Abbey National Group, Cahoot has no branches and operates purely as an internet and telephone banking service. Its products are highly competitive and flexible, offering good rates of interest, even on current accounts, so if you can do without a local branch this may be the site for you. They claim the site is best viewed with the Flash Player plug-in, but you can select a non-Flash version with no discernible disadvantage. It is a highly graphics-intensive site, though so may take a long time to load on older or slower equipment.

www.cahoot.com

Coutts

A highly upmarket bank, providing 'wealth management solutions' for private clients, each of whom is assigned his or her own private banker. An interesting site with a lot of information on investments and banking services, with online banking provided for existing clients. You can't apply for new accounts online, but you can complete an online form to request further information to be sent to you.

www.coutts.com

First-e

Operating offshore, this totally virtual bank has no branches but functions only online. Interest is calculated without paying tax.

www.first-e.com

Girobank BillPay

The quick and easy way to pay your bills using a debit (Delta or Switch) card, whatever bank your money is with. You can use it for regular and one-off payments to a wide selection of companies. Register with this site and you never need to write a cheque to pay a bill again!

www.billpayment.co.uk

Lloyds TSB

Another of the UK high-street banks is now online, with a wide-ranging site covering banking, insurance and many other financial concerns. Customers can operate online accounts and view details of new or alternative services. The site includes a handy branch locator and up-to-date list of interest rates for all accounts.

www.lloydstsb.com

MasterCard International

This site contains everything you could possibly want to know about MasterCard. Look into the future of banking, too, with electronic payments, smart cards and online transactions explained.

www.mastercard.com

MoneyExtra

This is not strictly a bank site, as it deals with all types of finance, but it offers an unrivalled comparison facility for bank accounts, allowing you to see instantly which bank offers the best deal for your particular needs. Each account suggested is described in detail, and links provided to the supplier's web site. The site also includes a lot of useful information on banking and finance.

www.moneyextra.com

Mybank.com

This American site provides a world-wide listing of links to individual bank web sites, so is a great place to start looking for a new bank, wherever you happen to be based.

www.mybank.com

Natwest

Another site offering all the usual banking services online plus useful information on holidays, running a business and other topics relevant to your financial life.

www.natwest.com

Online Banking

Do you want to find a bank that is open 24 hours a day so you can sort out your finances at a time that suits you, or do you want to know more about the one you are already with? Use this site to check out the banks. It gives you all the banks' web sites so you can find out more about each one.

www.netbanker.com

Visa International

Visit the Visa site to find out all about the services they provide. Visa International has the edge where electronic banking is concerned and does not fail to tell you so on the web!

www.visa.com

BEAUTY AND HAIR

Need a new look? Pamper yourself with this selection of sites, ranging from the cool chic of Clinique to homely advice for that hot date. Some are rather tongue-in-cheek, but all are worth visiting for a few new tips: if all else fails there's even plastic surgery. See also *Health, Fitness and Nutrition, Fashion*.

AFE Cosmetics and Skin Care

AFE offers lots of information plus a full line of the highest-quality skin-care and cosmetic products which, until recently, were only been available in professional skin-care salons. They are comparable in quality to the expensive European brands, but because they are manufactured in the United States they are offered at costs that are reasonable for consumers. You can also have an online make-up lesson at the cosmetics counter. As well as defining what the products do, you can also get a very thorough free skin-type test.

www.cosmetics.com

Avon

The well-known UK supplier of cosmetic products now has a web site from which you can order its range of cosmetics and associated products. The site has a good range and is easy to navigate. Delivery takes about five days.

www.avon.com

Beauty Link

Here you can consult the style guide on what's in fashion in the world of beauty. You can also find out which hairstyle suits you best, and even try out a few tried-and-tested beauty secrets. If you're under 21, Cyber Teen offers tips on beauty basics, skin conditioning and even relationship problems. You will need to register first but this is free and quick to do.

beautylink.com

Changes Lives

Divided into four sections – beauty shop, magazine, community information and interactive make-over – this site, primarily for women, gives a range of information on beauty needs and products.

www.changeslives.com

Clinique

This is the web site of Clinique Laboratories. Clinique was first launched in 1968 with prestige skin-care, make-up and fragrance products. The skin-care and make-up products have been designed to address individual skin types and needs and are all allergy tested and 100 per cent fragrance-free. The site offers information about Clinique, its products and which ones are right for you. Check out the health and beauty tips and even shop online (if you are resident in the US; currently no orders can be accepted from elsewhere).

www.clinique.com

Heather Kleinman's Cosmetic Connection

For cosmetic counselling, including monthly features, weekly product reports and a question-and-answer section, look no further. The highlight of this site is a comprehensive product-review section. Even though the product list has been compiled for American readers, there is plenty that European make-up users will find relevant.

www.cosmeticconnection.com

Cosmetic Surgery And Dentistry

Beauty is more than skin deep, so they say. However, if you are considering getting nipped or tucked, straightened or whitened in order to modify what nature intended, this is the site for you. It is devoted to cosmetic enhancement, including plastic surgery, dentistry and vision improvement, and is a good place to check out your options. Pick the body part you are interested in having altered, then read about the options available. There are many before-and-after shots to give you an idea of what is possible. Then pick your surgeon: you can even view comments from past patients and details of experience. From hair transplantation to breast augmentation, it is all covered in detail.

www.ienhance.com

The Make-up Diva

Although this is not the most extensive of sites, the advice here is realistic and relevant to the average woman. The Make-up Diva does not deal with specialist beauty issues, she simply brings you new answers to your make-up and skin-care questions every week. You can subscribe to a free newsletter sent by e-mail and view past questions. The site is well designed and very easy to navigate.

www.makeupdiva.com

Nailtech

Nailtech is a site for both professional nail technicians and consumers. There is a question-and-answer section for consumers who want to know more about caring for artificial nails, and there are links to other related sites. Look up the articles on nail care, including health and hygiene advice that is well worth reading before you book yourself in for that manicure. You may find the latest pictures from recent nail shows either appealing or appalling – so be warned!

www.beautytech.com/nailtech

Virtual Makeover

Do you fancy a complete change of hairstyle but are not sure what will suit you? Do you wonder what you would look like if your hair were a different colour? Do you wish you could to see what you would look like if you changed any of your features? If so then look up this site, order the demo, scan in your photo and start to change your look. The site is sponsored by *Cosmopolitan* and has links to other Cosmo sites. Be warned that it could take some time to load if you have an old computer or slow modem connection.

www.virtualmakeover.com

BEER

See *Drinks and Drinking*.

BOOKS

The internet is a great place for buying, exploring and reading books. Over the next few pages you can explore the following categories:

- Sites describing authors, illustrators and characters
- Bookshop/catalogue sites at which you can order or browse
- Sites providing the texts of online books and stories
- Sites providing book reviews, literary criticism or recommended reading (including help with literacy)

For books on a specific topic, such as DIY, it is also worth checking the sites listed in the relevant section of this book. For example, an arts site may offer specialist art books that the mainstream booksellers do not stock.

AUTHORS, ILLUSTRATORS AND CHARACTERS

These sites give information on particular authors, illustrators or characters and are often ideal for homework or research purposes. Many contain lists of links to other sites, which saves you the need to run your own search. If the person you require is not listed, try running a search on his or her name, and include the title of one of his or her works or the area in which you are interested, to reduce the number of hits (for example, Mary Shelley horror).

Aesop's Fables

Here are two great sites on these timeless tales. The first is an online collection of more than 650 fables, indexed in table format, with morals listed, and including images from the Dore illustrations and the beginnings of audio texts. In the second site, students studying computing in the fine arts were instructed to illustrate each fable in a traditional style and then in a modern style: some also wrote modern text to accompany their designs.

www.pacificnet.net/~johnr/aesop

www.umass.edu/aesop

Author and Illustrator Pages

Many readers are curious about the creators of the books they like. The 500+ links to author/illustrator sites included here will help to satisfy that curiosity.

www.scils.rutgers.edu/special/kay/author.html

The Brontë Web Site

This site is from Japan (!) and offers excellent photographs and links to all kinds of resources on the famous, literary Brontë family.

lang.nagoya-u.ac.jp/~matsuoka/Bronte.html

Harry Potter

There are many sites devoted to these phenomenally successful books, where you can read about the author, preview the books and find out other people's opinions.

www.scholastic.com/harrypotter/home.asp

www.mikids.com/harrypotter

www.usatoday.com/life/enter/books/potter/index.htm

Hergé and Tintin

Hergé (pseudonym of Georges Remi, 1907-83), the Belgian author and illustrator, created Tintin in 1929 and produced 23 volumes of the internationally famous *bande dessinée* by the time of his death. A must for lovers of Tintin and his adventures, this site contains links to a large number of Tintin sites around the world.

www.regiments.org/bd/tintin.htm

Index to Children's Book Authors and Illustrators

This site, part of the Internet School Library Media Center, provides an enviable selection of links to interviews, bios, crib sheets and other information on a wide selection of authors and illustrators. Find out whether you share a birthday with a famous author, or read authors' own descriptions of their work. Very useful for English homework and ideal for use by student, parent and teacher alike.

falcon.jmu.edu/~ramseyil/biochildhome.htm

Jane Austen Information: The Republic of Pemberley

Find here an electronic text of *Pride and Prejudice*, discussions of all Jane Austen's works, as well as information and links to other Jane Austen sites.

www.pemberley.com

Lewis Carroll

For anyone interested in the author of *Alice's Adventures in Wonderland*, this site must not be missed. As well as links to sites of interest, including the Lewis Carroll Society, you can join a Lewis Carroll discussion group, search for events in your area or discover more about the author himself; it even provides games and riddles based on Alice's adventures. For an online copy of the book itself see the section *Books: Online Books and Stories* below.

www.users.interport.net/~fairrosa/carroll.html

Louisa May Alcott Web

This site is an excellent collection of resources on the author of *Little Women* and many other books. Her books have been on the best-seller list for more than 100 years since her death.

www.alcottweb.com

Mark Twain and his Times

This site focuses on how 'Mark Twain' and his works were created and defined, marketed and performed, reviewed and appreciated. The goal is to allow readers, scholars, students and teachers to see what Mark Twain and others from his times said about each other, in ways that can speak to us today.

etext.virginia.edu/railton

The Peter Rabbit Web Site

This is the official and definitive site on the world of Beatrix Potter. Her favourite characters and other aspects of her work can be viewed at a wide selection of art exhibitions, theatrical performances, displays and local events. Find out everything there is to know at this address.

www.peterrabbit.co.uk

Robin Hood Project

The Robin Hood Project is designed to make available in e-format a database of texts, images, bibliographies and information about the Robin Hood stories and other outlaw tales.

www.ub.rug.nl/camelot/rh/rhhome.htm

Shakespeare

One of the best of many Shakespeare sites. Resources, discussion, quotations, lists and text of plays and a useful glossary with plenty of links is provided by this useful and informative site on everything about the Bard.

www-tech.mit.edu/Shakespeare/works.html

Simon Says (Simon & Schuster)

This site, by one of the world's largest and most prolific publishers, contains all sorts of information on books, authors and illustrators. Find out where and when your favourite authors are appearing next, or list new releases on a favourite topic; read reviews, do the crossword, even find a job! The SimonSaysKids section contains lots of helpful information for homework projects, as well as hints for parents, teachers and children alike.

www.simonsays.com

Snow White

This site examines the Snow White story in text and images drawn from the last 100 years.

www.scils.rutgers.edu/special/kay/snowwhite.html

Treasure Island

An informative site very neatly designed for children by a librarian. Here you can learn all about this novel by Robert Louis Stevenson and even submit your own pirate tales! It has a good list of links to related information too.

www.ukoln.ac.uk/services/treasure

Wizard of Oz

These two sites cover everything you need to know about to the Frank Baum's world of Oz (as in *The Wizard of Oz*). The first includes philosophical musings, creative writing and lots of artwork by the inhabitants of Oz, courtesy of primary school children in the US, and is a great way to introduce the story and its characters to youngsters. The second explores the incredible world of Oz in detail and has some great links to other sites.

seamonkey.ed.asu.edu/oz

www.eskimo.com/~tiktok/index.html

BOOKSHOPS AND CATALOGUES

The internet provides a great way to buy books from the comfort of your own home. Most of your high street favourites are here, along with some specialists to help you find precisely what you want. No more lugging heavy tomes home on the bus: these sites will deliver to your door, and often offer great discounts over shop prices.
See also *Reference, Shopping*.

Achuka

This is an extensive and enthusiastic guide to children's books, broken down by age group and genre. It has a listing of events and a growing online cuttings catalogue that points you to reviews of a long list of authors and their works. This is essential browsing for book-lovers of all ages.

www.achuka.co.uk

Advanced Book Exchange

An excellent source of out-of-print books. Although the site is Canadian, it has an extensive and world-wide list of partner bookshops, including many in the UK.

www.abebooks.com

Alphabetstreet

This popular site sells a lot more than just books; it is part of the Streets Online group which sells almost everything you can think of! The books section is particularly extensive though, and there are great offers on many popular titles. You can even buy, sell and exchange books so it's a great place for a bargain.

www.alphabetstreet.com

Amazon

Amazon.com is probably the most famous online retailer of books, music and more. If you do not know anything about a particular title, you can look up the various synopses, excerpts and reviews made available by publishers, authors and readers. The site has easy-to-use search and browse features, customised e-mail notification, personalised shopping services, secure web-based credit or debit card payment and direct delivery, often within 24 hours. Amazon.co.uk is the British subsidiary with more than 1.5 million locally published titles, providing the same service as Amazon.com but priced in sterling and distributed from a UK warehouse.

www.amazon.com

www.amazon.co.uk

Barnes and Noble

With world-wide despatch and discounts on all titles for sale online, it is easy to see why this company is currently the biggest bookseller in the world. If you want to know more about a book this site includes links to press releases and literary excerpts.

www.barnesandnoble.com

Bibliofind

An excellent site for finding out-of-print, rare or unusual books.

www.bibliofind.com

The Bookplace

Hammicks, the well-known UK high street chain of bookstores, stocks over 1.5 million books and its online shop, The Bookplace, has descriptions that are indexed by its search engines. Want to know the best title on a particular topic? Then put this site to the test! World-wide delivery.

www.thebookplace.com

British Magazines

Ideal for ex-pats, this is almost as easy as popping down to the corner shop for your favourite magazine, as they deliver over 3,500 British magazines throughout the world.

www.britishmagazines.co.uk

Children's Bookshop

Based in Hay-on-Wye, Herefordshire, UK, this real bookshop sells children's books and currently has about 15,000 titles. It specialises in 20th-century fiction and has a free book search service for finding books not in stock. The site has an online catalogue and ordering system, plus useful information and links on Hay-on-Wye. World-wide delivery; online currency converter.

www.childrensbookshop.com

Future Fantasy

The Future Fantasy Bookstore offers world-wide delivery and an order by e-mail service. The categories available include science fiction and fantasy, but they also cater for fans of horror and mystery.

futfan.com

Natural History Bookshop

This is the largest environmental mail order bookshop in the world. Search for any title here. It has thousands of titles describing and explaining the amazing diversity of the natural world: field guides, textbooks, monographs, reports, CDs, videos and cassettes on every environmental subject you can think of!

nhbs.com

Ottakar's

Another well-known bookshop, Ottakar's has a well-planned site at which you can browse, shop and read reviews or take part in a literary quiz. You can choose to have books delivered to your home (usually by next day), which incurs the usual postage charge, or to your nearest Ottakar's store, which is free.

www.ottakars.co.uk

Superbook

This site is great for finding 'remaindered' books at great discounts – up to 90% off according to the site. There is a huge range covering all topics, which is updated frequently. All books are in stock and can be delivered the next day.

www.superbook.co.uk

Waterstones

Another heavyweight in the high street, Waterstones has an easy-to-navigate site that will quickly find any book for you, even some that are out of print. They will deliver orders free to your nearest store. You can write your own reviews, and read those of other readers, and authors get the chance to tell you why you should buy their book. There are even e-books available for download.

www.waterstones.co.uk

WH Smith

The site for the major high-street chain selling books, stationery, CDs, games, etc.

www.whsmith.co.uk

ONLINE BOOKS AND STORIES

These sites contain whole story texts or condensed versions: a great way to see whether you really like a book before you buy it, or to check details of a character or storyline. The many children's sites are a great way to encourage young children to read and think up their own stories.

Bibliomania

At Bibliomania you can read some 60 classic novels as well as reference works. Science, economics, some biographies and ancient texts are all included here. To top it all, you will also find that there is a good selection of poetry at this site, and a great selection of literary quotations ideal for every occasion.

www.bibliomania.com

Book a Minute

Check out this site for amusing condensed versions of classic, children's and science-fiction literature. The classics section covers everything from Shakespeare to Steinbeck (sadly rather too condensed for school book reviews!), and there is also a bedtime section with bite-sized versions of everything from Dr Seuss to the Hardy Boys. The science fiction section gives you your favourite science fiction and fantasy stories at light speed and covers everything from Tolkien to Dragonlance. Good fun.

www.rinkworks.com/bookaminute

Children's Storybook Online

This site is divided into three sections, one containing stories aimed at young children, the next for older children, and a third for young adults. Read lots of exciting stories, many complete with illustrations and sound, try the colouring books and riddles, and shop for toys, books and many other items in their online mall.

www.magickeys.com/books

The Many Faces of Alice

This lovely site provides a full-text version of Lewis Carroll's *Alice's Adventures in Wonderland*, fully and aptly illustrated by young children at the Dalton School in New York with student essays and teacher notes. A great resource for schools.

www.dalton.org/ms/alice

Stories From The Web

This site, produced by the Library and Information Commission, is a great way to get children interested in story-reading and writing. Its colourful, fun format and animations grab the attention and it actively encourages children to get involved in book clubs and comment on what they've read. It has some great stories too!

hosted.ukoln.ac.uk/stories

Storytrain

This site is described as an illustrated, collaborative story project for creative children. It contains some great stories for young children to read and add to in words or pictures. Each is presented as a 'train' of contributions and there are to date over 100 stories to choose from. It is part of kids-space.org, which is a monitored, child-friendly site: contributions are written by children world-wide and are not edited, so sometimes the quality of the English is poor: but it's a great way to get kids interested in creative writing.

storytrain.kids-space.org

The Yarn

Don't just read it, write it, too! Read a chapter of the story and then choose one of two options: go on to the next chapter or write your own. See how the plot thickens! (Note the warning on the front page about content: this site may be unsuitable for children.)

www.theyarn.com

REVIEWS, CRITIQUES AND RECOMMENDATIONS

Many of the mainstream bookshop sites have a review facility, but the sites below are dedicated to reviews, recommendations and critiques rather than sales.

Arts and Letters Daily

This site is an intellectual guide to literature on the internet. It covers many different topics ranging through literature, philosophy, art, science, history and more. Some people may find the site controversial, but it is well worth a visit and may encourage you to join the discussions yourself.

www.cybereditions.com/aldaily

Books Unlimited

This site from *The Guardian* newspaper is full of interesting information. It has a range of news stories, literature reviews, and articles from both authors and celebrities. There are many interesting parts to this site, two of which are the author profiles – providing you with background information about your favourite writers – and the mood-matcher, which will pick you a poem in seconds to suit your mood.

www.booksunlimited.co.uk

Book Trust

The Book Trust offers free book lists, containing suggested and recommended reading, and runs book prizes and brilliant projects to encourage readers of all ages and cultures to discover and enjoy books.

www.booktrust.org.uk

British Literature

Specifically, this site's goal is to collect, in the most organised manner, a large collection of articles, information and photos covering every aspect of literature in the British Isles. The reason for creating the site is to create an internet resource useful to the world at large.

www.britishliterature.com

Children's Literature Web Guide

Want to find out more about any new children's books that are available? If so, then you will find this site very useful as it gives a critique of all recent publications, together with links to texts.

www.ucalgary.ca/~dkbrown

Federation of Children's Book Groups

This is a great starting place if you want to buy books for children or find out about how to encourage your child to read more. It provides lists of recommended books for different age groups, as suggested by the members and organisers of children's book groups around the country. It can help you find your local group and provide information on reading with children. Well worth a look.

www.fcbg.mcmail.com

Pick a Book

Author and publisher profiles, news, reviews and offers feature on this site. You can search by author, title, publisher, ISBN or classification to find the information you want on your favourite books, and also buy online.

pickabook.co.uk

Reading is Fundamental

This web site, courtesy of the National Literacy Trust, aims to help your child understand why reading is important and how it can be fun. It's a colourful, lively site that will appeal particularly to younger children, but offers information and recommendations for all ages. It also has a good list of other organisations that can help with learning to read.

www.rif.org.uk

Spike Magazine

Spike is about people, books and ideas. The site continues to update on a frequent but erratic basis, publishing interviews, features, reviews and new writing by both established and unpublished authors. The site features not only the famous and the up-and-coming, but also the totally obscure.

www.spikemagazine.com

BUSINESS AND E-BUSINESS

There are, of course, many thousands of business sites, of which we have selected only a few, covering useful and frequently requested topics. These sites will be of interest primarily to those running their own business, who are looking for information on other companies and business strategies, or want to look into e-business. If you are looking for a job, go to *Employment and Careers* instead.

Asian Net

This site contains all the information you need to conduct business with Asian companies. It contains a huge search engine of businesses and organisations in Asia, which will display information about the companies' products and services available to you.

www.asiannet.com

Big Yellow

Big Yellow is a massive directory, containing the contact details of 11 million US businesses. You can search by category and/or by business name. Click on any address to see detailed maps and driving directions too.

www.bigyellow.com

Biz Pro Web

This web site is to connect you with the resources available on the internet to help you with your business. It is specifically targeted toward the needs of small-business owners, professionals and home-office entrepreneurs so that you don't have to spend time searching for useful links.

www.bizproweb.com

Companies House

Companies House is the organisation to which all UK companies must report on an annual basis. Here you can find out about disqualified directors and the reporting details of any listed company, and order leaflets and forms. You can search for available company names and link to various related sites.

www.companieshouse.gov.uk

Companies Online

Find out all you need to know about over 100,000 public and private American companies.

www.companiesonline.com

Delphion Intellectual Property Network

The Intellectual Property Network (IPN) lets you search and view patent documents from the US, Europe and Japan that go back to 1971. You can also check out patent applications published by the World Intellectual Property Organisation (WIPO). The site has an entertaining gallery of obscure patents containing all things strange and wonderful.

www.delphion.com

E-commerce Guidebook

This site is an excellent resource for helping you get your business e-commerce-ready. At the site you will find reviews, a step-by-step tutorial for making your business ready for e-commerce, a list of companies offering payment gateways, and many links. The tutorial is an excellent place for people to start who are new to e-commerce as it provides the basic understanding necessary to get you started, and allows you to make a better decision about which company to go with.

www.online-commerce.com

Electronic Commerce

This site offers links and information to answer the many questions you may have and can help you understand the confusion and complexity of e-commerce. It also offers help and information on data processing and smart card technology.

ecommerce.about.com

Ergonomics

Ergonomics is the study of humans in relation to their environment, and ergonomic design centres on the efficient interaction between man and machine. This covers everything from correct posture and desk height to the elimination of possible causes of injury. This helpful site provides free training materials and risk assessment, and carries a range of ergonomic furniture; there's a mailing list for updates.

www.ergonomics.co.uk

Europages

This gives the basic details of 500,000 companies from 30 European countries, which are searchable by name or by product. The site also offers a company search by activity sector, plus links to online Yellow Pages from all over Europe.

europages.com

Internet Business Guide

Ideas, tips and instructions for creating, maintaining and promoting commerce-related web pages. There are news profiles, too. At this site you can find the resources necessary to establish home-based internet businesses and to find experienced merchants.

www.ibguide.com

The Institute of Logistics and Transport

The Institute of Logistics and Transport site, a good source of information both about the institute itself and all matters related to supply-chain management.

www.iolt.org.uk

Mondus

An online market for small and medium-sized businesses who are tired of spending too much time searching for new suppliers and want to expand their business. This site will help buyers purchase more quickly and conveniently while saving money, and help suppliers acquire new customers and increase sales.

www.mondus.com

MoreBusiness.com

A great source of information on getting started in your own business. The site is designed for Americans, so items such as the Tax Talk may be irrelevant elsewhere, but much of the information is practical and appropriate wherever you happen to be based. There are many useful tips provided by entrepreneurs and corporate businesses, and even templates for standard business documents, links to useful download sites and software reviews.

www.morebusiness.com

Sell it! on the Web

Want to start selling on the web? Then Sell it!, the number one e-commerce resource, is here to help! Peruse news, reviews and step-by-step guides about selling goods or services on the web. Also get free books, business ideas and newsletters. The world of e-commerce can be confusing but this site aims to make it easy for you.

sellitontheweb.com

SmarterWork

This site bills itself as 'the global market place for business services'. Clients can post details of projects they need to commission and experts can bid for the work.

www.smarterwork.com

TaxCafé

This site offers tax advice from leading UK tax experts: they guarantee an answer within 24 hours on any topic – just enter your question and pay the £19.95 fee. You can also search previous questions and sign up for e-mail newsletters for free.

www.taxcafe.co.uk

Training Zone

A comprehensive site dealing with aspects of human resources, particularly training and learning resources. A very useful place for exchanging ideas with other site users.

www.trainingzone.co.uk

UK Patent Office

The United Kingdom Patent Office is the official body for the granting of patents and for the registration of designs and trademarks in the UK (through its Designs Registry and Trade Marks Registry). It is also involved with domestic and international policy on intellectual property, including copyright, design right and other unregistered rights (through its Policy Directorates). This is the official site on which you can make searches but the information is not intended to be comprehensive and readers are advised to seek independent professional advice before acting on anything they find here.

www.patent.gov.uk

CARDS AND GREETINGS

Forgotten someone's birthday? Missed the post? These sites provide the answer: e-cards and greetings which simply drop into your recipient's inbox like a normal e-mail, but with far more pizazz. Not only that, they are free and environmentally friendly, too! Some sites also offer the more traditional cards for you to purchase and post.
See also *Flowers*, *Gifts*.

Blue Mountain

Sometimes it can be hard to find the right card for the usual occasions such as birthdays, weddings and births, but have you ever found yourself wondering where on earth you will be able to get a card that says 'Happy Left-handers Day'? Blue Mountain provides a wide selection of animated cards for all current and upcoming events – however obscure – including international and multi-denominational cards. You can even send chocolates and gifts with your card (they are delivered in the usual way though!).

www.bluemountain.com

Cardlady

Cardlady (previously Card Central) is a one-stop site for virtual postcards and greeting cards on the web. The site is a growing searchable database of many hundreds of card sites, whatever the occasion. It also links to sites for 'real' cards.

www.cardlady.com

Care Mail

Choose from the many cute animated cards, with optional music accompaniment, and with each card sent Care Mail will donate a portion of its advertising revenue to a wildlife charity. Care Mail has dedicated itself to saving wildlife around the world and to helping protect the remaining wild places. Through its network of talented artists, environmentalists and business leaders, and together with your help in making use of this free service, they have found a practical way to do this. If you can't find a card you like, you can create your own.

www.care2.com/send/categories

CraftPals cards

Part of a craft site, this has some beautiful e-cards and you can create your own text for most of them, making them somewhat more personal. You can attach music to any card from a wide list of tracks.

www.craftpals.org/card

E-greetings

Yet more cards to send and receive, including animated greetings. Particularly good on hello cards and cheaper than a phone call. You can add gift certificates to any card.

www.egreetings.com

Hassle-Free Cards

Ideal for those of us who perpetually forget those important dates. Just visit this site once, fill in all the birthdays, anniversaries and other occasions you like, and give a brief description of the style of card that would be most appropriate for each. Ten days before each date, they will select and post you a card for you to sign and send on. Easy-peasy! Each card costs £2.99 – a lot cheaper than a bunch of flowers to say 'sorry I forgot'! – and every fifth card is half price.

www.hasslefreecards.com

Moonpig

Customisable cards from this online retailer, £1.99 each including postage, direct to the recipient. The site has a 'naughty filter' to allow you to restrict what you want to see, and cards are available for a huge range of occasions and recipients. Well worth a look. You need to register to use the facility, but can browse without doing so.

www.moonpig.com

Virtual Insults

If you feel that the majority of greetings cards on offer are filled with over-the-top sentiment or are too 'nice', help is at hand. This site provides plenty of choice, and there are insults for all occasions for anyone who has ever wanted a card to say what they really feel!

www.virtualinsults.com

CHARITIES

Many charitable organisations now have their own web sites, and this is a great way to find out more about what they do and make donations or purchases from their various online stores. Here are our favourites: if you can't find what you want here, use a search engine to locate your own particular favourites.

Some of the sites listed below appear not to be for charities at all, but just general shopping sites. However, each donates a percentage of its profits to nominated charities, so they are a great place to shop and help others at the same time. Some other charity sites can be found in the *Health, Fitness and Nutrition* section.

Age Concern

Age Concern cares about all older people and believes that later life should be fulfilling and enjoyable. The British-based organisation provides a number of its fact sheets online, with topics ranging from going on holiday to organising a funeral. Also gives contact information and details of various courses for the over-50s. Works closely with partner organisations around the world.

www.ace.org.uk

Childnet International

This is a British charity that helps children all over the world, especially in poorer countries and regions. It hopes to help these children learn more about life and their studies, using the internet as a work tool. There are many projects going on and you will find out all about them and about the charity here. You can even make a donation to them online if you wish. It also has some good links for parents worried about their child using the internet. The site is available in German, Spanish, English and French.

www.childnet-int.org

Free2Give

This is one of the sites at which you can do all your usual net shopping but give to charity at the same time. Products offered include insurance, food, travel, gifts, wine, and much more – many from sites recommended elsewhere in this book – and up to 10% of the price you pay is given to the charity of your choice. It doesn't cost you any more than shopping directly at the individual sites.

www.free2give.com

Great Ormond Street Hospital

Renowned world-wide for its level of care for sick children, the Great Ormond Street Hospital in London relies almost totally on donations from the public. Visit its lively site to find out more about its work, its history and how you can help.

www.gosh.org

Hospices

Hospices provide care for the terminally ill, often on a short-term basis to allow their families a break. This can be a life-saver to tired relatives who have nowhere else to turn. There are many such organisations in the UK, mostly funded primarily or exclusively by donations from the public, and all staffed by caring, dedicated and often low-paid professionals and volunteers. This site provides links to many of those that have a presence on the web. Check it out to see what you can do to help.

www.hauraki.co.uk/hospice_uk

Hunger Site at the UN

Information on world hunger. Visit this site often, as one click on the site (per person, per day) means that a sponsor will pay for a meal for a starving person.

www.thehungersite.com

Macmillan Cancer Relief

Macmillan nurses are famed as being caring, considerate professionals in the field of cancer care, but few people realise that their work for the Macmillan organisation is entirely funded from donations for their first three years (after which the NHS steps in). While all recruited nurses have extensive nursing experience, the first years with Macmillan involve a lot of training in this very specialised area of care, so donations are always needed and welcome. This site provides eye-opening detail into the work of this valuable organisation, including not only nurses but also doctors, dedicated Macmillan wards and hospitals.

www.macmillan.org.uk

Naomi House

This is the site for one of the UK's leading children's hospices. Entirely funded by donations, it offers respite care to families of terminally ill children. Visit this site to find out more about this centre of hope, and how you can help keep it open.

www.naomihouse.org.uk

National Children's Bureau

The National Children's Bureau (NCB) is a registered charity which promotes the interests and well-being of all children and young people across every aspect of their lives. Its site contains valuable information on equal opportunities, participation and young citizenship and other issues of concern to children and parents. Well worth a visit.

www.ncb.org.uk

NCH Action for Children

NCH Action for Children improves the lives of Britain's most vulnerable children and young people by providing a diverse and innovative range of services for them and their families, and campaigning on their behalf. Find out exactly what they do at this site.

www.nchafc.org.uk

Refugees

You can access information about the plight of refugees from around the world at the site of the United Nations High Commission for Refugees. Read first-hand accounts of people forced to flee persecution and up-to-date news on conflicts world-wide. For holding discussions in the classroom, the site includes a guide for teachers on the subject. It certainly brings home the awful reality of life.

www.unhcr.ch

SmartChange

SmartChange is a new service that describes itself as 'a channel to help people get more involved in positive social change'. Recognising the problem a lot of people have with just handing over donations to charities, it aims to help its customers 'feel like investors in community, not just donors'. Find out more at its web site.

www.smartchange.co.uk

U Shop U Give

This is another shopping site that donates a percentage of your spend to one or more of its charities. A great way to shop online and help others at the same time. At this site, up to 10% of your bill, and up to 50% of the site's commission are donated.

www.ushopugive.com

CHILDREN

These sites are primarily of interest to young (pre-school and primary) children and will help to build their interest and skills in using the internet and computers, as well as providing more general entertainment or education.

For help with literacy, see also *Books: Reviews, Critiques and Recommendations*. For topics relevant to older children, see *Teenagers*. For help with homework, see *Homework Research and Revision*, or specific subjects. For fun sites of interest to kids and adults alike, see *Fun*.

BBC Little Kids

Part of the enormous BBC Online site, this site is aimed particularly at young children and provides plenty of activities featuring their favourite TV characters. The emphasis is mostly on fun, helping pre-schoolers become familiar with the computer and its various uses. There are many other areas of the BBC site for children, both educational and fun, so it is worth exploring. Links are provided to other related sites, and all content is child-friendly.

www.bbc.co.uk/littlekids

Bob the Builder

Bob and his gang of talking machines appear in one of the most popular cartoon series around, and here all Bob fans can play games, download pictures for colouring and even send Bob postcards to their friends. A lively, fun site ideal for pre-school children.

www.bobthebuilder.org

The Bonus Supersite for Kids

This American site is well equipped with a limited browser that only allows the user to access the kid-safe sites. There are various sections: explore, inspect, colour, imagine and play. All contain educational projects and games, making this a great site for fun and learning.

www.bonus.com

Children's Literature Web Guide

Want to find out more about any new children's books that are available? If so, then you will find this site very useful as it gives a critique of all recent publications together with links to texts.

www.ucalgary.ca/~dkbrown

Crayola

The site of the famous crayon manufacturer – although actually they produce far more than just crayons – offers kids of all ages a wealth of information, games and activities. The pre-school section will help your youngsters to learn their letters, phonetics and numbers, with screens to print off and colour in using their own crayons.

www.crayola.com

Disney

If you want to know more about the Walt Disney Company and all its movies, other products and theme parks, this site catalogues it all. It's the official Disney web site with games, stories, films, musical theatre, videos, competitions and, of course, information on all the Disney theme parks. This is quite graphics-intensive and many of the games require plug-ins, so to avoid disappointing young children with lengthy waits for their favourite character, check it out yourself and download the required software first.

www.disney.com

Dungeons and Dragons

The popular role-playing game is now becoming a movie, and this site gives you all the information you need to be ready: you can even download your own DND browser. Unless you have a speedy modem, select the 'Humble' version of events from the front page: the Flash version can take an age to load up.

www.seednd.com

Fantastic Fractals

Did you know that a fractal is a complex self-similar and chaotic mathematical object that reveals more detail as you get closer? Well you do now! Learn about fractals with the step-by-step tutorials or use the site to download software that will enable you to generate some amazing graphics. Ideal for kids of eight and over, this is great fun for adults too.

techlar.com/fractals

Funschool

This site is packed full of educational games for the young: it is an American site so is arranged by school 'grade' rather than age, but with a little exploring you can find the most suitable starting point for your child.

www.funschool.com

Global Gang

This site is aimed at getting children and teenagers interested in what is happening in the wider world. The site is set up by Christian Aid and through the use of good news and games they aim to raise children's awareness of important global issues. The site also aims to put children in touch with other children in different countries all over the world.

www.globalgang.org.uk

Greatest Places

Check out this site for the greatest places in the world: do you agree with them or is your own area far better? Ideal for introducing primary children to different countries, landscapes and traditions around the globe, and encouraging their interest in geography, science and other cultures. Good for homework research too!

www.greatestplaces.org

Harry Potter

This is the 'official' Harry Potter site (operated by Warner Bros.), giving regularly updated information and sneak previews of the forthcoming movie. You can sign up for advance information by e-mail and they intend to launch a Hogwarts School Online site soon, which will be accessible from this site. There are many other Potter sites to explore; some of these are listed under *Books: Authors, Illustrators and Characters*.

www.harrypotter.com

Kids Recipes

Do your kids like to cook? Need some new ideas? Try this site, part of the excellent myrecipe.com, which has recipes specifically tailored to children for them to make and enjoy. As it is an American site, some of the measures may be unusual, but most recipe books will show you how to convert to the European equivalents. One particularly handy feature is the ability to scale all recipes to the specific number of servings you require – so no need to eat macaroni cheese for three weeks (unless you want to, of course).

www.kidrecipe.com

Mathematical Magic

For schoolchildren and teenagers. Find out how to perform all sorts of tricks without becoming a member of the magic circle. Here practice does not make perfect, a basic understanding of maths does!

www.scri.fsu.edu/~dennisl/CMS/activity/math_magic.html

Something Strange to Make and Do?

When you are feeling creative but don't know what to make or do, try out this site for some very strange ideas – especially the kind of science projects you are unlikely to do at school, such as making stink bombs and fake blood! Note: some of these projects are somewhat dangerous, so it's not really suitable for very young children!

freeweb.pdq.net/headstrong

A Space for Children to Play

This site is designed to be a sharing space for children on the internet. There are illustrated stories by children from all over the world and pictures for the children to write further stories about. There is even a concert hall where they can put sound files of their own musical performances online. There should be enough on the site to keep them occupied for more than 20 minutes!

www.kids-space.org

Star Child

Attention all budding young astronomers – look up this site before you next look up at the stars. StarChild is a fun-filled site on all aspects of astronomy that is easy to use, entertaining and extremely educational.

starchild.gsfc.nasa.gov

Swapit

This site, heavily plugged on TV, allows children to exchange things they no longer want for things they do – assuming someone else has what they want for sale. The site is carefully monitored and provides an ideal way for kids to find new toys and interests at minimal cost. It is particularly useful for items such as computer games, although common sense dictates that you are unlikely to find anyone willing to exchange the latest releases for last year's Furby. If your child has tired of a particular hobby, try this site to exchange that old stamp album for something completely different.

www.swapit.com

Thomas the Tank Engine & Friends

This is the official site of the children's favourite Thomas the Tank Engine. The site is full of fun and games with the children's favourite steam trains. There are puzzles and riddles, a chance to paint and colour pictures – and of course a trip round the depot to meet Thomas and all his friends.

www.thomasthetankengine.com

UK Kids

It's hard to think of much that they have left out of this site. There's games, film reviews and music plus more 'serious' features on careers and school.

www.UKkids.co.uk

Wild World of Wonka

This site, based on the popular Willy Wonka books by Roald Dahl, is committed to developing the premier web site for kids, making the site an entertaining and educational forum for children to learn. Here you can use magical colouring-in to explore a vast range of information and music. There's a load of stuff here and most of it can be downloaded to play offline to save your telephone bill. Note: you will need the plug-in Flash Player to access the best bits of this site – you will be prompted to download it if you don't already have it installed, or you can get it from www.macromedia.com/software/flash

www.wonka.com

Winnie the Pooh

All A.A. Milne's characters are here, and there are great games to play – come and join the fun! There are stories and poems, games and puzzles; you can chat to other Pooh fans or send e-mail to Piglet. This site is an unofficial celebration of all things Pooh, rather than a sponsored or merchandising site.

www.winniethepooh.co.uk

Xplore Kids

A great fun site with lots going on, children can investigate science, sport, an underwater world and everyone's favourite: the world of dinosaurs. They can also contribute their own stories to the site. A good one for keeping them busy on a rainy day.

www.xplore.com/xplore500/medium/kids.html

Yahooligans

This is a version of the well-known search engine Yahoo, aimed at the youngsters now using the internet. You use the site exactly as you would the main search engine but the links are more fun and interesting and also educational for kids of any age. This is a search engine that will be enjoyed by adults as well as children.

www.yahooligans.com

You Can Find Out Why

Here you'll find the answer to many everyday questions, such as why feet smell or how a refrigerator makes itself cold. Great for school projects! It is part of the Bonus Supersite (see page 137).

www.beakman.com

COMPUTERS AND SOFTWARE

These sections will help you find elusive software and new hardware, plus answers to almost any computer-related question. You can compare prices for computer-related goods, find a new service provider or simply learn more about how it all works. The sites are grouped in the following categories:

- Graphics and images
- Hardware and supplies
- Security
- Sites for Mac users
- Software suppliers and download sites
- Terminology and problem-solving
- Other computer sites

For internet-related information, see *Internet*. You might also find some of the sites listed under *Reference* useful for more general information.

GRAPHICS AND IMAGES

These sites provide free graphics and images, which you can use on your own web site or in other documents.

Animated Gifs of Michael Shaikun

This is a good site to obtain more and more graphics for your own web page designs. Not only are there animated gifs here but there are collections of icons, backgrounds, text – anything you need to make your web page load more slowly!

gifs.net

Art Today

This site normally charges a flat fee for downloading images, but gives you a free three-day trial period (which should be enough for you to download most of the items you will need). It boasts 1.2 million files, including clip art, photographs and animations, so there should be plenty for you to choose from. If you need new graphics regularly, you can subscribe for a small fee and have access for one year to their entire catalogue.

www.arttoday.com

Clip Art

If you have a presentation to make, you can always make documents and overhead transparencies clearer and easier on the eye by adding clip art. Use these sites to find all the pictures you want.

www.clipart.com

www.clipartconnection.com

GifsNow.com

This site has a huge number of gif files (one of the best formats for the web) including animations, icons for your web site, 3D images and more. Images can be downloaded individually or by category. You can download trial versions of graphics software here too.

www.gifsnow.com

HARDWARE AND SUPPLIES

These sites allow you to shop online for new hardware, as well as peripherals such as printers and scanners. Some are more general shopping sites that provide price comparisons across suppliers, and many also offer software.

Big Rom

This computer supplies company promises really low prices combined with quality goods and a reliable service. It is part of the Which? Webtrader network, so you can shop here with confidence.

www.bigrom.co.uk

Buying Guides

This is one of the most comprehensive buying resources ever published, with a computer section covering both hardware (parts) and software. It is the only tool created to guide each customer through the entire buying process, from the realisation of their need for a computer product to intelligent fulfilment of that need in order to make the best buying decision possible.

www.buyingguides.com

Computer Manufacturers

All the main computer manufacturers have their own web sites on the internet – in fact, many of them have sites in different countries all over the world. At their sites you can find a vast amount of information on all the companies' products and they are often the best place to get support for your computer, including updated drivers for your hardware. Many of the companies are based in America but from their main site it is possible to connect to a site closer to home for faster downloads. Some of the computer manufacturers' sites even allow you to buy new computer systems, base units, monitors or other hardware online.

www.compaq.com

www.hp.com

www.dell.com

www.gw2k.com

www.toshiba.com

Micro-warehouse

Both hardware and software are on sale from this site, with a good range of software products, next-day delivery (free for orders over £30), and a quality service. Not the best place for games, but good for general software.

www.microwarehouse.co.uk

SECURITY

These sites provide either security products, such as anti-virus or password protection, or information on security. For 'safe surfing' products, see *Internet: Security and Protection*.

Blacklist of Internet Advertisers

This site is intended to curb inappropriate advertising on Usenet newsgroups and via junk e-mail. It works by describing offenders and their offensive behaviour in order to help people avoid their 'services'. The list is posted regularly to several newsgroups, stored on a number of FAQ archives around the world, and the most recent version is always available on the web.

math-www.uni-paderborn.de/~axel/BL

Scambusters

Internet Scambusters is a site created as a result of watching hundreds of companies get blatantly wrong information and baseless hype while trying to learn how to use the internet to promote their businesses successfully. If you want to learn from other people's mistakes, subscribe here to find out what others have done wrong and how to avoid being taken in yourself.

www.scambusters.org

Symantec

Symantec offers both home and business users the computer software they need to help with their networks and security. Symantec offers award-winning solutions for corporate help desks, mobile and telecommuting professionals, as well as the industry's leading anti-virus and protection applications.

www.symantec.com

Tracing Software

Have you ever wondered where the signals you are sending are actually going or have you wanted to trace that computer address that is giving you a headache? NeoWorx have come up with the answer. Their software, NeoTrace, traces the route your data takes all around the world and displays it to you graphically. You have to purchase the software but you can download a demo version first.

www.neoworx.com

Trend Micro

Home of the award-winning PC-cillin anti-virus software, this site has tons of information on viruses, virus protection and general security. You can download trial versions of its various products, or order full versions online.

www.trend.com

Virus Database

This site provides useful information on many viruses and how to prevent virus damage. It includes a database of all known viruses to date.

www.virusdatabase.com

SITES FOR MAC USERS

The following sites contain valuable information for those using a Mac.

Mac Connect

The first and largest national service provider exclusively for users of the MacOS in America. Here they are dedicated to providing Macintosh users with access to a superior data network with excellent Mac support from folks that love the Mac as much as you do! MacConnect provides dial access with over 1,000 access numbers, world-class Mac-centric web hosting, and full-time high-speed connections nationwide.

www.macconnect.com

MacFix-it

MacFix-it is more of a troubleshooting site than a news site. Here's the type of information you will find: troubleshooting tips, hints, work-arounds and solutions of any sort; news about documented bugs, conflicts and problems with existing versions of popular software and hardware; announcements of new and/or updated products. Their Download Library is a collection of troubleshooting-related freeware and shareware utilities and a lot more.

www.macfixit.com

Mac Orchard

This site is a careful list of the most vital internet applications and links for Macintosh internet users, as well as internet software reviews contributed from the Mac Orchard's audience. Also available is a very good FAQ about the site for new users of the site and Macintosh machines.

www.macorchard.com

Mac World

This is the online version of the magazine *Mac World*. You can find out all the latest information for the Mac machines and software, and you can even subscribe to the magazine from the site. This site is also available in German, Italian, English, Chinese, Russian, Swedish and Spanish.

macworld.zdnet.com

SOFTWARE SUPPLIERS AND DOWNLOAD SITES

Surf to these sites to find new software, handy tools and plug-ins.

Adobe

Here you can find some of the best and most professional imaging and publishing software on the market. This the home of the most widely-used professional graphics software – PhotoShop – as well as one of the internet's most-used plug-ins, Adobe Acrobat Reader. You'll find information on the software available and software to download as well as patches, help and tutorials on how to use your software.

www.adobe.com

Browser Watch

One of the leading sites for information about browsers, plug-ins and ActiveX controls, this site offers up-to-the-minute news in the browser and plug-ins industry, as well as one of the most complete lists on development of different plug-ins and browsers. A quick check of your browser allows you to find the plug-ins or browsers you want quickly and effortlessly.

www.browserwatch.com

Dave Franklin: Hunter Gatherer!

Here is a site that all Windows and Linux users should check out. Dave Franklin collects the addresses of all the latest software for Windows and Linux PCs. Whatever you need he should be able to take you to it. There are a huge number of categories to choose from on his site. If there is some software you would like to see here, you can either e-mail Dave or use his submit page to inform him of the software, though new listings are added every day.

www.davecentral.com

Download.com

The download facility of CNET.com (previously accessible as download.com) offers quick and intuitive access to more than 20,000 Windows, Macintosh, DOS, Linux, Palm OS, Windows CE and BeOS programs that are available for download over the internet. The programs are evaluated and categorised by the people at CNET, and include the information you need to help you decide whether a program is suitable for your system and needs. You can download the software you want from one of several web and FTP sites around the world, and there is a reliability guide which points you towards the download location most likely to be successful.

www.download.cnet.com

Free Stuff Center

This site boasts all sorts of free stuff, from books to web tools. It's not all computer-related, but it's the best place to start if you want to fill your hard drive with innovative downloads – it even has a section promising free cash!

www.freestuffcenter.com

Microsoft

This is the largest company involved in the computer business and on their site you will find downloadable versions of many of its software products – such as word processors, spreadsheets, games and many more. The site also contains lots of utilities for you to download, as well as all the information you may need to solve any of your problems with its software.

www.microsoft.com

Net Resources

A huge range of computer-related products is available from this site, all available for you to download free of charge. So if you find yourself missing a file or DLL in your computer set-up then the chances are that you can find it on this site. It also offers loads of free cut-and-paste Java scripts for the web designers out there, and a wide range of anti-hacker tools.

www.uforesources.com

Netscape

This is the home of the popular and well-used browser suite of software, Netscape Communicator. Here you will find the latest version free to download. You will also find tutorials on using the suite of software to its maximum potential. The site also doubles up as a search engine with a full and comprehensive site list.

www.netscape.com

QuickTime

QuickTime is the standard for digital video and streaming media. On this site you can see examples of how QuickTime is used in live programming and on-demand programming on the web. The BBC, Bloomberg and WGBH Boston use QuickTime in their digital media offerings, as do industry giants such as Pixar, Lucasfilm, Macromedia, Microsoft, Disney and CNN. This is an essential plug-in for your browser to enhance your multimedia experiences on the web.

www.apple.com/quicktime

Real Player

RealNetworks is the pioneer and established market leader in streaming media technology on the internet. Their Real Player software allows you to watch video clips and listen to live music or radio while you are on the internet. Once you have downloaded the software, just go to the guide page to see what's on. The Real Player software is available free of charge, though you can upgrade by paying for the latest release. The third site listed below is a huge listing of available Real Player shows for you to listen to and watch once you have the software installed.

www.real.com

www.realaudio.com

www.realguide.real.com

Shareware.com

Shareware.com allows users to search a variety of existing internet software archives containing 250,000 freeware and shareware files. These files are organised by archive and are not categorised. File descriptions at Shareware.com are provided by third parties and may not include system requirements or other relevant details.

www.shareware.cnet.com

Software Paradise

Concentrating on sales of software, this site offers a wide range at good prices with plenty of special offers.

www.softwareparadise.co.uk

Tucows

Tucows is one of the world's best collections of internet software available for people to download. It offers software for all Windows, Macintosh and BeOS internet software. All the software available for you to download is both performance-rated and checked for viruses. You can choose to download from servers in many locations.

www.tucows.com

TERMINOLOGY AND PROBLEM-SOLVING

These sites provide a forum for questions and answers, free downloads to solve common problems, or help you to jargon-bust by providing plain-English definitions of technical terms.

Allexperts

Experts here will answer any questions related to computers, browsers, word processing and graphics programs: simply select the link to Computers, Software and the Internet to find a whole list of topics to suit your every need. To put it simply, this site is a one-stop shopping source for free questions and answers on virtually any topic!

www.allexperts.com

AnalogX

This site provides free, downloadable tools for Windows PCs, many for use with internet connections, most of which provide some kind of analysis or block annoying messages. A particularly useful one is HyperTrace, which allows you to identify where blockages are on the net (so helping you to find out why your internet connection is running so *s-l-o-w-l-y*).

www.analogx.com

BBC Webguide

A section of the massive web site created by the British Broadcasting Corporation, this section gives you a guide to the information available on the web on the arts and culture, nature, business and finance, children's information, reference, science, sport, travel – and television and radio!

bbc.co.uk/webguide

Computer and Internet Zone

Having problems with your computer system? If so, then visit the Computer and Internet Zone with its question-and-answer board. You can also browse the highlights of current news topics, all relating to the computer and internet industries.

www.cizone.com

Emoticons

Emoticons are those little pictures made from punctuation that many e-mail and chat room users litter throughout their messages – anything from the basic smiley :-) to total surprise :-o or even a tongue in cheek comment ;-^) If you find such things baffling, visit one of the following sites offering definitions.

www.utopiasw.demon.co.uk/emoticon.html

www.robelle.com/smugbook/smiley.htm

FAQs

This archive contains all the newsgroups' Frequently Asked Questions (FAQ) postings in hypertext format and in FTP archive textual format.

Each FAQ is converted into a single hypertext document. All FAQs are scanned for various references and have hypertext links automatically inserted when such references are found.

www.faqs.org

Help-site

Help-site contains links to hundreds of computer-related documents and sites. If you are looking for a FAQ list, a tutorial, a manual or an official or unofficial support site, as long as it is for a computer-related subject, you have come to the right place. This is not another free-for-all links site, however. Only the more useful sites and documents will be added, allowing you to find the information you need much more easily.

help-site.com

Modem Help

Modem Help is a support service for individuals who need assistance using their modem and communications software. The web site is a free service for everyone looking for modem-related support information. There is an exhaustive link library and support forums where people can help each other. Their technicians maintain the support links and participate in the forum discussions.

www.modemhelp.com

Netspeak

A dictionary of jargon for the techno-minded.

www.erols.com/amato1/AC

PC Mechanic

PC Mechanic is one of a minority: a unique site on the internet. There are not many sites like this one that offer such a wide variety of computer hardware information in one place. Not only that, but also the information and tutorials are written in plain English for the newcomer to computers. They also offer (for a small fee) a downloadable book which contains all the site's tutorials and information.

www.pcmech.com

PC Show and Tell

Puzzled about how to fulfil a task or action with your software or even on the internet? PC Show and Tell will guide you through the answer, step-by-step, while you actually see and hear how to do it. This site is your best source for understandable and quick computer help – and it's free of charge! They have shows for Word, Excel, PowerPoint, Outlook, Hotmail, ICQ, Internet Explorer, Yahoo and more!

www.pcshowandtell.com

PC Technology Guide

The idea of this guide is to cover the PC's major internal components and peripheral devices and, as its name implies, is more concerned with PC technologies than products – at present just hardware technology. In general, specific products feature only in the context of major technological innovation. Topics are covered at the overview rather than detailed technical level and the guide is aimed more at the PC hobbyist than the IT professional.

www.pctechguide.com

Protonic

This site gives free technical support to anyone who has a problem with their computer. Very useful and willing to help users of all ages.

www.protonic.com

Technology Dictionary

This is an online encyclopedia that contains everything you need to know about computers. This site is a must for experienced users as well as novices. Search for definitions to more than 7,000 high-tech terms! So, if you are not sure what CCYY is, or what data ageing means, check it out here. It is part of the web site for *Computer User* magazine, so you can also find lots of other helpful information by clicking the link to the home page.

www.computeruser.com/resources/dictionary/dictionary.html

Webopedia

This is an online encyclopedia of computer technology and information together with an extensive links page. The site's online encyclopedia and search engine is dedicated to computer technology and nothing else.

www.webopedia.com

Windows Annoyances

Windows Annoyances is a web site devoted not only to pointing out the flaws in Microsoft Windows but also to providing solutions to those flaws. It is not just based on the information in the web site but expanded with much more information and examples, and includes coverage of Windows NT 4.0.

www.annoyances.org

ZD Net

This is one of the best places to start researching anything that is computer-related. ZDNet produces original, compelling content and communities of common interests in technology and is consistently ranked by Media Metrix as the number one web site in the news, information and entertainment category.

www.zdnet.com

OTHER COMPUTER SITES

This selection of sites provides useful information about computers that doesn't fit into the categories previously specified.

Computer History and Development

Where would we be now if we did not have computers? For better or worse, computers have infiltrated every aspect of our lives and today they do much more than simply compute. But where did all this technology come from and where is it heading? To understand and appreciate fully the impact computers have and what the future holds, it is important to understand their evolution. This is also a useful site for detailed background information on computer projects.

www.digitalcentury.com/encyclo/update/comp_hd.html

Easter Egg Archive

This site contains hundreds of software Easter eggs for all computers, operating systems and applications. What is an Easter egg? In computer terms, it is any amusing tidbit that software writers hide in their creations. They could be in computer software, movies, music, art, books or even your watch. There are thousands of them, and they can be quite entertaining, if you know where to look. This site will help you discover Easter eggs in the things you see and use every day, and let you share Easter eggs you discover with the rest of the world.

www.eeggs.com

Pkzip

This popular shareware program allows you to 'zip' or compress files when you are sending them, making it quicker for them to reach their destination (and more likely to arrive in one piece). Many sites use it or Winzip, its Microsoft equivalent, to reduce the size of files available for download. Normally you will not need the program to install such downloaded files, but it is useful to have if you regularly send files by e-mail or FTP.

www.pkware.com

Product ReviewNet

This site tracks product reviews from a wide variety of consumer magazines and posts the summaries online. Simply enter the product name to receive the information.

www.productreviewnet.com/home.html

Recycling

These days we are all aware of the need to recycle as much as possible. But how about computers? The following sites offer information on recycling of computer and printer parts, cartridges etc.

www.computer-aid.org

www.esel.co.uk

www.microweb.com/pepsite/recycle/recycle_index.html

www.rapidrecycling.demon.co.uk

www.takeii.demon.co.uk

Slashdot

Only for the computer enthusiast, this is a magazine-style site full of news and features about what is happening in the techno-world.

www.slashdot.org

W3C

This is site for the Worldwide Web Consortium, the people who made the internet what it is. Come to find out about all the latest and up-and-coming standards and tools used on the internet.

www.w3.org

Web66

This is one of the internet's oldest and most complete lists of school web servers. You will find links to schools in countries all over the world and their web sites – don't be put off by the front page's reference to US school gradings. The resource centre also has everything you need to get started with setting up a Windows NT server to handle your school network and internet needs, as well as information about the world-wide web, browsers, servers and other useful topics.

web66.coled.umn.edu

Wired

This site is the top technology site on the web and is well known for its ground-breaking news stories on the subject of technology. You can even subscribe to its free mailing list, which will then deliver the news to your e-mail account.

www.wired.com

COOKERY AND KITCHENWARE

This section lists sites that give recipes and cookery guidance or feature cookery products and appliances. You can find further sites of interest in the *Food* section, and you might also like to look at the section on *Drinks and Drinking* for something to complement your meal!

Allrecipes.com

This American site covers everything from recipes to kitchen appliances. It boasts the largest online kitchen store in the world, with many items that are difficult to find elsewhere, and prices are competitive (although you will need to check with them regarding the shipping cost outside the USA for any particularly large items). Well worth a look.

www.allrecipes.com

Barbecues on the Internet

Everything that you ever wanted to know about outdoor cooking is at this entertaining American site. Find out about marinades, cooking tools and even barbecues in history, together with some tasty American recipes for you to try. There are even some excellent FAQs and monthly wisdom from an expert on the subject. The site is aimed at both beginners and experts on all aspects of barbecues and their success.

www.barbecuen.com

BBC Food

Another great part of the extensive BBC site, this provides recipes, programme link-ups, tips from celebrity chefs and much more. You can enter competitions, join in a culinary chat, or even Ask the Chef.

www.bbc.co.uk/food

Culinary Connection

There are over 73,000 recipes to choose from at the Culinary Connection, so there is something for everyone. The site covers many culinary categories and each section contains recipes listed alphabetically by title. In addition, there are links to other food-related sites, a selection of affiliated online shops and topical food and health news.

www.culinary.com

Internet Chef

Do you find yourself stuck for culinary ideas or wondering how to create a certain dish? Then take a look at this site and you will never have those problems again. Choose from over 30,000 recipes and read the cooking tips. If you wish, you can get involved in the kitchen talk or look up the many links.

www.ichef.com

My Meals

You can enter any special dietary requirements you have into this site and it will make a selection of recipes suitable specifically for you. Particularly useful for those with a food allergy or when you have an awkward guest for dinner.

www.my-meals.com

MyRecipe

A vast selection of recipes for menus of all kinds, not only main meals but breads (including muffins, tea breads and other yeast bakes), cakes, kids' food and much, much more. It's an American site, so all the recipes are in cup measures and there's quite a lot of extra information about who wrote the recipes and what people think of them, but it's a great source of recipes, nonetheless. A particularly handy feature is the ability to scale all recipes to the number of servings you require, so even the most mathematically challenged of us have no excuse!

www.myrecipe.com

RecipeXchange

There is a glut of cookery web sites on the internet if you want recipes and cooking tips, but this one is definitely worth checking out. RecipeXchange contains thousands of tasty recipes submitted by cooks around the world, and you can search the list in a number of different ways, including by Tummy Index (an indication of the fat level!). Why not submit some recipes yourself? You can join in at the live cookery chat rooms or read the many articles on food.

www.recipexchange.com

The Repertoire

You will find that this upmarket 'culinary workstation' serves up a feast of food facts and recipes, without too much intrusive advertising. There are helpful articles, recipes and guides to the most delicious uses of bread, fish, meat, game, cheese, wine, vegetables and preserves. There is also a handy guide that shows what foods are in season and some useful conversion tables to help you navigate the recipes.

www.therepertoire.com

Scott Sargeant

This well-known cookshop offers a wide range of equipment and accessories at its web site, and you can browse and purchase online.

www.scottsargeant.com

Seasoned Cooking

This is the online version of the *Seasoned Cooking* magazine. The site is mainly about cooking but there are also more general pointers on how to keep a healthy body and mind. In fact, the web site is full of interesting and informative articles on healthy eating, it has a searchable recipe index and a full archive of back issues online. The advertisements can be annoying but you soon learn to ignore them.

www.seasoned.com

Spice Advice

Do you want to know more about spices and their uses? This site is an encyclopedia of spices and gives details of their origins and purposes together with recipes and tips on what is best combined with what. Unfortunately the online ordering is available only in the US, but there is lots of useful information here.

www.spiceguide.com

United Cutlery

Are your forks fading? Spoons lost their sparkle? If so, try this site for a new look. Buy on the web and save up to 50% off the retail price of these fabulous cutlery sets: there are 15 patterns available in hallmarked silver, silver plate and stainless steel. All are guaranteed for life.

www.cutlerysets.com

Vegans

If you have a vegan guest coming for dinner, or if you are vegan yourself and need to know more about how to follow a healthy diet, look up vegan.com for lots of recipes and tips. The site will show you how to get your recommended daily intake of calcium from vegetables instead of milk, for example. It is well worth looking at: just be prepared for all the accompanying political issues.

www.vegan.com

DANCE

There's a great range of dance information out there, including advice from the pros and lists of events. If you can't find the type of dance you're interested in listed below, try using a search engine, specifying the exact name of the dance style (for example, breakdance, Kuchipudi, belly-dancing). See also *Entertainment, Music, Theatre*.

Ballet Companies

This site is simple in design and contains pages devoted to the biggest national, local and touring UK ballet companies. It also contains useful and interesting performer pages and listings information. It is an indispensable guide to ballet and will appeal to ballet dancers and enthusiasts alike.

www.ballet.co.uk

Ballroom Dancing

Use this ballroom dancing resource to find a list of competitions around the world. It also has a ballroom media gallery and information about dancing organisations and publications world-wide. You can even view the content in various other languages.

www.dancescape.com

Dance Index

Focusing on music and dance, this site has all kinds of information on dance throughout the world, in all styles, including extensive lists of forthcoming events throughout the UK.

www.ftech.co.uk/~webfeet

Dance Service

This site is an impressively large resource, covering contemporary dance in Britain. There is information for dancers as well as dance fans and a useful dance directory. You will also find it contains a comprehensive collection of internet links, articles, reviews, a dance discussion area and much more.

www.danceservice.co.uk

Dance Videos

This page is actually part of a site entitled *Ballroom and Country and Western Dancing* but it offers a mind-boggling selection of dance videos for all kinds of dance from hula to hip-hop, plus exercise and fitness videos. All can be ordered online and shipped anywhere in the world (see the Ordering instructions for details of which format to select). By clicking on the Home link you can find instructions on dance steps and articles on various types of dance. (Most of the remaining information on the site is specific to the US.)

www.centralhome.com/ballroomcountry/video_store.htm

Indian Dance

This site, part of an extensive Indian Heritage site, gives a huge amount of information on the various forms of Indian dance, many of which have their basis in religion. It also has several links to related sites, so is ideal for research into this fascinating topic.

www.saigan.com/heritage/dindex.html

International Folk Dance Resource Guide

Find out about the many different types of folk dancing including Morris dancing, country dancing and various international varieties at this site.

www.io.com/~hbp/folkdance/fd.html

Morris Dancing

You may have thought morris dancing to be a peculiarly English tradition, but this site brings together dance groups from around the world, and even includes links to clog-makers! Fascinating stuff.

www.morrisdancing.org

Worldwide Web Virtual Library: Dance

As the title suggests, this is a virtual library of dance web sites. Browse through the library's index to find information on exactly the type of dance in which you are interested.

www.artswire.org/Artswire/www/dance/dance.html

DISABILITY

See *Health, Fitness and Nutrition: Disabilities*.

DIY AND HOME MAINTENANCE

Need a new toolkit? Got a leaking tap? Then check out these sites, all of which offer help to the DIYer and guides to those tricky tasks. Also see *Home Improvements and Interior Design*.

B&Q DIY Guides

B&Q is Britain's largest DIY retailer. If you want to learn how to do it yourself, whether in the home or garden, then check out this site. You will find detailed guides to every task from painting and decorating to making your house more secure. Voted the best retail site of the year and recently expanded to include online shopping, full product lists and an interior design section.

www.diy.com

DIY Fixit

With clear, step-by-step instructions, even those who blanch at the thought of a flat-pack should find help here.

www.diyfixit.co.uk

Do it Yourself

This site contains all the information you need to carry out projects on your own home, in any of 19 different areas. These include lighting, electricity, flooring, kitchens, plumbing, painting and woodworking. Each area contains user-friendly advice guides, relevant books and links to web sites. Should you need further help, go to the forums where you can post your tricky DIY questions and have them answered.

www.doityourself.com

Do It Yourself, Do It Right

This site will appeal to anyone who enjoys making things with their hands as it provides project plans and patterns for a variety of DIY projects. All project plans for sale in the catalogue/showroom contain professionally drafted drawings, hints and tips on problems, and a list of the tools required for the job. Also contained within the package is a construction sequence with detailed step-by-step instructions, which has been written with the novice in mind. Finally, it is good to know that each project has been carefully designed, constructed and tested before making the plans available for purchase!

www.do-it-yourself.com

Global Power

This is a massive home improvement superstore offering secure online shopping, with no minimum order and fantastic savings on thousands of brand-name products. It is very easy to navigate and provides advice as well as orders, whatever your DIY needs: from power-tools to shelves, hardware to pet care. Deliveries are free within the mainland UK. Check out their extensive guide to DIY safety before starting work to help avoid nasty accidents.

www.globalpower.co.uk

Handy Home Advisor

Home Advisor gives advice on DIY, home improvements, good housekeeping and interior decoration. A must for all home owners!

homearts.com/helpers/homecare/00homcc1.htm

Homebase

A down-to-earth site from the Sainsbury's subsidiary, offering the same goods as in-store, including special offers. Similar in content to the B&Q site, with product listings, design ideas and how-to guides.

www.homebase.co.uk

Home Improvement Encyclopedia

Do you watch the DIY programmes in complete confusion about what is going on? If so, then before you attempt to do any DIY yourself, visit this encyclopedic site. The site is organised by area and gives enough information on most of the jobs that you are likely to tackle. The animated examples are especially helpful.

www.bhglive.com/homeimp

SalvoWEB

Not for the fainthearted, if you are a serious DIYer and are restoring a period property, this site could be useful. It provides extensive information on finding and using reclaimed and salvaged building materials, including a list of dealers throughout the UK, as well as architectural antiques for the home and garden. Great if only the real thing will do.

www.salvo.co.uk

Screwfix

The ultimate site for finding tools, materials and other DIY accessories, at great prices. No-nonsense information and easy ordering, with free next-day delivery if you spend more than £45.

www.screwfix.com

DRINKS AND DRINKING

Need a beer? A new cocktail or the best vintage wine to impress your date? How about a change of coffee? These sites tell you all you need to know about drinks and drinking, from the non-alcoholic to the practically volcanic.

BEER

Beer Information

Are you a connoisseur of beers? Do you wish to know more about the multitude of different beers available? If so, then this site has all the information you need.

www.beerinfo.com

Beerstalker

Concentrating on real British beer, this site offers a complete listing of bottled beers brewed in the UK, along with ciders, wines and spirits, with a mail-order service.

www.beerstalker.co.uk

BreWorld

This is Europe's largest web site devoted to the brewing industry, which has all the 'news, information and entertainment regarding the brewing industry'. It also includes a beer database, a list of the top ten beers, articles from *Grist* and *Beerscene*, a bulletin board, information on beer-making and a beer-specific search engine.

www.breworld.com

The Campaign for Real Ale (CAMRA)

CAMRA now has its own site on the net, covering every aspect of real ale and where to get it. It includes polls on beer-related issues, guides to pubs, brews and festivals, beer news, and details of how and where to join your local CAMRA group. It even has pages on real cider. A true Oktoberfest of a site!

www.camra.org.uk

The Good Pub Guide

Register here and open up the book to discover thousands of pubs around the UK. You can search the site by region or locality and state preferences according to recommendations in quality of beer, food, value, surroundings, etc. It has been well designed, is quick to use and is an excellent basic interactive pub guide for the UK.

www.goodguides.co.uk

London's Real Ale Guide

London's Virtual Real Ale Pub Guide includes over 250 pub reviews in the London area. Each review gives a brief description of the pub, the atmosphere, the clientele and even the toilets. These pages have been thoroughly researched over several months and are occasionally changed as they find new pubs or revisit pubs that have altered since they first visited.

alt.venus.co.uk/vpub/welcome.htm

Pubsmaster

This site lists pubs, wine bars, clubs and other drinking locations throughout the UK. Just select the type of establishment you want to visit, enter the town name or postcode, and it will provide you with a list. Great for when you are away from home or just want to try somewhere new. It's best not to be too specific as some areas have only a few places listed.

www.pubsmaster.co.uk

Real Ale

Another site all about British pubs, beer festivals and the like. You can find reviews, pub locations and ratings and all kinds of related information at this useful site and can even subscribe for updates.

www.beerguide.co.uk

Real Ale Guide

This is a comprehensive site that will tell you all you need to know about beer. Find out what is on offer, where to get it and when. Check out their brewery of the month or browse the information on independent breweries. There is a pub directory, a guide to upcoming beer festivals, pub news, a trade directory, a landlords' forum, articles about ale, a section about related societies and associations and lots more.

www.real-ale-guide.co.uk

BEVERAGES AND SOFT DRINKS

Beverage Recipes

This site, part of the excellent myrecipe.com, contains loads of different recipes for drinks, from the alcoholic to the chocoholic. All have been submitted by people who've tried them for themselves, so they must be drinkable! A great source of new cocktails and party drinks.

www.beveragerecipe.com

Coffee.com

This site, from Peet's Coffee and Tea Co, tells you all you need to know about coffee and tea, including how and where it is grown, the different types, and how best to select a blend to suit you, brew and drink it. There's also a link out to Peet's own web site, from which you can order any of their blends for delivery world-wide.

www.coffee.com

Coca-Cola

Home of the favourite thirst-quencher, this site has some great graphics and sound-effects that will have you running for the fridge. It has fun games and details on all current promotions, and other parts of the site contain information on the company, its products and its policies.

www.coca.cola.com

Evian – L'Original

What could be more boring than a water site, you ask? Think again. This lively site from the French spring-water company has great sounds, sports information (they sponsor a baffling range of events), up-to-the-minute fashion and plenty more to entertain you. Oh, and there's a few pages about the water, too.

www.evian.com

The Tea Council

Who can resist a good cuppa? This eye-opening site, run by the Tea Council, provides a huge amount of information on the nation's favourite beverage, including lists of tea traders, steps for making the perfect brew, and an illustrated history of tea consumption. It also tells why tea is so good for you! Fascinating, and a great resource for homework.

www.teacouncil.co.uk

COCKTAILS

Cocktails at the Mining Company

This site has a 'mine' of information on the subject of drinks: cocktail recipes, ideas for cooking with spirits, guides to consuming spirits, help for would-be bartenders, links to online shops and the chance to e-mail virtual drinks.

cocktails.miningco.com

DRINKING AND BARTENDING

AA, Al-Anon and Alateen

The first of the sites listed is for Alcoholics Anonymous, or AA, the world-wide organisation for those with an alcohol problem. It is a lively, helpful site giving sensible advice and encouragement, and includes questionnaires to help you decide whether you are drinking too much. The second site, run jointly by Al-Anon and Alateen, provides help for those who are concerned about another person's drinking – a family member or friend, or a young person in particular.

It gives a rundown on the organisations' approach and a world-wide listing of member offices. The sites are also available in French and Spanish.

www.aa.org

www.al-anon.org

I-drink

I-drink is a quick and easy reference tool for information on mixing drinks for yourself and your guests. From traditional favourites to the latest trendy concoctions, you can look like an expert in no time. The information on 5,865 drinks has been compiled from recipes submitted by professional and amateur bartenders everywhere. The next time you are planning to entertain a few friends or throw a big party, you can enter all your bar ingredients in their quick checklist, then let the program match your ingredients against their database and display all your options. You will be surprised at the number of drinks you can make, even with a limited number of ingredients, and will have more fun and enjoy your new bartending skills.

www.idrink.com/home.htm

The Virtual Bar

Search the archive containing over 3,000 cocktails by ingredients, drink type or name. The site is also home to Corky the bartender, who provides a guide about alcohol, a virtual jukebox, a selection of toasts for all occasions and, most importantly, a list of hangover cures.

www.thevirtualbar.com

Web Tender

This is a great site to find out how to mix that elusive drink. Webtender contains over 4,800 different drinks for you to try, including cocktails, alcoholic drinks, soft drinks and many more. If you find that your favourite drink is not listed here, then why not submit your own drink using the form supplied?

www.webtender.com

SPIRITS

Bacardi Central

Home of the fabulous Cuban Rum, browse this site to the accompaniment of catchy salsa music and you'll soon be grabbing for a glass. The site covers the history of the company, as well as providing many Bacardi recipes (simply enter your own ingredients and they'll work it out for you!) and party suggestions: you can even play games or relive old Bacardi ads in the Gallery. You are only allowed to enter the site if you are legally allowed to drink alcohol.

www.bacardi.com

Classic Whiskey

A great site this, providing information on whiskey and whisky alike, as long as it's Irish. You can read about the history of whisk(e)y, how it's made, and where it comes from, all accompanied by some great Irish tunes. You can even shop online for your favourite brands, as long as you are legally entitled to.

www.classicwhiskey.com

Hallmark of St James

This classy site deals in rare and fine liquors, spirits and the best whiskies. You can take a tour of their newly refurbished premises, view details of their own pubs, or shop online for any of their products. They even offer personalised labels for that special occasion.

www.hallmarkofstjames.com

WINE

Australian Wines of Distinction

This site is an excellent resource of information on the major wine producers of Australia. The makers listed here are Penfolds, Lindemans, Winns, Seppelt, Seaview, Devil's Lair, and Coldstream Hills. All the wines produced by these makers are listed with good descriptions of the wines and the estates.

www.australianwines.co.uk

Berry Bros and Rudd

Berry Bros & Rudd offer exceptional wines, hand picked to reflect both the quality and individuality of regions such as Bordeaux, Burgundy and Champagne, as well as North America, Argentina, Australia, New Zealand and others. You can order from their selection of fine wines over the internet at the BBR Internet Wine Shop, bringing 300 years of personal service, expertise and an unbeatable range of wines online.

www.bbr.co.uk

Bring-a-Bottle

This no-nonsense site keeps it simple: you want wine, we've got it. No editorials, recipes or competitions here, only reasonably-priced, popular wines, mostly from the New World, for next-day delivery anywhere in the UK for a flat fee of £6.99 (free if order is £300 or more).

www.bring-a-bottle.com

German Wine Page

Full of information and opinions on German wine, this site offers help in making selections and buying German wine, including information about vintages and producers, as well as lots, lots more. It also contains good links to other German pages, some wine-related and some in English.

www.winepage.de

Virgin Wines

An extensive site that lists around 20,000 wines for sale. The site includes Recommended Wines, about 500 wines which are claimed to represent the best quality and price, have been properly stored and come from reputable suppliers. You can order online, with delivery in around a week.

www.virginwines.com

The Wine Anorak

Jamie Goode, also known as the Wine Anorak, has assembled a selection of features, links and reviews here. Jamie also talks about his own travels to various wine-growing regions and you can see his personal notes on the wines he has recently tasted.

www.wineanorak.com

Wine Lovers' Page

This site has everything from basic guides on getting started, to organising your cellar with a sophisticated selection of wines. You will find articles on books about wine, discussions on wine, food and wine, wine on the internet, wine pronunciation, wine and its vintage and, of course, on the enjoyment of wine itself. There is also a huge wine grape glossary to help you find the wine that is to your taste. This site is useful for both the amateur and the connoisseur alike.

www.wine-lovers-page.com

Wine Pages

The Wine Pages is one of the world's most popular online wine resources. An independent site, it is updated daily with features, tasting notes and wine news. The site is run by wine tutor Tom Cannavan, who has compiled a handy and instructional wine drinker's guide. He even offers an online course in wine, as well as well-written notes on popular wine regions.

www.wine-pages.com

Wine Place

This site provides a good introduction to the world of wines for the beginner. It has well-written, easy-to-swallow guides to the tasting, storing and drinking of all types of wine. There are also handy hints on the correct pronunciation of wines, how to hold a wine party, as well as lots of other regular features and links to more sites.

www.wineplace.nu

Wine Searcher

If you have a yearning for a particular label, start here. Wine merchants list their finest wines with this site, allowing you to compare prices and stocks for all your favourites. They claim to list 250,000 wines from several hundred suppliers, so whatever you want you are bound to find it here.

www.wine-searcher.com

Wine Spectator

This claims to be 'the most comprehensive wine web site in the world' and it certainly packs in the facts about its subject. You will find daily wine news, weekly features, a vast searchable database of wines, tips on choosing the right wine for the right meal, an archive of articles from past issues of the magazine as well as information on wineries and wine auctions. Make sure you know what you are looking for when you visit this huge site, although it is fairly easy to navigate, despite its size.

www.winespectator.com

EDUCATION

These sites give general information on educational opportunities and resources for all ages, or provide information for students on school or college life. See also *Children, Teenagers*, and specific subjects (e.g. *History*). If you are a parent seeking information on the National Curriculum, see the sites under *Parenting*. If you are looking for sites to help with homework or revision, see *Homework Research and Revision*.

American Institute for Foreign Study

Here you will find information about cultural exchange programmes, summer jobs in the US and studying abroad for both American and non-American students. The American Institute for Foreign Study® (AIFS, Inc.) and its family of companies organises cultural exchange programmes throughout the world for more than 40,000 students each year.

www.aifs.org

Anything Student

For both students and graduates, this site contains magazine-style articles, information and advice on careers and student life in general, with hyperlinks to other related sites of interest.

www.anythingstudent.co.uk

BBC Education

Designed to work in support of the National Curriculum, the BBC offers a high-quality site filled with research and revision information, games and stories. There's also an e-mail service for posing questions to teachers.

www.bbc.co.uk/education/schools

BECTA

This site is run by the British Educational Communications and Technology Agency, who are responsible for creating and co-ordinating information communication technology (ICT) within the UK education system. It provides valuable information for teachers, students and parents on the place of ICT within the National Curriculum and how and where ICT is being used in schools. It also contains information on ICT training for teachers and support staff.

The second site listed below provides an extensive database of educational software packages. You cannot purchase or download the software – this is only a catalogue for information – but it is a great way to identify the packages you need for a particular area of study, by subject, target age, operating system and format.

www.becta.org.uk

besd.becta.org.uk

BT Education

BT, or British Telecom, provides far more than just a telephone service. It actively supports technology-based learning in schools and sees learning as a key part of competitive advantage. It provides workshops to more than 3,500 schools: an estimated one million children will receive training in skills essential for life in the 21st Century. The site also includes an extensive list of educational resources, and details of BT's graduate recruitment and work experience schemes.

www.bt.com/world/education

Bunk.com

An essential piece of kit for all students, this includes comprehensive listings of off and on-campus digs for all UK universities and colleges. Absolutely everything is covered, down to pots and pans – even local cashpoints and supermarkets!

www.bunk.com

Connecting Students

This American site contains puzzles and links to all kinds of sites on all kinds of subjects. It is a great starting point for homework research.

www.connectingstudents.com

Datalake

This web site allows you to search for universities and colleges worldwide via its learning stream. Increasingly, this is possible by subject, department, faculty and course. Useful to students and widely used by them, Datalake is also a resource for locating wider research expertise for a variety of applications. This operates in parallel with a job locator (Earning) – with links made between learning outcomes and available work at all stages of your search.

www.datalake.com

Digital Education Network

The Digital Education Network enables students to get information on study programmes around the world. You can also search for a wide range of other educational service providers including student advisors, education agents, accommodation agencies, publishers, examination boards and funding organisations.

www.edunet.com

Dreamlife

A personal development web site with online classes by experts world-wide. A good way to improve your life skills without having to attend expensive seminars.

www.dreamlife.com

Essay Writing

An essay can have many purposes, but the basic structure is the same. You may be writing an essay to argue a particular point of view or to explain the steps necessary to complete a task. This site gives you the steps to guide you on how to construct your essay.

members.tripod.com/~lklivingston/essay

GCSE Answers

This site aims to help students preparing for GCSE exams, in particular in maths and English. It provides suggested questions and answers, tutorials on specific topics and links to many other helpful sites.

www.gcse.com

Hobsons

This is the premier site for details of thousands of career and education opportunities in the UK and around the world. Hobsons is a British and US-based company with over 25 years' experience in publishing educational and recruitment guides for students making career and course decisions. A guide to UK boarding schools is also produced.

www.hobsons.co.uk

LearningStore

A UK-based site, this stocks over 1,200 different educational software packages covering everything from hobbies to business management, so you should be able to find something to help with your studies.

www.learningstore.co.uk

Learning Tutorials

Arts and crafts, sport and leisure, travel, technology and health are among the topics covered here and you can find tutorials on anything from shining your shoes to soothing a teething baby or restructuring your business. You can also e-mail the information to a friend.

www.learn2.com

McGraw–Hill

McGraw-Hill offers online training for business, and here at its site you can learn all about the different courses on offer. McGraw-Hill online learning offers you quality course information and expert instruction using state-of-the-art technology on the web. Online learning allows you to study where you want and when you want, to study at your own pace, and to interact with instructors via e-mail and discussion groups.

www.mhonlinelearning.com

MindEdge

This web site is here to help you make sense of the revolution in education that is taking place on the internet. It is a great source of information on courses and course descriptions that are being taught on the internet, as well as at all the colleges and universities, although many of the colleges and universities listed are American.

www.mindedge.com

National Grid for Learning

A government portal designed to provide a focal point for education on the web. It contains links to sites providing information on everything from life-long learning to museums and galleries and the National Curriculum. Whether you are studying, teaching, managing or supporting others in their learning, you should be able to find what you need here.

www.ngfl.gov.uk

Open University

The OU is primarily a British site but it has pioneered a system of study – OU-supported open learning – which brings its courses and other study materials within the reach of the entire population of the European Union, Switzerland, Gibraltar and Slovenia. Also available are a growing number of courses world-wide on the internet.

www.open.ac.uk

SAM Learning

This site – the only educational site supported by the National Association of Head Teachers – offers information on all major exams, broken down by subject and then topic. It offers explanations and sample questions – with drag and drop so you can complete the answers – to help you revise. Some of the information designed for use by schools (rather than at home by students) is only available by paid subscription.

www.samlearning.co.uk

Schoolzone

Schoolzone was set up by a group of enthusiastic teachers and parents in Oxford, who could see the need for safe, differentiated internet material which teachers, students and parents can access easily, without anyone trying to sell them anything or exploit anyone in any way. Here you will find all the potentially useful sites – more than 30,000 at the last count – sorted into subject groupings.

www.schoolzone.co.uk

Student UK

A site for the college or university student with news, features, information on entertainment and general advice on student life. Some of the content is unsuitable for children.

www.studentuk.com

Student World

Designed for students and staff at colleges and universities, you'll find a range of information here from advice on money to news, culture and reference information. Good links to other related sites.

www.student-world.co.uk

Time to Learn

If you want to upgrade your computer and internet skills or learn new ones, this is the place. They provide self-study courses – up to five free with the new Individual Learning Account. Courses include Microsoft Office, desktop publishing, graphics, web design and more.

www.timetolearn.co.uk

Universities and Colleges Admission Service for the UK

Anyone looking for higher education courses can find full information on the UCAS web site, including contact numbers, course searches and other information about degree, HND and other courses.

www.ucas.com

Virtual School

Revision courses in Key Stage 3, GCSE and A-level subjects, with material sent by e-mail and tuition completed online using the NetMeeting facility. You can register for each course online, or request more information if necessary.

www.virtualschool.co.uk

EMPLOYMENT AND CAREERS

Need a change of direction? A promotion or an entire new career? These sites will help you identify what you're best at, how you can use it and where the jobs are. Some even give tips on how to present yourself for the best first impression. See also *Business and E-Business*.

Big Blue Dog

Established by the *Evening Standard*, you can log into an e-mail service to receive details of jobs that match your requirements. There's also online CV composition and even a jobs astrologer!

www.bigbluedog.com

Career Solutions

At this site, discover what you really want to do and how to get somebody to pay you to do it! Career Solutions contains lots of useful information and provides clear steps to getting what you want in the job market. The site also points out other free sources of career advice and advises you of what to do if you lose your job.

www.careersolutions.co.uk

CV Search

A great way to get your CV noticed by the employers who really need you! Employers compose the CV they would want to receive from their ideal job candidate and CV Search matches it as closely as possible with those it has on its books. If you're not in, you can't win!

www.cvsearch.net

Graduate Base

If you're a graduate and don't really know what you want to do with your degree – or your life for that matter – help is at hand! This site is packed with information on career options and how to choose them, plus interactive tools, a jobfinder and much more.

www.graduatebase.com

Hot Jobs

This site lists technical jobs in different career channels world-wide. It is very user-friendly and easier to search than most. Browse and find yourself a new job!

www.hotjobs.com

JobServe

Every day, IT recruitment agencies from all over the UK and Europe send details of their latest requirements to JobServe. The details are entered into a database; a neatly formatted list is then generated and sent out, overnight, by e-mail to anyone who wants it. JobServe is based in the UK but often includes overseas vacancies.

www.jobserve.com

JobShark

Here you can search for jobs, register your CV to receive e-mail about suitable jobs, or find useful information on job-hunting and the companies using the service. Employers can register to receive CVs that match specific requirements. It is part of a world-wide network, so is ideal if you are looking for a job in a far-flung destination.

www.jobshark.co.uk

International Guild of Butlers

This site is aimed at people who are in the profession or are thinking of making a move into it. The guild is dedicated to improving and promoting the interests and reputation of its members and the buttling profession. The guild also offers a free advisory service to its members, employers of butlers and members of the public on any matter related to buttling.

www.butlersguild.com

Innovative Cruise Services

This is the web site of the longest-established Cruise Job Consultancy. All its information is factual and constantly updated. The staff are professionals who have worked in the cruise industry for many years. The company is wholly committed to helping you to the best possible chance of getting a position and, more importantly, identifying the right job for your capabilities. There is no searchable list of jobs, but you can order their comprehensive guide to cruise careers or request further information on particular jobs.

www.cruiseservices.co.uk

Job Hunter's Bible

This American site is a great source of information on how to go about looking for a new job or career, and where to look. It is based on a best-selling book on the same topic, but this way you get to read the information for free! Some of the information is USA-specific but it is generally very useful to the first-time job hunter or for those seeking a change of direction.

www.jobhuntersbible.com

Jobsite

Created in 1995, Jobsite is the longest-established multi-sector internet recruitment platform in the UK. Jobsite attracts hundreds of thousands of candidates every month from all industry sectors including sales, marketing, management, accountancy, secretarial and administration, as well as IT, telecommunications and engineering. Jobsite provides both job hunters and recruiters with the most powerful range of internet recruitment services in the world.

www.jobsite.co.uk

Just Engineers

This claims to be the UK's leading engineering recruitment site, and invites engineering professionals from all disciplines to register and receive full access to details of thousands of jobs, plus help with career development. Employers can match their vacancies with your skills and experience.

www.justengineers.net

Milkround

Interesting and useful site providing details for graduates looking for work. Quick to access, with a database to store your CV and send it to companies.

www.milkround.com

Monster.com

Monster.com is one of the leading global online networks for careers, connecting the most progressive companies with the most qualified, career-minded individuals. Features include resumé management, a personal job search agent, a careers network, chats and message boards, privacy options, expert advice on job-seeking and career management and free newsletters.

www.monster.com

www.monster.co.uk

New Monday

Another comprehensive portal, with a definite European feel. All the usual CV and job matching services are here, plus a career channel feature, expert Q&A (a sort of jobs agony aunt), details of training and much more. An upbeat, friendly site offering more than the usual database search.

www.newmonday.com

Overseas Job Express

This online version of the newspaper for overseas job seekers offers a multitude of excellent resources and advice which is regularly updated. Only OJE gives you vacancies that are genuinely open to non-citizens of your target country. The site has hundreds of fresh jobs online and over 1,500 in every issue of the paper. It gives you all the tools you need to help you get a job abroad.

www.overseasjobs.com

People Bank

Ideal for both employers and job-seekers, there's a wide range of jobs listed here for anyone in the employment market at any level. Several household names use this site for their recruitment, including Sainsbury's, Moat House Hotels and Nestlé.

www.peoplebank.com

Price Jamieson

If you are looking for positions in media, marketing and communications, then the Price Jamieson site is for you. You can easily browse international listings here that are updated weekly.

www.pricejam.com

Professional Contractors Group

This portal is aimed at professional consultants and contractors in the fields of IT, engineering and associated businesses, and those seeking to use their services. It offers business-to-business contract matching for independent consultancy and contracting companies, their clients and agents. If you're looking for staff you can search for free; if you want to register as a consultant you need to join the Professional Contractors' Group, who run the site. They represent independent contractors and campaign on their behalf for fair treatment on tax and employment legislation.

www.pcgroup.org.uk/portal

Reed Employment

An effective site in which you can store employment opportunity details and link your requirements to specific jobs. A huge range of jobs and careers are covered, from junior to executive level. It offers regular e-mail updates.

www.reed.co.uk

Review Computer Recruitment

Review was formed in 1990 and is a specialist agency in the computer personnel recruitment industry. The company specialises in the growing markets of internet technologies, UNIX, relational databases, server networks, PC/Windows, client server and object-oriented design areas. It deals with all aspects of technical recruitment.

www.review.co.uk

The Riley Guide

This site is a directory of links to job-hunting resources from around the world, including job listings, CV and interview techniques, how to organise your job search, etc. It contains tips on how to use them and the information is extremely comprehensive but there is rather a lot of text to read through, so while useful it is not a quick-search tool. It is, however, highly recommended even by other job site owners.

www.rileyguide.com

SHL Online

SHL is a world leader in the objective assessment of people, jobs and organisational context. This site is therefore useful to the individual who is applying for a graduate appointment or who has been asked to take assessment tests, and particularly for companies who want to use better assessment in their recruitment procedures. This site will show you examples of tests, offer hints and tips and tell you what employers will be looking for.

www.shlgroup.com

Top Jobs

This site offers job opportunities with exclusive employers in various parts of Europe and further afield. You are able to register with Top Jobs and automatically receive e-mail notification of jobs that fit your criteria as soon as they become available.

www.topjobs.net

University of London Careers Service

This comprehensive site, run by the University of London, contains a Virtual Careers Library that directs you to many resources. The topics covered include career choice, further study, and job-hunting resources, professional bodies and trade associations, and employer web sites.

www.careers.lon.ac.uk

Work in America

If you are looking for work in America, this free site is the place to start your search. America's Job Bank has links to more than 1,800 US State Employment Service Offices and 100,000 vacancies.

www.ajb.dni.us

Work in the UK

If you are looking for work in the UK, you can search for British jobs at the Jobsearch site. It covers a wide spectrum of fields and is a good starting point.

www.jobsearch.co.uk

World Careers Network

This site is aimed at university students looking for resources to help them find a job after university. Once you have registered, you will have access to a guide on how to get on, together with many resources such as employers in-depth, news and market research, briefing books for each employer, contacts world-wide and lots more.

www.wcn.co.uk

ENTERTAINMENT

Looking for something new to do, or somewhere to go? These sites have it all, from event guides to online entertainment. Other entertaining sites can be found in the sections *Children, Dance, Films, Television, Video and DVD, Fun, Music, Radio and Broadcasting*, and *Theatre*.

All Tickets

This site has tickets for all major sporting, musical and other entertainment events in the UK (and some further afield), even those supposedly sold out. It lists a wide range of events and if your particular event is not listed offers to find tickets for you. You cannot book online but can e-mail a booking enquiry.

www.alltickets.uk.com

Aloud

The site gives details of events that are being held throughout the year, and has a magazine-style format with interviews, features and links to related sites. You can search for events by artist, location or genre (everything from pop to theatre) and book your tickets online.

www.aloud.com

Alton Towers

Need some thrills? This site gives you a virtual tour of the famous theme park, including many of its best rides, complete with sound effects and animation. Information is provided on events, resources and accommodation, and you can book your tickets online. As the site is quite graphics-intensive, it will take a long time to load on older or slower computers.

www.altontowers.com

Ananova Going Out

Part of the Ananova site, which covers everything from news to TV guides, these pages provide wide-ranging information on events, exhibitions and cinema listings throughout the UK.

www.ananova.com/whatson

Bananalotto

If you like the lottery, you'll love Bananalotto – it's free and there's £1 million to be won each day! You can even gain extra prizes by recommending it to your friends.

www.bananalotto.co.uk

Comedy Online

This is a great site devoted to London comedy clubs and pubs. It features listings and venue details, together with a wide selection of interviews, features and background information. You can also become a member.

www.comedyonline.co.uk

Entertainers.co.uk

Need to book an act for a function? Not sure what you want? This site provides all you need to know. A wide range of acts and artistes are on offer, and you can book some of them online (others must be arranged by phone).

www.entertainers.co.uk

Gala Bingo

OK, so bingo isn't to everyone's taste, but if you like it, try this site. Bright and wacky with sound effects and music, if you can't make it to your local bingo you can play the virtual version here for virtual cash prizes! The site has details of promotions and loads of facts about Gala, including contact numbers for all their clubs.

www.gala-bingo.co.uk

Legoland

This site includes all kinds of information on the Legoland theme park (in the UK) including maps and information on opening times and what you can find at the park. You can buy your tickets online, not only saving money but also bypassing the inevitable queue at the gate.

www.legoland.co.uk

PlanIt for Kids

Every parent's dream – a portal packed with kids' stuff to do in your area, so you will never have to hear the words "I'm bored" again! Activity centres, classes, workshops, sports, museums, it's all here. Fun, fast and friendly. Although the front page asks you to choose from one of only a few major cities in the UK, areas quite a distance from the city centres are covered, so just select the city that is closest to you (for example, some places in Suffolk, Hertfordshire and Kent are covered under London). You can also add your favourite places to the site.

www.planitforkids.com

Ticketmaster

Book all your seats for plays, shows, rock concerts, exhibitions and sporting events being held all over the UK from this one site. You can also buy tickets for shows in America, Australia, Canada, Ireland and Mexico using the appropriate Ticketmaster sites, accessible from the UK site.

www.ticketmaster.co.uk

Time Magazine

This is the official site of the US-based magazine *Time*. The site itself is free and has the same good stories as the printed magazine. There are lots of subjects covered, such as movies, health, news, politics and more. The site also boasts a good range of links to each story.

www.time.com

Time Out

With everything you need to know about what is going on in the entertainment world in London, *Time Out* magazine has become something of a byword. This is its web site, which offers the same depth and quality of entertainment information for those in London.

www.timeout.com

What's on When

This site covers events around the world, not just concerts and shows but cultural events and celebrations too. A great way to find out what's on today or while you're on holiday, plus all the usual listings for films, gigs and theatre. You can search by location, event or category. A great resource wherever you happen to be.

www.whatsonwhen.com

Yack

Pay regular visits to this site to find out when and where online events and celebrity chats are taking place.

www.yack.com

ENVIRONMENT AND NATURE

This section covers all sorts of environmental issues, concerns and resources. Many of the sites also have extensive lists of links to other sites on similar topics. You might also find some of the sites listed under *Science* to be relevant to certain environmental projects.

Center for Ecoliteracy

This American institution, based in Northern California, was set up to foster the experience and understanding of the natural world through education. It works with schools and other organisations to teach them how to respect our environment and create sustainable communities. A good source of information for those researching ecosystems and the impact of technologies and man-made disasters on the environment.

www.ecoliteracy.org

Climate Ark

This portal provides links to hundreds of sites, articles and resources on climate change, from its causes and impacts to solutions and conservation. It is run by a non-profit organisation and provides a great starting point for research into this topic.

www.climateark.org

Earthquakes

The activities of the British Geological Survey's (BGS) Global Seismology and Geomagnetism Group (GSGG) cover a broad spectrum of research and information services concerned with earthquakes and man-made seismic disturbances. This site will tell you everything you may want to know about earthquakes. Find out what causes earthquakes and where they strike. See what devastation they leave behind.

www.gsrg.nmh.ac.uk

Eco-friendly Paper

One of several 'green paper' sites available on the web, this one, courtesy of Costa Rica Natural, offers a bewildering array of natural and recycled papers – including banana, coffee and cigar paper – for office and home printing use, together with a wide range of accessories including notebooks, writing paper and sketchbooks in a range of designs. You can order online: all products are illustrated and full details given including size and weight.

www.ecopaper.com

Eco-Portal

This portal brings together lots of academic papers, research info and statistics on various ecological and environmental topics, and allows you to search for what you need. All the items listed have been reviewed by the portal, so there is no spurious content. A great resource when you need specific information.

www.eco-portal.com

EcoWorld

This site promises information and answers about the earth's energy and food supply, species, ecosystems and projects to preserve them. It also provides a guide to earth-friendly products and services, tours and green investing, with links to approved providers.

www.ecoworld.com

Environmental Media Services

EMS is a non-profit organisation that aims to provide top-quality information to journalists and the media about environmental issues and concerns. If you are researching a particular issue, search its database for links to related articles and sites.

www.ems.org

Environmental Atlas

The Environmental Atlas is an internet-based tool for researching world-wide environmental policy. It uses a standard set of criteria to categorise environmental conditions and policies and offers quick access to information about a single country as well as comparisons between countries. An excellent resource for people concerned with the environment.

www.rri.org/envatlas

Environmental News

The Environmental News Network collects the news concerning our world and contains facts, essays, radio shows and a calendar of events. Everything available on the site deals with the environment, and with all the details in one place this is an essential visit for the environmentalist. You will find that the factual information is often seasonally related.

www.enn.com

Environmental Organisation Directory

This simple directory provides thousands of links to environmental sites covering every conceivable topic. Make this the starting point for your ecological research.

www.webdirectory.com

Environmental Sites on the Internet

This award-winning Swedish site provides a vast library of links, giving an enormous amount of information on every aspect of the world environment, including greenhouse gases, oil spills, acid rain, electric vehicles, land care in Australia and much more.

www.lib.kth.se/~lg/envsite.htm

Environmental Sources

Here is a large directory of pressure groups, government organisations and magazines, plus a large information section including some interesting miscellaneous entries, as well as features on pollution and transport. This site is a useful resource for anyone interested in improving and protecting the environment.

www2.eng.cam.ac.uk/~tpl/env.html

The EnviroWeb

You should be able to find out about any environmental issue here. The EnviroWeb claims to be the largest online environmental information service anywhere.

envirolink.org

Forest Conservation Portal

Another portal offering links to sites of related interest – this time for forest conservation, and rainforests in particular. Over 500 sites are listed and this is an excellent resource for homework or general research on the depletion of the world's forests and what we can all do to protect them.

www.forests.org

Friends of the Earth

The largest international network of environmental groups in the world, Friends of the Earth is represented in 58 countries and is one of the leading environmental pressure groups in the UK. Friends of the Earth is a charity which commissions detailed research and provides extensive information and educational materials. If you care about what happens to our planet, the Friends of the Earth web site will inform you of lots of interesting, if sometimes alarming, facts and figures. You will find the site up-to-date on all green issues, such as the debate on the production and consumption of genetically modified food. Enter your postcode to view the pollution records of local factories and discover what chemicals they currently emit.

www.foe.co.uk

Green Guide

Here you will find lots and lots of advice pages for eco-friendly living. The site will eventually feature directories of green products and services in Britain, Ireland, America, Canada and Australia.

www.aim-irl.com/greenguide

Greenpeace International

This site gives you the low-down on all current campaign events. Whether you want to know more about Greenpeace itself or what they are up to, check out this official site. You can also find out how to join Greenpeace or make a donation.

www.greenpeace.org

Myst@RainForests

This site is all about the most important ecosystems in the world, the rainforests. From breathtaking pictures of the Amazon to the island tropics everywhere, Myst@RainForests brings it to you. It is an educational web site that provides information about saving and protecting the earth and the rainforest inhabitants.

www.geocities.com/RainForest/Vines/1009

Nature Conservancy

All you ever need to know about nature and how to conserve it. This American site covers nature projects world-wide, giving helpful tips on conservation and details of ongoing conservation projects.

www.nature.org

OneWorld.Net

This highly professional-looking site, which is sponsored by BT, carries environmental and related news, campaign information, tips on how to be more green and links to providers of green products and services. You can even search for jobs in human rights, environment, and sustainable development.

www.oneworld.net

Ozone Depletion

This site offers you the answers to all your questions about the ozone layer. It covers everything from 'What is the ozone layer and why is it important?' to 'What can we do to help protect the ozone layer?' The site is very clear and helps even the scientifically challenged understand the problems and concerns associated with this topic.

www.geocities.com/RainForest/Vines/4030

The Mineral Gallery

Explore rocks and minerals at this site, which includes both pictures and detailed information, as well as the chance to purchase rock specimens.

mineral.galleries.com/default.htm

Natural History Bookshop

This is the largest environmental mail order bookshop in the world. Search for any title here. It has thousands of titles describing and explaining the amazing diversity of the natural world: field guides, textbooks, monographs, reports, CDs, videos and cassettes on every environmental subject you can think of!

www.nhbs.com

Pew Center on Global Climate Change

This is the web site for the American centre whose aim is to raise awareness of climatic changes, and provide guidance on what steps companies and individuals can take to reduce greenhouse gas emissions that have led to global warming.

www.pewclimate.org

Planet Ark News

If you take an interest in environmental issues and you like to keep up-to-date with what is happening in the world, this site is worth visiting regularly. It gives you the daily environmental news from

Reuters, the London press agency, and provides a host of resources for research. It is run by the Planet Ark charity, originally set up in Australia and supported by many famous names.

www.planetark.org

Volcano World

At this site you can ask a vulcanologist anything that you want to know about volcanoes. Check out any current eruptions and see what it is like to be at the crater's edge.

volcano.und.nodak.edu

FASHION

If you're concerned with your image or designer trends, or simply need a new outfit, check out these sites. You might also find the following sections useful: *Beauty and Hair, Shopping*.

Best of British

This portal provides a showcase for British designers and manufacturers, in association with *The Daily Telegraph*. It covers not only designer fashion but also accessories, toiletries and even home and garden, and has an excellent 'traditional British' section.

www.bestofbritish.com

Cosmopolitan

Cosmopolitan offers monthly features with copious illustrations. It includes fashion news, updates from the catwalks and current style debates. A magazine not to be missed by the fashion devotee.

www.cosmomag.com

Designer Deals

Many of the designer outlet sites are American-based and while they seem to offer good prices, once you add on the shipping costs and currency exchange fee, they don't necessarily offer that much. Here is an alternative: a UK-based site offering designer deals with up to 75%

off the recommended prices (it also ships world-wide and details of its shipping costs are provided).

www.designerdeals.com

Elle International

This site contains snippets from all 27 international editions of the glossy magazine Elle.

www.elle.com

Fashion Icon

This punchy, fun American site gives information and opinions on all the latest trends from street culture to the heights of designer gear. It provides chat boards, latest news and you can search the archives for anything you've missed on the catwalks.

www.fashionicon.com

Fashion Live

Here you can preview the latest collections online from all the world's best fashion designers, find out about haute couture in Paris, or read the features on ready-to-wear collections. You can discover who is showing on the catwalks and search the online database for up-to-date information about your favourite designer. The site also features online fashion TV which shows non-stop fashion clips from a variety of designers.

www.fashionlive.com

Fashion Net

This site contains so many fashion links that by the time you have looked at all of them, the new season's collections will be uploading! Not only fashion news, but jobs, bios, city guides and runway videos.

www.fashion.net

Figleaves

This site offers over 70 brands of underwear and hosiery for both men and women. From the designer frillies to the downright sensible, all you need is here. You can order online and delivery is free. If buying for that special someone, you can get them to wrap it for you, and they even offer to take the blame if you order it late, by saying the order was delayed in the warehouse!

www.figleaves.com

Firstview Collections Online

If you want to see what is in this year in fashion then why not sign up and subscribe for the Firstview service? Once you have subscribed you will be able to preview thousands of photos of the world's top designers' most recent collections – straight from Milan, Paris, New York and London.

www.firstview.com

Hawkshead

This well known retailer of casual affordable men's and women's wear inspired by the great outdoors provides a voguish, fashionable and easy to use catalogue packed with superb clothing. The 'Hawkshead Life' section is very commendable, featuring ideas for living, free time, competitions and feedback.

www.hawkshead.com

Landsend

This is the site for the well-known leisurewear retail outlet and offers online product selection. For women, there's a personal model service into which you key your details (hair colour, complexion, figure, etc.) so they can offer a selection of clothes to suit you.

www.landsend.co.uk

Levi's Europe

This is an interactive site for the great jeans company featuring their TV ads and a brochure to help you choose the style and cut that's right for you. Once you've decided on a pair you can see them in glorious QuickTime video and find out where to buy them in Europe with a European storefinder. You can even buy the music for the adverts here as well.

www.eu.levi.com/index.html

Paul Smith Fashion

Paul Smith's mission has always been to make his shops the individualistic antidote to retail uniformity. The Paul Smith web site is the same! Check it out to see his latest fashion creations and one very well-designed web site. For best effect, you need the Shockwave Flash plug-in, but a link is provided to allow you to download it if you don't already have it installed.

www.paulsmith.co.uk

Pink Ice

No outfits, simply high-quality accessories. From handbags to jewellery and pashminas, this shocking pink site has it all. You can browse its extensive catalogue and order online in sterling or dollars and the goods will be delivered to your door. They even gift-wrap if you are purchasing for someone else.

www.pink-ice.com

Platform Diva

Whether you love them or loathe them, maybe the long history of the platform shoe will convince you that they, indeed, will always be around. Strap on your platforms and teeter through the styles of the 1600s, 1930s, 1970s and 1990s at this site. You can test your platform knowledge by taking the online quiz.

www.geocities.com/platform_diva

Ready2shop

This site offers a unique 'Match to Me' service designed to help hide the bits of your body you dislike and emphasise the good parts. From the information you provide, the site owners will suggest items to suit you from an extensive selection of high street and designer fashion, accessories and beauty products (they also have a Kidswear section). You can also browse the product lists yourself and read their various tips for how best to wear and accessorise particular styles. All products have been personally vetted by the site owners. You cannot shop online but can create a list of the items you like (including style numbers) to take with you when you shop.

www.ready2shop.com

Sensuelle

What's an outfit without hosiery? No wrinkly nylons or popsocks here, this site offers only the best French tights and stockings, made by Le Bourget of Paris for a touch of pure luxury. Some wonderful designs to suit every outfit – be sure to use the scroll bars to search each collection thoroughly.

www.sensuelle.co.uk

Vogue

If you are interested in fashion, then you should regularly check out the Vogue site. It gives daily tips and past and present fashion features. It also has a brilliant search tool that can be used if you want to see what you can get for your money. Find out what the high street stores have in stock, as well as what the top designers are offering. You can also link to the various other Vogue sites across the world.

www.vogue.co.uk

Women's Wire: Style

This site offers you a diverse selection of regularly updated features examining current trends in fashion and beauty. It is down to earth in its recommendations, and never takes itself too seriously – a refreshing change from some sites. It simply provides accessible advice and information for women for whom style is an interest rather than an obsession.

www.womenswire.com/style

Yves Saint Laurent

A lavish site from the French designer Yves Saint Laurent that enables you to take a front-row seat at the catwalk shows. It is just goes to show you how expensive the designs must be because the site does not even try to sell you any of the clothes! Ever heard the expression: 'If you need to ask the price, you can't afford it?'

www.ysl-hautecouture.com/va/index.html

FILMS, TELEVISION, VIDEO AND DVD

Are you a fan of the big screen? Or maybe you prefer to watch your idols from the comfort of your own home. Use these sites to check out the latest releases or find out more about the golden oldies or your favourite screen pin-up. See also *Entertainment, Fun, Music* and *Theatre*.

Ain't It Cool News

Check out this film site for all the latest insider movie news. It has a somewhat anarchic style and tends to concentrate on non-family movies so some of its content is unsuitable for children.

www.aint-it-cool-news.com

All Movie Guide

This directory of the movies comes complete with reviews and synopses, so you can find out all there is to know about your favourite films, however old. The site is huge but do not be put off by this as it is very easy to navigate your way around and pinpoint relevant information, such as plots, reviews, biographies, etc. It is available in six different languages: French, German, Italian, Spanish, English and Portuguese. It also has a DVD section.

www.allmovie.com

Black Star

Online store for video and DVD purchases delivered free anywhere in the UK.

www.blackstar.co.uk

BBC Online

BBC Online provides a huge number of services, bringing information, entertainment and education from the BBC to the web. The BBC home page acts as both a gateway to all their online content and a frequently updated guide to the key programmes and stories of the day. There are individual sites for all the major entertainment and education programmes on the BBC.

www.bbc.co.uk

CDDirect

This is the place to buy your CD players, PlayStations, Nintendos and DVD players, as well as the CDs, DVDs and games to play on them.

www.cddirect.co.uk

Drew's Scripts-O-Rama

Are you wondering how you can find film scripts on the internet? Perhaps not, but if you are now interested in gaining access to the scripts of your favourite films, look no further than this site. Drew has done all the hard work for you by finding the necessary links to hundreds of scripts and it is all free of charge.

www.script-o-rama.com

DVD

This site is the best source of DVDs on the internet, including Region 1 discs from America which cannot be obtained in the UK. Delivery is free throughout Europe.

www.play247.com

Empire

This is the web site for the video and film magazine where you will find news, competitions, features, cinema and video releases and links to movie-related sites.

www.empireonline.co.uk

The Greatest Films

This site is a true labour of love designed by an amateur film buff. It contains a list of the 100 greatest films and 200 greatest film moments (see if you agree). For most of the films listed there is a long description and plot synopsis. Worth a look just to see if you agree with the choice.

www.filmsite.org

Hollywood Reporter

Want to know the latest Tinseltown gossip? For daily reviews and previews, plus a look at the showbiz directory, check out the Hollywood Reporter site.

www.hollywoodreporter.com

Internet Movie Database

A very comprehensive database that should not be missed by any movie-lover. It has information on more than 100,000 movies and a million actors. When you have found your favourite movie, you can watch full 'filmographies' of the entire cast and crew.

www.imdb.com

James Bond

Here you will find a fan's page about the most successful British agent. James Bond 007 is known throughout the world and this site contains everything you will ever need to know. You can find out about the actors who have played James Bond, the villains, the films with reviews, find out about all the gadgets used by Bond, and of course all the lovely Bond Girls.

www.geocities.com/Hollywood/5727

Morecambe and Wise

If you loved this famous duo, check out this tribute site, created by fan Tim Lomas. It includes a gallery, bios, film and radio credits, and a shop for memorabilia.

www.morecambeandwise.co.uk

Movie Bloopers

Perfect for trivia fans, here you can find details of mistakes and continuity errors in all your favourite films. (Use this to impress your friends the next time you watch them!)

www.moviebloopers.com

Mr Showbiz

If you want to know what is going on in the world of the movies, check out this American site. It provides movie reviews, features, obituaries, news and a lot of celebrity biographies.

www.mrshowbiz.com

The Oscars

Interested in the Academy Awards? Have you ever wondered what else the Academy does? If so, then this site is for you. It has information about the public exhibitions and events, the Student Academy Awards, the annual screenwriting competition, all publications, plus the world-class research library and film archive.

www.oscar.com

Popcorn

This site, from Carlton.com, features comprehensive searchable listings of what's on at cinemas nationwide throughout the UK. It also has the entire low-down on the movie industry, with all the glitz, glamour and gossip. The site itself features film reviews, hundreds of pictures, video trailers, audio interviews with major stars, and a personalised e-mail alert.

www.popcorn.co.uk

Screen It! Entertainment Reviews for Parents

Despite the title, the site does not tell you how good a film is. Instead, it takes a moral stance and simply rates the film on various scales. Find out whether a film is suitable for viewing by children (and for that matter, by some adults too!) because of the degree of alcohol and drugs, disrespectful and bad attitudes, sex and nudity, profanity, smoking and tense family scenes.

www.screenit.com/search_movies.html

Showbizwire

For the latest showbiz news on the celebrities to all the film, theatre, television, music and video productions, Showbizwire gets its information from around 50 major sources.

www.showbizwire.com

Silents Majority

Do not bother to adjust the volume when watching the films discussed at this site! You will find that the first page steers you to current feature stories, but go beyond this and see that the site links areas on the stars and the technology. There are also some regional showings of the old classics.

www.mdle.com/ClassicFilms

Sky Broadcasting Corporation

This site gives you details of all Sky channels and much more. Find out about the world of entertainment here.

www.sky.co.uk

Star Wars

The official site for the *Star Wars* films, this also has a directory for any sites related to *Star Wars*, with information on every conceivable aspect of the films.

www.starwars.com

Tomb Town

This site is a virtual 3D world. TombTown is the only 3D interactive virtual reality cemetery on the web where you actually visit a 'real' cemetery. You experience the cemetery by wandering about, looking at tombstones, listening to birds chirp and crickets sing, and by visiting residents. Famous personalities such as Marilyn Monroe, Plato, Bela Lugosi, Doc Holliday and Jerry Garcia. Also available is the chance to register your own plot for a small fee.

www.tombtown.com

FINANCE AND INSURANCE

If you need advice on what to do with your money, how to organise your tax affairs or how Granny's stocks are doing, check out these sites. See also *Banking*.

Accountant's Home Page

The Accountant's Home Page is a series of pages dedicated to collecting and making available internet resources of interest to accountants. Here you can access an information database with resources on e-commerce, tax law, and the accounting, manufacturing, construction and service industries.

www.computercpa.com

Bloomberg

Bloomberg is organised into three primary channels: markets, money and life. The markets channel offers comprehensive coverage of world-wide financial markets. The money channel features audio and video interviews with market experts as well as articles from the award-winning *Bloomberg Personal* magazine. The life channel covers wine, cigar and art industries, sports, weather and world-wide real estate listing. Bloomberg has sites in Australia, Germany, Italy, Japan, Latin America and the UK.

www.bloomberg.co.uk

Charcol

Part of the UK's largest independent mortgage broker, the online wizard at this site helps you to find the best deal for you.

www.charcolonline.co.uk

Company Sleuth

A legal inside look at your investments, competitors, partners and clients. Company Sleuth's have the ability to stake out and track the publicly traded companies you choose. They will even send you daily reports, via e-mail, on their business activities, financial moves, internet dealings and legal actions.

www.companysleuth.com

CNBC

Financial market news, tickers, charts and analysis are to be found on this site, which offers vital information for the private sector.

www.cnbc.com

Dow Jones

This site brings together an expanded collection of news, information, resources and services. You can also personalise the features that make them relevant to your specific business interests. This is a free site, offering information and resources selected by *Wall Street Journal* editors for any business question. For those times when deeper research is required, the site provides access to premium services and pay-per-view information that's all easily and effectively organised and presented to help you find precisely what you need.

www.dowjones.com

E-mail Tax

An advice site run by professional accountants who will calculate your self-assessment tax bill for you.

www.emailtax.co.uk

Eagle Star

The major insurance company sells insurance online as well as offering information and answering any of your questions on insurance.

www.eaglestardirect.co.uk

Egg

Although a relative newcomer, Egg has quickly established itself as one of the major players in internet financial services. Loans, savings, accounts, investments and all other major banking services are available at this well-rounded site. It also has links to approximately 150 retail-outlet sites.

www.egg.com

Fantasy Stock Market

Fantasy Stock Market promotes investment education to individuals through active participation and competition which is enhanced by an interactive and easy-to-use web site. Players who sign up are given $100,000 in fantasy money to trade stocks and mutual funds listed on the New York, Nasdaq, American and other US stock exchanges. Fantasy Stock Market will then track the portfolio and rank them against other players.

www.fantasystockmarket.com

Finance News

This site from CNN provides you with all the financial news you could ever need. The site contains stock quotes, market numbers, top news and financial help. Here you can find everything financial from important information for business travellers to the latest stories involving small businesses.

cnnfn.com

Financial Message Board

If you want to find out information about a company or discuss the future prospects of the company and share knowledge about it with others, this is a good place to start. This board is not connected in any way with the companies listed, and any messages are solely the opinion and responsibility of the poster.

messages.yahoo.com/yahoo

Financial Times

The online version of the UK newspaper, *Financial Times*, which is the first source of reference in City banking circles.

www.ft.com

Find Information

Designed to give you all kinds of financial information, here you'll find a financial information net directory, as well as guidance on investments, insurance, savings, loans and other financial advice. They have a site of the week section which rates all the most recently updated sites.

www.find.co.uk

Fool.com

An award-winning and popular site devoted to investors and investment. It offers detailed information, discussions and portfolios and is a good place to start researching stock issues.

www.fool.com

FTSE International

More commonly known as the Footsie, this company exists to provide a database of world stock market indices.

www.ftse.com

Inland Revenue

The official site of the Inland Revenue where you can find the answers to all your tax-related questions.

www.inlandrevenue.gov.uk

Insurance Reinvented

If you have just received an insurance quote and want a second opinion, you may be able to get one here before you sign up. The site covers motor, travel and home insurance and breakdown cover.

www.insure.co.uk

Interactive Investor

The ultimate goal of Interactive Investor is to provide you with all the information you need to make an investment decision by providing the best available information on current investment and the best tools to monitor and manage investments effectively. On its site it provides performance and price information for stocks as well as collective investments such as unit trusts, investment trusts, ISAs and pensions.

www.iii.co.uk

Life Search

This company aims to beat your existing quotes for life insurance, whatever your age and cover. Enter the details on their site and they will quote you immediately.

www.lifesearch.co.uk

London Stock Exchange

The web site of one of the largest stock exchanges in the world.

www.londonstockex.co.uk

Moneygator

A site on which you can see comparisons of mortgages, credit cards and personal loans on offer from more than 40 leading lenders. They also provide useful information on the various products and you can apply for loans etc. online using a single form and with no broker fees to pay.

www.moneygator.com

Money Extra

Money Extra is a leading UK personal finance web site and aims to give you fast and easy access to the best financial products and services using independent and impartial comparisons. The services are provided free of charge because it receives sponsorship revenues. The company specialises in financial services e-commerce and the provision of electronic information and transaction services for the life, pensions, investment and mortgage-lending markets. There is also an international section.

www.moneyextra.co.uk

National Savings

Checked your Premium Bonds lately? This Government-backed personal savings specialist, which traditionally has operated via the Post Office, is moving into the world of e-commerce. You can check for any unpaid Premium Bond prizes, and offers details on 280,000 unpaid prizes. Other features include a savings selector, a savings calculator and information on products and tax rates.

www.nationalsavings.co.uk

UK Screentrade

Screentrade offers you the chance to have a number of competitive, personalised quotes prepared for you in just a few minutes. Then you can compare prices and cover, and see just what you're getting for your money – you'll probably be surprised how policy features differ. All you do is key in your details once and you're in touch with some of the biggest names in the market. Then you can buy online or over the phone, whichever suits you best.

www.screentrade.co.uk

ShareDetec

This site monitors other financial and investment sites for updated information, rumours and moves, saving you the need to search several sites. If up-to-the-minute info is what you need, check out this site for details of its various products.

www.sharedetec.com

Silicon Investor

At this site you can read up on timely performance data and other useful statistics on technology companies of all sizes. There is also a chat forum, where active investors can share their views and get advice about the prospects for specific companies and the technology sector itself. Silicon Investor claims to be the world's largest financial discussion site.

www.siliconinvestor.com

Simpler Pensions

Established by the National Association of Pension Funds Limited, this site aims to simplify and demystify company pension schemes for both employer and employee.

www.simplerpensions.org.uk

Utility Bills

This site saves you money! Now that the electricity and gas markets are deregulated, you can choose your own supplier, rather than being tied to your local one, so they have to compete on price. At this site, enter details of your annual usage to find which supplier offers the best deal for you, whatever your preferred payment arrangement. With more suppliers entering the market every month, it's definitely worth shopping around. Many of the suppliers also allow you to link directly from this site to their own to sign up immediately.

www.unravelit.co.uk

Virgin Direct

This site offers a variety of financial products, all fully described, from a number of different lenders. One of its best features is the glossary, which explains financial and insurance terminology in plain English. You can also download Richard Branson's guide to investments.

www.virgin-direct.co.uk

Wall Street Journal Interactive

WSJ.com is the online edition of the *Wall Street Journal*. It not only contains the same information as the printed version but also has charts and data archives that really make it worth looking at. Anyone wanting to find out about investing on the stock market would do well to look at this site. You can try it free for 14 days, after which you have to pay.

www.wsj.com

UK Invest

Excellent information site for investors on almost all money-related subjects. Its sister site netmortgage.co.uk offers great deals on mortgages and remortgages, plus in-depth explanations of the various products and options available to you, and is accessible from the main site or separately.

www.uk-invest.com

www.netmortgage.co.uk

FLOWERS

The following sites offer UK-wide or world-wide delivery, usually on the same day, with payment by credit or debit card. If you fancy something different, see the sections *Cards and Greetings* and *Gifts*.

Flowers2Send

This Leeds-based company sends flowers by mail anywhere in the UK, at reasonable prices. You can see exactly what you get: all 22 of their arrangements are illustrated on their site. Order by noon for delivery the next day.

www.flowers2send.com

Flowers Direct

Next-day delivery anywhere in the UK is offered from Flowers Direct, where you can choose from a range of prices and arrangements. They also provide useful advice on which flowers to choose, the meaning of various flowers (choose candytuft or hydrangea at your peril!) and how to make your cut flowers last longer.

www.flowersdirectuk.co.uk

Interflora

Fleurop-Interflora is the world's biggest online flower shop. This world-wide flower-ordering organisation will get your message and flowers to that special person within hours of receiving your order, no matter where they live: just have your credit card number and the delivery details ready. Note that payments are processed in Swiss Francs, so you may have to pay a currency exchange fee to your credit card company – check with them first if you are unsure.

www.interflora.com

Internet Florist

This American-based site offers deliveries world-wide at reasonable prices and has a huge selection of arrangements and accompanying gifts. Just select the 'International' button to view the list of countries they cover and select the one you require. Some of their prices seem a little high – especially when you add the handling fee – but remember they are quoted in US dollars, so they will be cheaper for some countries than others.

www.iflorist.com

Teleflorist

With same-day or next-day floral deliveries anywhere within the UK, this is a nicely laid-out and easy-to-use site with a good selection of arrangements (try one of their 'zodiac' range for something a little different. If you order flowers regularly you can set up an account with them, and you can also help charity by selecting certain products for which 10% of the purchase price is donated to the British Heart Foundation. They also offer hampers for various occasions.

www.teleflorist.co.uk

Virtual Florist

At this site they offer you a chance to send a virtual flower bouquet: a floral image by e-mail that is easy, fun and totally free! You can select and send a floral image with a personalised message. There are plenty of tasteful arrangements and space to compose a short poem to accompany them. If you prefer the real thing, they provide a link to Internet Florist (described above).

www.virtualflorist.com

FOOD

Be warned, some of these sites will set your stomach rumbling! Whatever your culinary pleasure, you are sure to find it on the web. Food-lovers everywhere are publishing recipes, tips and dining experiences, while food producers and providers are queuing up to tempt you with their various epicurean delights. For the cooks amongst you, don't forget to check out the selection of sites under *Cookery and Kitchenware*. You might also like to browse the section on *Drinks and Drinking*.

Ben and Jerry's

The madcap homemade ice-cream merchants are at it again, this time online. A great fun site for the kid in all of us, Ben and Jerry's UK site offers help on choosing your favourite flavours, lists of stockists and links to sites that deliver (sadly not yet throughout the country, but maybe soon), and great competitions and features.

www.benjerry.co.uk

Chocoholic's Delight

Chocoholism is an issue that should be addressed. So for all you chocoholics out there, get some help: check out this premium site for lots of information and mouth-watering recipes! This sophisticated chocolatier even allows you to upload contact details for your friends and family directly from a Palm PC so you can send them confections with just one click! However, unfortunately they do not yet offer an international delivery service so you can only order if you are within the USA. They do, however, provide contact details for all their international branches so that you can order by phone.

www.godiva.com

Clearspring

Dedicated to vegetarian foods from around the world, this site offers a catalogue of goods that are available by mail order from London. There is also a database of interesting and unusual recipes.

www.clearspring.co.uk

Dine Online

This independent UK dining and travel e-zine offers a selection of British and foreign food reviews. The informative articles recommend and review specific world-wide venues as well as cover broader food issues. There is also an equally good but smaller section of wine reviews and suggestions for the perfect meal.

www.dine-online.co.uk/welcome.html

Domino's Pizza

All this fancy food giving you heartburn? Why not opt for an old favourite: pizza delivered to your door. Domino's has an online ordering facility that puts you directly in touch with your local branch and allows you to select everything you want without the need to shout it down the phone! There are even games to play while you wait for your order to arrive. If you're not in the UK, use the main US site listed below, and click on the 'non-US locations' button to find the site for your local branch.

www.dominos.co.uk (UK only)

www.dominos.com (US and elsewhere)

Epicurious Food

This massive site contains everything you could possibly want to know about all things edible. There are informative sections on drinking and food etiquette, together with a helpful food dictionary. The cooking classes offer illustrated step-by-step recipes that will take you gently through the creation of some exotic dishes, while the gourmet section reveals the secret to creating more complex culinary works of art.

food.epicurious.com

Food Lines

This site provides sound, reliable food and nutritional information. Food enthusiasts can also obtain information about food-related trade shows, festivals, events and contests held around the world, and search the world for recommended restaurants. There are links to other food, nutrition and recipe sites and you can purchase speciality food, nutrition and health products and services from vendors. Try out a food quiz and crossword to see how much you have learned.

www.foodlines.com

The French Hamper Company

View this site for a selection of fabulous French food and drink for every occasion, both business and pleasure. You can choose from a large range of pre-packaged hampers, but the company also caters for special requests all year round. Recipes in French and English are included with your order so that you can make the most of everything you have in your hamper.

www.frenchhampers.com

Global Gourmet

This is an e-zine with articles about food, wine and diet, as well as a full archive of previous issues. Global Gourmet has profiles and recommendations of culinary web sites and cookbooks amongst its regular features.

www.globalgourmet.com

Haagen Dazs

Reputedly the best ice-cream in the world (it certainly has the most stylish TV ads), Haagen Dazs is now online. This site has plenty to entertain you while you tuck in to your favourite tub: movie clips, tips for nights in and out, the story of the company and much more. What a pity you can't order online...but you can find your local stockist and, if you're lucky, a local Haagen Dazs café.

www.haagendazs.co.uk

Hampers

This site has links to some of the best hamper providers operating in the UK, whether for business, as a gift for delivery or the standard budgeted Christmas blow-out. A one-stop shop for basketed goodies, whatever the season.

www.hampers.uk.com

Henriette's Herb Page

A mainly text-based site, containing tons of information on growing and using herbs of all kinds. It is well organised and hence is easy to use. The herbs are broken down by use – medicinal, culinary, etc. – and listed by name. If the content interests you, try their newsgroup alt.Folklore.herbs.

www.ibiblio.org/herbmed

Iceland

The first major UK food retailer to ban GM foods from its own-brand range, also one of the first on the web. Order online for next-day delivery if you live within 10 miles of one of their stores (three miles within the M25). If your freezer's not big enough, don't panic, you can order a new one here too!

www.iceland.co.uk

Iorganic Food and Wine

This site offers a great selection of organic food and wine and delivers the next day. It also has a number of articles on organic foods and farming.

www.iorganic.com

Le Gourmet Français

The UK's leading internet gourmet specialists. On offer, a wide range of gourmet food for discerning palates, including gift hampers, organic food, and prepared meals and soups, all delivered to your door. There is a good recipe section and the site also has its own chat room for gourmet gossip. Not one for the calorie-counter: as the site puts it, 'People on diets are trying to follow the path of feast resistance!'

www.gourmet2000.co.uk

Mail a Meal

Guaranteed non-fattening! This site is dedicated to sending free food postcards. Say it with food by mailing a meal to your friends from their mouth-watering selection. Say 'Sorry' with some chocolates, say 'I love you' with a romantic candlelit dinner, or 'Get well soon' with a bowl of soup. Fun and no fat.

www.mailameal.com

Menu Master

Type your location and you will get a list of all the local restaurants, food pubs and takeaways in the area. Very useful if you are travelling and do not know the area. Don't be too specific with the address details as some areas have only a few places listed.

www.menumaster.co.uk

Organics Direct

An easy-to-navigate site, offering organic foods, wine, clothing and bedding online for fairly quick delivery.

www.organicsdirect.com

Real Meat

This site offers ethically produced meat and poultry, on sale exclusively online (they don't supply to supermarkets) with a minimum order quantity.

www.realmeat.co.uk

Sainsbury's

The major UK food retailer now has its own web site offering an excellent range of quality foods to order online for next-day delivery. You can set up a shopping list of your favourite items and use it to reorder every week, or change to suit your mood.

www.sainsburys.co.uk

Schwartz

This site from the UK's major producer of herbs and spices is full of information regarding the products they offer, recipes using their herbs and spices and a section on everything you could need to know about the your favourite herbs and spices. There is even a section on special offers where you can buy related goods, although this is only open to UK residents.

www.schwartz.co.uk

Speciality Foods

Exactly what you would expect, this site is an entry-point to small, specialist UK sites offering unusual foods from organic meat to home-made pickles and vegetarian Parmesan cheese.

www.speciality-foods.com

Taste

For everyone who loves eating and drinking, this site – sponsored by Carlton and Sainsbury's – contains food facts, recipes, information on UK restaurants, shopping and wine tasting. Check it out for any food-related topics.

www.taste.co.uk

Tesco

One of the first of the major UK food retailers to expand into the online shopping market, Tesco offers online ordering and delivery the next day. You have to have a Clubcard and be over 18 to order by credit card. The site also includes recipes, shopping tips and special offers.

www.tesco.com

Thorntons

This site is the Thorntons online store where you can purchase gifts and special treats from a selection of their delicious confectionery. Simply fill your shopping basket and place your order, together with a free personal message which can be sent with any gift.

www.thorntons.co.uk

Urbanbite

Currently covering only London and Amsterdam, but promising to extend to the whole of the UK and Holland fairly soon, this site offers you all the convenience of your local restaurants but with none of the legwork. Just choose the food you fancy and the restaurant you'd like it from and they do the rest – takeaway or deliver. If your area isn't covered yet, visit them and leave your postcode and e-mail address and they'll let you know when your area goes 'live'.

www.urbanbite.com

Veggie Heaven

The place where you can find over 230 of the tastiest vegetarian and vegan recipes, the leading UK vegetarian restaurant guide, amazing facts and figures – and more. Created by Rosamond Richardson, one of the UK's most innovative vegetarian cookery writers.

www.veggieheaven.com

Waitrose Direct

The food section of the John Lewis Partnership sells a vast range of high-quality foods. Investigate its site for online purchases.

www.waitrose.com

Wild Thymes

This Suffolk-based site offers all the herbs and spices you could ever need, including an organic range, tantalising recipes, competitions and gift sets – even catering packs for restaurants or serious spice users. A great search facility, easy navigation and free delivery all add up to an absolute must for spice lovers.

www.wildthymes.co.uk

FUN

Here's a selection of sites to make you smile, from the outright funny to the weird and wonderful. Other fun sites can be found in the sections *Children, Entertainment, Hobbies* and some more unusual sites in *Strange and Unusual*.

Abacus

The abacus is a calculator, the earliest known use of which is about 500BC in Babylonia, although the abacus as we know it today appeared about AD1300 in China. However, it was the Japanese in Korea who began to make serious use of the Chinese abacus in about AD1600 and to continue its evolution. Addition, subtraction, division and multiplication can be performed on a standard abacus, which is still in use today by shopkeepers in Asia and in Chinatowns world-wide. Its use is also taught in certain schools in Japan and the US. In fact, it is used to teach mathematics to blind children in situations where a sighted person would use pencil and paper. This site offers instructions on the use of the abacus.

www.ee.ryerson.ca:8080/~elf/abacus

Anagrams

At this site you can use the free generator, the anagram genius, to see what anagrams can be made out of your name. You can also use the anagram archive to search those elusive words that are stopping you from finishing that crossword you started at breakfast.

www.anagramgenius.com

April Fools on the Net

Pranksters will love this one: archives of all the best net hoaxes and jokes (vote for your favourites), plus 'foolish' tips, shopping and links to comic sites. As it says, 'This site is not to be taken seriously'!

www.2meta.com/april-fools

The Avenger's Handbook

If you want to get even with someone, or if you are just looking for some good laughs, then this site is for you. It contains revenge schemes, tactics, ideas, tips and guidance that would scare or pester most offenders into surrender. What it does *not* do is take any responsibility for your actions! This site is not recommended for children.

www.ekran.no/html/revenge

Chickenshop

Need an outfit for a fancy dress party? Or just fancy a giggle with some foaming sugar? The Chickenshop site offers fancy dress and party supplies of all kinds, including wigs, makeup, props and costumes, all delivered to your door. They also arrange firework displays and will always make sure your event goes with a bang!

www.chickenshop.co.uk

Colossal Humour

This is a mailing list for jokes, humorous stories, and entertaining anecdotes. List members send in humorous contributions, which are periodically collected into collages. The collages then are mailed out to the list on a less-than-regular basis – usually once a month. You can subscribe for free or just read the archives. Note that some of the content is unsuitable for children.

www.humournet.com

Disney

For everything about Disney with a style and quality you come to expect of this mega institution.

www.disney.co.uk

Dragons

If you are interested in dragons, this site offers a central source with hyperlinks to a whole range of dragon images, a history of dragons, and lots of other dragon-related information.

www.draconian.com

Dream Emporium

This site contains a wide range of topics to do with dreams and their interpretation. The topics include how to interpret your dreams; keeping a dream journal; nightmares; sleep disorders such as sleep walking, sleep talking, sleep paralysis and night terrors; lucid dreams; dream symbols; helping children with their nightmares.

www.dreamemporium.com

Fantasy Animation

Devoted to Japanese animation, this site offers lots of pictures of all the weird and wonderful creations – including, of course, Pokémon and Digimon – plus game-playing tips and a message board.

www.fantasyanime.com

Fortean Times

Fortean Times is a monthly magazine of news, reviews and research on strange phenomena and experiences, curiosities, prodigies and portents. This site contains highlights and news from the printed publication.

www.forteantimes.com

Funny

Want a good laugh? Then go to this online comedy directory with links to other 'funny' sites on the web. If you regularly need cheering up, sign up for its free e-mail service, which promises to send you a new joke every day!

www.funny.co.uk

FunnyMail

Want to start each day with a smile? FunnyMail will e-mail you not only jokes, but also quips, funny quotes and one-liners, and free fun stuff.

www.funnymail.com

Guide to US Theme Parks

Park-by-park advice on how to avoid the crowds, which attractions to ride on first and how to ride the attractions for maximum thrills. You can also get the latest from insiders about up-and-coming US park mergers and future rides.

www.screamscape.com

Humor Database

This site was started as a high-school science project but the project proved to be so successful, a company bought it! You can find thousands of jokes here and search by content, keyword, author or by humour number. Humor Database has links to other similar sites too. Some of the content is unsuitable for children, but you can quickly see which thanks to its rating system (similar to that used for films).

www.humordatabase.com

Humour Links

This is like a search engine for funnies! It provides links to hundreds of humour-related sites offering jokes, fun stuff, comedy from particular countries or in particular styles, funny films, and much more. The offbeat news section is particularly good.

www.humourlinks.com

HumorScope

Have you found that your horoscopes are getting too boring or too cynical for you? Try HumorScope, where the readings are changed daily and scientifically worked out by spinning a carrot. Also available by e-mail.

www.humorscope.com

Insect Recipes

You could try out these recipes – if you feel so inclined! Recipes include Rootworm Beetle Dip, Banana Worm Bread and Chocolate Chirpie Chip Cookies made with crickets!

www.ent.iastate.edu/Misc/InsectsAsFood.html

Joey Green

This American site will give you hours of fun finding out some amazing uses for ordinary things you have lying around the house. Joey also has a great selection of weird facts and there are message boards for you to exchange further weird ideas with fellow readers.

www.wackyuses.com

Joke Wallpaper

If you are getting bored looking at the patterns that came with your operating system, you'll find many new ones to choose from at this site. You can download free images for either Windows or Mac.

www.jokewallpaper.com

Nutty Sites

A fun and non-commercial site with dancing hamsters, lizards and cows as well as magic tricks. A real antidote to a rainy day.

www.nuttysites.com

Off the Mark Cartoons

These cartoons by Mark Parisi, which appear in newspapers across the world, cover subjects as diverse as beanie babies, tattoos and the stock market! A great archive of over 1,000 cartoons, plus merchandise and a good selection of links.

www.offthemark.com

Peeping Tom

Fancy peeping through some of the net's many cameras? They are watching many different people and events 24 hours a day, seven days a week. However, beware: you could end up watching life instead of getting on with it!

www.coolbase.com/peepingtom

They Killed Kenny

Comedy Central's *South Park* reached cult-worship status overnight. If you can't get enough of it, or want to know more about this bizarre show, then check out its web site. The site includes special events, the South Park booster club and a chat room.

southpark.comedycentral.com/southpark

Trivia Collections of Unusual Facts

If you have ever wondered about anything trivial, then this site is for you. Here you will find a selection of categories of trivia for your personal delectation, ideal for entertaining family and friends at those opportune moments.

www.corsinet.com/trivia

UK National Lottery

This site contains everything you need to know about the UK lottery. It will not give you the winning numbers to subsequent draws (what a shame!) but you can access previous ones together with numerical analysis and statistics. This may help you put a strategy together, or just pick six numbers at random and hope for the best!

lottery.merseyworld.com

Urban Myths

An Urban Myth is a form of legend. It is a bizarre story that is told time and time again. The people then begin to believe it is true and continue to pass it on. This site is the most extensive collection of these tall tales. If you visit this site, you can see how many times you have been duped!

www.urbanmyths.com

Useless Knowledge

This site contains lots of useless facts, useless quotes – everything on it is useless actually, but it is a good read. You'll never be stuck for something to say again!

www.uselessknowledge.com

The Weekly

The Weekly is a funny mag of made-up things that is published each Monday. It does not contain true news stories but it is a very entertaining read if you want something to make you smile.

www.theweekly.co.uk

Write Like an Egyptian

Nom en Hieroglyphes is a fun site to visit. It allows you to type in your name phonetically and receive the corresponding hieroglyphics. However, the instructions are given in French and English in alternating paragraphs so it is a little confusing. What you must not miss is the Album in English link, which you will find at the bottom of the page. This gives you a tour of the pharaohs.

webperso.iut.univ-paris8/~rosmord//nomhiero.html

Yuk Yuk

Chad Frick's weird interactive cartoons are all available at this site (you will need the Shockwave plug-in to get the best effect). Click on passing objects to stop and interact with them; click on characters repeatedly for new dialogue. When they start to repeat, click on something else. Click the arrows to continue walking. Hit the Reload button on your browser to start over.

www.yukyuk.com

Yahoo Games

This site allows you to play classic games such as chess, bridge and backgammon with other people around the world. It is a free service which does not require any special software. A standard web browser and an internet connection are all you need and then it simply takes a moment to register in order to obtain your log-on name. Once you have done this, you can enter a game at the site and have hours of fun!

play.yahoo.com

GAMES AND GAMING

These sites offer online games, downloadable games, or information on games for other platforms such as PlayStation and Nintendo. For more traditional games, see *Toys and Play*.

All Game Guide

This site allows game players quick access to news and reviews, hints and tips, screenshots and downloads of games, and is easy to navigate. It includes games from the past, the present and hints on what the future holds.

www.allgame.com

Computer and Video Games

This is a PC and console online gaming magazine. It is UK-based and updated daily with news, reviews, tips, voting and forums.

www.computerandvideogames.com

Crime Scene

This site features fictional crime cases. It is a unique combination of interactive storytelling and gaming. Choose a level of participation and become a case detective or a case viewer. You can then examine the evidence and share your tips, leads and observations. The current case is updated each week with items such as: evidence, photos, coroner's reports, witness interviews and surveillance videos.

www.crimescene.com

Emulators Online

If you're a born-again gamer, or just an old-timer, you've probably got stacks of old games from defunct systems such as Atari 8-bit and STE just lying around waiting to be resurrected. Now's your chance. This site has software and all the necessary instructions to temporarily turn your PC into an Atari so you can relive your youth.

www.emulators.com

Free Games

A list of links to sites with free games available to download: not just the standard computer games but ones based on card and board games, too.

www.freegames2000.com

Game FAQs

Are you frustrated with the new game you have just bought because you cannot get past the first screen? Do you feel like returning it or even throwing it out because you are totally fed up with it? Help is at hand at this site. You'll find cheats and walk-throughs to hundreds of games designed for both PC and games consoles.

www.gamefaqs.com

Games Domain

This is a comprehensive British-based games site that provides news, reviews, freebies, chat and a contacts and resources list. It is one of the few sites that really makes good use of its user contributions.

www.gamesdomain.co.uk

Game Spot

Game Spot states: 'the best, the worst, the coolest, the hottest – if it's new in computer gaming, you'll find it here!' Apart from news and reviews, it contains a designer diary section, beta centre and 3D model gallery to enhance your gaming experience. With an almost exhaustive amount of information across all platforms, it has everything you will possibly need.

www.gamespot.com

Happy Puppy

This could be renamed Huge Dog considering the size of this long-established game site. It contains an enormous amount of varied information for game players of all persuasions and platforms. From tips and cheats to downloadable demos, this site has it all.

happypuppy.com

Hot Games

This is an online magazine with a sharp edge and a great sense of humour. Subscribe to their e-mail service, Cool News, to receive all the latest news and information on the games world.

www.hotgames.com

Jamba

Self-styled as offering big games, big prizes and lots of fun, this site offers you games such as Armageddon and *Catchphrase* which you can play once you register on the site. More than just a computer-gamer's site: this is now managed by the Carlton media organisation as part of Carlton.com.

www.jamba.co.uk

MSN Gaming Zone

Microsoft Network brings you this site, which allows you to play others at popular games across the net. You don't have to be an expert at the action games: simpler ones like Hearts and Blackjack are also on offer. The site also features game reviews, chat and news on gaming events.

www.uk.zone.msn.com

PC Game Finder

This is a specialised search engine indexing everything the web has to offer for over 3,500 PC games. Look up a game to get all of the facts, files and links that you may ever need. The site gives you direct access to the latest reviews, demos, patches, cheats and much more. In order to carry out a search, look up a game by title, by company, by A-Z, or by browsing over 150 detailed categories. You can also check GameScoop to see what's new every 24 hours.

www.pcgame.com

Software First

PlayStation 1 and 2, Nintendo, Dreamcast and Gameboy games are all stocked on this site, together with books, videos and CDs.

www.softwarefirst.co.uk

Sony Station

This is one of the best and most popular games sites on the web (specialising in PlayStation for obvious reasons) and well worth a visit. The ads can be annoying though.

www.station.sony.com

Total Games

This site claims to be 'the home of video games', which may seem a little presumptuous, but it is certainly crammed with information for all formats. You can play online or download new software, read reviews and interviews, and get all the latest cheats and tips. They have some great competitions too.

www.totalgames.net

GARDENS AND GARDENING

All you green-fingered enthusiasts out there – don't think the net is not for you! Take off those gardening gloves for a moment and check out these sites. You can pick up some tips for your own garden and search for the latest in garden technology and products, as well as peeking at some of the most glamorous gardens in the world. You might also be interested in the sites listed under *Environment and Nature*.

Archadeck

Decking is becoming very fashionable and this company offers a wide range to suit every property and garden, plus accessories and heating. It is an extensive web site covering every aspect of decking and you can submit your requirements to the company via an online form for a quote or further information.

www.archadeck.co.uk

Australian National Botanic Gardens

Even if you never get the chance to visit, you will know everything about the Botanical Gardens at Canberra by the time you finish looking at this site. The site includes information on all flora and fauna projects right through to fire procedures! Although the site is not that well ordered, nature lovers will find it is really worth wading through.

www.anbg.gov.au

Baby Bio

Baby Bio is one of the major UK producers of plant foods and pest-control products. The site offers advertising of its own products, of course, but also useful question-and-answer information on plant care and coping with plant and gardening problems.

www.bio.uk.co

BBC Gardening Online

The BBC produces some of the best gardening programmes in the world, whether for TV or radio. *Gardeners' World, Ground Force, Homefront in the Garden, Gardeners' Question Time*, you can check them all out at this site, together with advice from the presenters, a handy jargon-buster feature, and plenty of plant and design information. A one-stop shop for expert help with your garden. You can also sign up for an e-mail newsletter to let you know about new features on the site.

www.bbc.co.uk/gardening

Capital Gardens

This site offers a good range of garden products and accessories for sale, with an efficient search engine to help you navigate through the stocks. There is normally a charge for delivery unless you live in London.

www.capital-gardens.co.uk

E-garden

Sensible and straightforward advice, with sources for gardening products and supplies are offered on this site, including features from TV gardeners Richard Jackson and Geoff Hodge. It has a great section of handy guides that explain common gardening problems and how to solve them.

www.e-garden.co.uk

Garden Experts

The Expert Gardener magazine now has this site which is part of a larger web site on all aspects of gardening, including news, features and a chat room. Once you register, you can access information about the magazine, get gardening advice or buy gardening products.

www.igarden.co.uk

Garden Furniture

This company offers a wide range of stylish and practical garden furniture traditionally crafted in beautiful natural teak. It will withstand all the British weather can throw at it, and arrives fully assembled for you to use straight away. Delivery is free. You can get a preview of their range at the web site and then order their brochure for the full collection.

www.teaktigertrading.co.uk

Garden Guides

This site is a great resource for gardeners everywhere with articles, guide sheets and tips for all things gardening-related, such as planting hardy perennials, composting and arranging beds. Great stuff, with a free newsletter posted to your inbox every week if you wish to subscribe. Note that as it is an American site you will be unable to purchase from the seed shop (they only deliver to the US and Canada).

www.gardenguides.com

Gardening 365

Find out about plants, gardens and gardening events in the UK, search the web for garden information or a gardener in your area, or discuss gardening topics. This site has a magazine-style format so features change regularly. You can also buy plants, seeds and garden equipment online.

www.oxalis.co.uk

Garden Web

This is a US-based site, so some of the information is of regional relevance, but there is also a lot of useful information for all gardeners, including planting, plant care and pest control. The site contains a number of message boards for discussions on gardening-related topics, so bring all your problems here and see if anyone has the answers!

www.gardenweb.com

Gardening Encyclopedia

Here you will find an illustrated gardening encyclopedia, problem-solver section containing the answers to 700 horticultural ailments, and a guide to other sites at gardening.com to help the novice and the expert alike. Again it is primarily American content.

www.gardening.com

Gardening UK

With plant of the month, articles, information and details of events and supplies, this site offers much to interest the keen gardener – and it is based in the UK!

www.gardening-uk.com

Horticultural Index

All aspects of horticulture are covered in this wide-ranging index, including products, colleges, nurseries, shows and equipment.

www.ukexnet.co.uk/hort/index.htm

Internet Garden

The Internet Garden has been designed to provide a useful starting point for gardening enthusiasts in search of quality information that is quick and easy to access. It has a search facility and links to other useful sites as well. A well-designed site with some stunning images.

www.internetgarden.co.uk

Harkness Roses

A fascinating site from this famous rose-grower, with articles of all sorts for rose fans as well as all kinds of roses on sale. Easy to find your way around and an excellent site for rose gardeners. It also hosts the site for the Royal National Rose Society – just click on the link.

www.roses.co.uk

Royal Botanic Garden, Edinburgh, Scotland

The Royal Botanic Garden Edinburgh was founded in the 17th Century on an area the size of a tennis court. It now extends to 31 hectares at its original site, plus specialist gardens at three very different locations in Scotland (Younger, Logan and Dawyck), and is one of the world's finest botanical gardens. Check out the site for all the latest news and information on education, events, publications and research as well as links to other sites and associated organisations.

www.rbge.org.uk

Royal Horticultural Society

This site, from the UK's premier organisation for gardeners, offers information on plants, RHS gardens and events, the science behind plant growing and much, much more. You can join the RHS online and browse their online book and garden shops (in conjunction with grogro.com).

www.rhs.org.uk

Shrubs for your Garden

Online sales of shrubs, perennials, turf, etc. for your garden from a Cheshire-based nursery. A good range with competitive prices and quick delivery. Take a tour of their nursery to see how your plants are produced, packaged and shipped.

www.shrubsdirect.com

Thompson and Morgan

One of the UK's most prolific seed and plant distributors, Thompson and Morgan now offers you the chance to browse its enviable selection and order online for quick delivery. Each plant is fully described including tips on where best to place it for the best growing conditions. The site also contains information for commercial growers and details of the company and its range of products.

www.thompsonandmorgan.co.uk

The Urban Wildlife Garden Site

This site is dedicated to the promotion of organic techniques which attract wildlife and endeavour to live with nature. The aim is to encourage the biodiversity of nature in urban communities, creating an oasis of sites for wildlife of all kinds. Although the site has not been updated for some time, the information is contains is still useful.

www.geocities.com/RainForest/4645/ecogarden.htm

Walling and Paving

This company offers all sorts of paving and walling solutions, from flagstones to dry walling and granite setts. A specialist offering only the genuine article.

www.dolmens.freeserve.co.uk

GENEALOGY

Ever thought about tracing your roots? These sites will help you to track down those long-lost ancestors and maybe find some distant relations you never knew about. It's also worth checking the sites maintained by your local or county library, as these often include information on local names and families.

Access Genealogy

With advice for those starting out and a huge database of records, you can sift facts and figures to your heart's content. It's an American site but as many Americans can trace their families back to Britain and Ireland, it has a lot of useful information for us too.

www.accessgenealogy.com

Ancestors.co.uk

This is the web site of Ancestors Ltd, based in Kent. They can research family trees world-wide and investigate house history, company history and intestacies, plus missing persons and adopted children. They also design and manufacture merchandise for the heritage market. They have full, secure online ordering facilities to enable you to purchase from their range of products and services.

www.ancestors.co.uk

English Origins

This site, run in conjunction with the Society of Genealogists, provides access to its vast database of genealogical information for English and Scottish families. You can search the surnames index and join their discussion lists for free; some other services you have to pay for.

www.englishorigins.com

Everton's Genealogical Helper

A very good American site, designed especially for the beginner. There's access here to a vast database of information to help you track down your ancestors, wherever they came from.

www.everton.com

Genealogy

This American site is dedicated to bringing the best and the most comprehensive resources and services on the web. It is the place to go whether you are a beginner or an experienced genealogical researcher.

www.genealogy.com

GENUKI

One of the longest established and best-known genealogy resources on the web, GENUKI offers a huge amount of information for the UK and Ireland, based on church records, birth, marriage and death certificates, land and property ownership and even medical records. Whoever you are looking for, you are bound to track them down here and you'll discover some fascinating facts along the way.

www.genuki.org.uk

Royal and Noble Genealogical Data

Are you related to royalty? At this site find genealogical data for the British Royal Family and just about all the European Royals. It is worth visiting the site on a regular basis because the data is not static but is being constantly updated. You will also find links to other related sites.

www.dcs.hull.ac.uk/public/genealogy

Ultimate Family Tree

If you want to trace your family tree, then this site is for you. The Ultimate Family Tree provides a variety of searches to help you get the most out of the site, together with a glossary of genealogical terms and abbreviations. This is essential because you will come across current legal terms, as well as those that are archaic or now obsolete!

www.uftree.com

GEOGRAPHY

These sites are ideal for geography homework, and for answering those pub quiz questions on far-away places. We haven't listed sites for particular countries: you can find these yourself using a search engine. Try searching on the country name plus the aspect you're interested in (e.g. Australia AND climate AND beach).

If you find somewhere you'd like to visit, take a look at the sites under *Travel and Holidays* to track down that elusive deal.

About.Geography

This geography portal, part of the huge 'About.com' portal, allows you to search for almost anything connected with geography. It has various categories of information to get you started and boasts 700 links to geography sites. It also has an unbeatable glossary of geographical terms.

www.geography.about.com

Arab Net

The aim of Arab Net is to provide the most comprehensive online resource on the Arab world, primarily dealing with countries in the Middle East and North Africa. There is a general overview of each country together with information on its culture, history, geography, government, business potential and transport facilities. There is also a guide to attractions and sights for the tourist or business traveller.

www.arab.net

Flags of all Countries

The site gives large and small pictures of the flags of every nation in the world. You can click on the flags to see a map of the country plus other useful information, and link to sites selling flags and related information.

www.wave.net/upg/immigration/flags.html

How Far Is It?

Although part of a site specifically for Bali and Indonesia, this page is worth a separate mention as it works for anywhere in the world. Use it to find the latitude and longitude of any two places and then calculate the 'as-the-crow-flies' distance between them. It then displays them for you on a map.

www.indo.com/distance

Mapquest

This award-winning web site can help you get to where you need to be each day. By simply typing in a starting point and destination, or even just a city and state, you can get driving directions, create customised maps, view nearby businesses and points of interest, and plan trips away.

www.mapquest.com

Map World

This company produce maps and globes of every kind which you can order on the site. They have an e-mail catalogue and e-mailing list and when you input the details of the sort of material you want, they will provide information and pictures on what is available, including full specifications and prices.

www.mapworld.com

Multimap

An excellent online atlas for the UK including postcodes, London street names with links to world atlas. You can search by name or on the outline of the country.

www.multimap.com

National Geographic

Full of incredible photos, like the magazine, this web site is one you should not miss. Updated each month with new reports from foreign countries and archaeological digs, the site contains online forums where you can contribute to debates. The site also has an impressive archives section where you can look at the highlights from back issues.

www.nationalgeographic.com

National Geographic Maps

The National Geographic Map Machine is without a doubt the best resource for online maps. The source enables you to choose any destination on the globe and view a political or physical map of the region. You can even see it from above for a real bird's-eye view! There is also the Map Machine Atlas containing country maps, facts, flags and profiles.

plasma.nationalgeographic.com/mapmachine

Volcanoes of the World

This site offers a geographical breakdown of all known volcanoes – and there are more of them than you might think! More often than not they are docile and the kind of destruction that is always depicted in films is not likely to be seen. However, you will find the photo library of this site fascinating as it contains some fairly scary images of Mount St Helens.

vulcan.wr.usgs.gov/Volcanoes

WebCam Central

This site hosts a listing and some previews of fixed cameras bringing pictures from dozens of countries around the world, from Brazil to Russia and the United States.

www.camcentral.com

The World Fact Book

The CIA has produced this extensive guide which is an excellent resource full of information on the world's countries. Information includes cultural, political, economic and geographic topics plus some very good maps.

www.odci.gov/cia/publications/factbook/index.html

GIFTS

The web is full of sites offering products and gifts to every taste. (See *Internet: Search Engines* for an example of how to find a specific type of product.) Many deliver to your recipient's door, and some will even gift-wrap for you. A selection of general or unusual gift sites is shown below: for gifts of a specific type, check out some of the sites listed in other categories (for example, some of the fashion sites offer gift-wrapped accessories; some of the food sites will send gift hampers).

Cool Diamonds

A gift that's sure to please! You can now purchase loose or set diamonds online from this established jeweller in Hatton Garden, London, and there are selections to suit most budgets. This site comes with many recommendations and plaudits and is well-designed, allowing you to search not only by price but also by design, quality and carat.

www.cooldiamonds.com

Fire Box and Boys' Stuff

Men are notoriously difficult to buy for. So try these sites, dedicated to gadgets and gifts that men will adore. Whatever your budget, these will help you find something for the man who has everything.

www.firebox.co.uk

www.boysstuff.co.uk

Forget Flowers

Forget flowers, say it with sweets! This unusual site from Swizzels Matlow gives you the opportunity to send a gift-boxed 500g of their all-time greats (Love Hearts, Drumsticks, Parma Violets, etc) to anywhere in the world. It's not exactly cost-efficient compared with scooping a basketful from the pick-and-mix at your local supermarket, but has far more impact!

www.forgetflowers.com

Gift Baskets X

More than just hampers and bubble bath, this site offers a mind-boggling array of themed gift baskets that can be delivered anywhere in the world (shipping charges are extra). Ideal for those difficult-to-please friends or even a business colleague you are trying to impress.

www.giftbasketsx.com

Gift Mania

A manic selection of weird and wonderful gifts guaranteed to raise a smile. How about some 'Dirty Girl' bubble bath? Or a giggling Mona Lisa pillow? From the tasteful to the downright hilarious, there's something for all tastes here. An American site, so allow plenty of delivery time and remember that shipping costs will be added.

www.giftmania.com

Gift Store

Chocolates, flowers, games, cards, ties, cufflinks and other gift items delivered direct on the day you choose. A great selection, with seasonal offers, this is a UK site so you can be sure that all items featured can be delivered with ease.

www.giftstore.co.uk

Love Darling

Feeling mushy? If you need a gift for a loved one, try this site, which features all sorts of romantic and cuddly ideas. It is American, so be sure to allow plenty of time for shipping (they will e-mail you a quote for shipping costs before processing your order, so you can choose to cancel if it's too extortionate).

www.lovedarling.com

Present Picker

If you are stuck for gift ideas for the person who has everything, then help is at hand at the present picker site. From this site you can use a gift wizard which will ask you some simple questions, then provide a list of gifts from various companies and links to their web pages where you can purchase the gift of your choice.

presentpicker.com

Pressie

A UK-based site that rivals all its American counterparts, with a huge range of quality gifts covering everything from champagne to jewellery, lava lamps to wine. Enter details of who you are buying for and what the occasion is and it will suggest gifts for you. There are various delivery options, most of which involve an extra charge.

www.pressie.com

Red Letter Days

A gift with a difference: treat your recipient to a day out doing something they'd really enjoy. An air balloon trip; a theatre night or sporting fixture; a day learning how to drive a classic or racing car; even a lesson in how to mix dance tracks at the Ministry of Sound! This is the most established name in the UK for 'experience' gifts, and they have an astounding range.

www.redletterdays.co.uk

Scottish Gifts

Scotch Corner, the retail outlet, also has this web site on which you can find anything and everything Scottish.

www.scotch-corner.co.uk

Star Names

How's this for romantic? You can name a star for your loved one and have it recorded in the Cosmic Library for all time.

www.starnames.co.uk

GOVERNMENT, POLITICS AND INTELLIGENCE

Whatever your political leanings, find out more about politics, political and intelligence issues and the machinations of government at these sites. From news to scandal, latest propositions to historical research, warmongering to party politics, you should be able to find it all here.

Some issues are also covered on sites listed under *Environment and Nature*.

10 Downing Street

The official site for the home of the British Prime Minister. Here you can find information on the workings of the British Government, the latest government campaigns and press releases, plus historical facts about the building itself and its former occupants. It also has a Kids section, dedicated to explaining politics to the younger generation (although this is by no means as kid-friendly as the American version at the White House site!).

www.number-10.gov.uk

All Politics

This site is devoted just to news about politics brought to you by CNN and *Time* magazine and supplies you with the latest political news from inside America. You can take part in a quick poll or research events through in-depth special reports and Congressional quarterly articles.

cnn.com/allpolitics

Amnesty International

Amnesty International crusades for human rights all over the world and this is its official web site. Find out here about the injustices it is fighting and see what you can do to help.

www.amnesty.org

CAIN: Conflict Archive on the Internet

Northern Ireland has been a political hot potato for many years, and its conflict has been both bloody and prolonged. This site, operated by the University of Ulster, provides archived information on the whole history of the Troubles, ideal for homework research or for those just seeking more knowledge on this ongoing issue.

www.cain.ulst.ac.uk

Central Intelligence Agency

If you want to know more about the CIA, then this is the site for you. It gives all sorts of facts, such as details of the CIA's role in international affairs and its history.

www.odci.gov

The Commonwealth

This is the web site of the Commonwealth, the unique family of 54 nations around the world. It is also the official web site of the Commonwealth Secretariat in London. Here you will find information about member countries, Commonwealth activities and projects. Also explore the rest of the site to access details of their programmes and activities, read their latest releases, features, reports or publications, to find out more about their forthcoming events and to see who their partners are.

www.thecommonwealth.org

The Euro

This is the European Commission's internet site dedicated exclusively to the Euro, useful whether you are a citizen interested in your future currency or a specialist working on technical preparations for the changeover. The site is regularly updated with applicable documents as they become available, and also provides access to an electronic version of Infeuro, the Commission's own newsletter on the Euro, plus other sites with useful information on the single currency. The site is available in 11 languages.

europa.eu.int/euro

Europarl

This site is the home of the European parliament so if you have ever wondered what new laws are being passed that may affect you, or wanted the most current news and activities, then this is the place to go. It is available in a variety of different European languages.

www.europarl.eu.int

The European Telework Development

The ETD site aims to construct a European network of national web sites for each participating country. Some of these are ones that already exist and with which the ETD has agreed to co-operate; others are new ones directly supported by the ETD. Each web site should contain the following: relevant national information important to the country concerned; and also selected European and ETD information in the local language. Some countries have provided their national pages in their own language.

www.eto.org.uk

FedWorld

If you want to locate any US federal government documents, contacts or servers, use the FedWorld government site.

www.fedworld.gov

The Gallup Organisation

For over 60 years, the Gallup Organisation has been the world leader in the measurement and analysis of people's attitudes, opinions and behaviour. Check out the site if you wish to take part in any of its opinion polls or fill out the questionnaires. You can see the results of past surveys or go to the Gallup bookstore to purchase books written by Gallup researchers and consultants. Access is also provided at this site to Gallup clients who are receiving research results and consulting services by means of a secure extranet web site.

www.gallup.com

INCORE

This site provides information on ethnic conflicts around the world and how their resolution is being managed. It's an ideal starting point for when you need background information on a particular issue. It is operated jointly by the University of Ulster and the United Nations University.

www.incore.ulst.ac.uk

InfoWar

If you are interested in warfare issues and in finding out what is going on, this site is for you. It has information on hacking activity, industrial espionage, terrorism and military propaganda.

www.infowar.com

Intelligence International

This site is for a magazine produced with the same name. The magazine is the world's leading independent source of political and strategic intelligence so expect the same from the web site. During the 64 years of its existence *Intelligence International* has built up an unrivalled network of intelligence sources covering almost every country in the world. It is this network that has enabled the magazine to be the first again and again with vital news – long before the mainstream press and electronic media.

www.intelligence-net.com

International Security Organization

The Organization for Security and Co-operation in Europe (OSCE) is a security organisation of 55 participating states which span the geographical area from Vancouver to Vladivostok. It is the primary instrument for early warning, conflict prevention, crisis management and post-conflict rehabilitation. The OSCE approach to security is comprehensive and co-operative. It deals with a wide range of security issues, including arms control, preventive diplomacy, confidence and security-building measures, human rights, election monitoring and economic and environmental security. Here you can find out all about them and their latest projects and concerns.

www.osce.org

Jane's Information

Jane's is the leading unclassified information provider for military, government and commercial organisations world-wide on the subjects of defence/geopolitics, transportation and law enforcement. You can get brief updates of everything that is occurring in these sectors from this site.

www.janes.com

NATO

At this site you can find out all about the North Atlantic Treaty Organisation, founded in 1949, soon after the Second World War. Also available is all the information on projects that are currently being carried out by NATO.

www.nato.int

National Security Agency

This is the site of America's most secret service. Here is also the home of the American National Cryptologic Museum containing documents on the Cuban Missile Crisis and probably more secrets than even the most hardened conspiracy theorist could imagine. A high-technology organisation, NSA is on the frontiers of communications and data processing. It is also one of the most important centres of foreign-language analysis and research within the American Government.

www.nsa.gov

Number Ten

Now this is more like it! When the political fallout gets a bit much, come to this site to cheer yourself up. It features the more humorous items to appear in Speaker's Corner over the last few years, plus assorted other features. Their 'Distort the Prime Minister' facility is a personal favourite.

www.numberten.org.uk

Open Government Information

If you need to find any UK Government authority, then look no further – just open this huge directory and use the Search facility to find what you want.

www.open.gov.uk

UK Politics

This online site, provided by the magazine *UKPOL*, provides links to a huge catalogue of information concerned with UK politics and the political scene, from central government to local issues. You can find out more about your own MP, view the various party manifestos and details of governments past and present, and pick up tips on how to get your voice heard on issues. A great starting place for any political research.

www.ukpolitics.org.uk

United Nations

This is where you can find out all about the United Nations and how it helps countries in the world. There is a lot of information about current activities, news and international law and plenty of geo-political information. Within the site is the 'United Nations Cyberschool Bus', an area aimed at children who wish to learn more about the world and about the UN. It includes a discussion area, an interactive database containing up-to-date information about many countries, plus a virtual tour of the UN, an online introduction to the UN and its work.

www.un.org

www.un.org/Pubs/CyberSchoolBus

The White House

Go on a tour of the White House or air your views on any political matter using the White House's official suggestion form. Do not expect your questions to be answered by the president himself, but you never know: someone in there might be taking heed of what you are saying! When you are fed up with the official site, try the second site listed – it's a spoof along similar lines to the Number Ten site listed above.

www.whitehouse.gov

www.whitehouse.net

HEALTH, FITNESS AND NUTRITION

There are many thousands of health-related sites on the net, from the official sites of medical and pharmaceutical organisations and support groups to those set up by 'get-rich-quick' quacks. Here are some of the more useful, personally vetted by the authors. If you are looking for information on a specific health problem, it is worth running a separate search specifying the name of the illness or its symptoms.

See also *Beauty and Hair, Parenting, Pregnancy and Childbirth* and *Senior Citizens*. Some fitness sites are also listed under *Sports*. Some of the sites listed under *Women's Interests* have information specifically related to women's health.

ALTERNATIVE AND COMPLEMENTARY MEDICINE

More and more of us are turning to non-invasive or non-chemical treatments these days, for everything from a sprained ankle to persistent headaches or even relief from the symptoms of many terminal illnesses. These sites offer help and information on a range of treatments.

Culpeper

The Culpeper name is known throughout the world for high-quality information and goods on herbs, and this web site offers information on and sales of herbs and herb products for medicine and cooking, as well as seeds and books. A very well-organised and pleasant site.

www.culpeper.co.uk

Good Health Directory

Information on a range of complementary health issues and therapies, with links to other useful health-related sites.

www.goodhealthdirectory.com

Homeopaths UK

With both an online pharmacy for homeopathic products and a directory of homeopaths in the UK, this site is an interesting one for those involved with alternative medicine.

www.homeopath.co.uk

Home of Reflexology

The ancient healing art of reflexology has been known to man for many thousands of years. It was first practised by the early Indian, Chinese and Egyptian peoples who observed that congestion or tension in any part of the foot mirrors congestion or tension in a corresponding part of the body. The Home of Reflexology provides details of reflexology organisations, together with information on reflexology and other reflexology related links.

www.reflexology.org

Homeopathy Home

This site provides comprehensive information and links to every homeopathy resource available. Site sections include a directory of addresses and contacts, reference area, services and supplies over the internet, discussion forums and links to other sites and societies.

www.homeopathyhome.com

Quackwatch

This site is concerned with presenting the truth about alternative therapies and questionable theories related to health. It includes a large number of articles on a wide range of topics and is constantly updated. There are links to other sites and a comments page. Questions can be posted and are usually answered very quickly.

www.quackwatch.com

Think Natural

The UK's premier web site devoted to natural health and body care, offering thousands of natural health products that you can order online. Think Natural also provides a huge amount of information, including encyclopedia content from Dorling Kindersley and contributions from their expert journalists and natural health practitioners.

www.thinknatural.com

DISABILITIES

These sites give valuable information on coping with mental or physical disability, facilities and resources for the disabled and their carers, and links to organisations for disabled people throughout the world. For information on a specific disability, run a search on the name of the condition or injury. For information on charities that deal with specific disabilities, see *Charities*.

Disabled Data Link Group

This site is an advice and support group open to disabled people around the world, though it does focus mostly on the UK. The group provides services including companionship, information on disability aids, motoring help and the rights of the disabled. An excellent site for information.

web.ukonline.co.uk/ddlg.uk

Disability Net

This site is an excellent resource for those with disabilities. The site contains information and news in all areas including job listings and links to local, national and international groups. An interesting part of the site is the penfriends section.

www.disabilitynet.co.uk

Disability Network Inc

This American-based site describes itself as 'an information highway for the disabled and their families' and features chat rooms and frequently updated health news, as well as a vast number of links to related sites. Some of the information is specific to the US, but most of it would be useful to disabled people, or anyone needing to know more about disability, wherever they are in the world.

www.disabilitynetwork.com

DTour

This site is for disabled people who wish to visit the country of Ireland. The site contains a huge directory of property, and guides to transport around the country. In its current form it focuses mostly on the wheelchair-bound, but it has plans to extend in future to those people with hearing and visual impairment.

ireland.iol.ie/infograf/dtour

EmPowerNet

This is the web site for the charities consortium of users of disability equipment. It has a wide range of information on prosthetics, orthotics, wheelchairs AND rehabilitation, and on campaigns to promote equal access for the disabled, still sadly not a reality in this country. A useful site for the disabled, and an eye-opener for those seeking information on what it is like to be disabled in Britain today.

www.empowernet.org

National Information Centre for Children and Youth with Disabilities

NICHCY is a national information and referral centre that provides information on disabilities and disability-related issues for families, educators and other professionals. A US-based organisation, it specialises in children and teenagers and this site is a useful reference point for anyone to investigate.

nichcy.org

National Rehabilitation Centre for the Paralysed

This centre is dedicated to rebuilding those lives shattered by paralysis, whatever the cause, through the use of exercise rather than drugs or surgery. It provides valuable, no-nonsense information on the effects of spinal cord injury on mental as well as physical health, and the prospects for improvement. A useful site for those researching the effects of injury as well as those directly affected by paralysis.

www.paralysis.co.uk

SpeecHTML

This site advertises software for people with sight problems. The software is a written version of HTML that turns text from web sites into speech so that people can dial up and interact with web sites by phone. There's a free one-month trial of the service designed for visually impaired people and those who don't have access to the net.

www.speechtml.com

Spinal Injuries Association

This organisation has one of the most comprehensive spinal injury sites on the net. You can browse through the information and links to other sites, and add your own experiences and photos. It has a guides to legal help, holidays, sports and leisure and universities, and features its own message board and chat room where you can meet other site visitors.

www.spinal.co.uk

GENERAL HEALTH AND MEDICINE

These sites often follow a directory-style or magazine-style format, giving both general health information and details of specific illnesses and treatments.

Health Gate

Health Gate states that it is committed to providing you with health information you can trust. Consumer health and medical information at Health Gate is brought to you from several reliable sources. They contract freelance health and medical writers to write new and informative articles about health issues facing consumers today. Many of their writers have advanced degrees in health-related fields or work in the health-care professions.

www.healthgate.com

Health in Focus

This site is aimed specifically at British people and offers a wide range of health-related information, gathered into categories such as News, Chat, Clinical Focus, and Health Tips, with sections specifically for men, women and alternative health. The content is provided primarily by healthcare professionals and checked by doctors and patient support groups.

www.healthinfocus.co.uk

Health World Online

The most comprehensive global health network on the internet. Although it is US-based, it provides a huge and useful resource for both alternative and conventional health information, wherever you happen to live.

www.healthy.net

NHS Direct

This site supports the 24-hour NHS Direct helpline recently set up in the UK. Use it to find information on common illnesses, conditions and treatments, the NHS itself and how it operates, and the usual nutritional and healthy living advice. It is very simple to use and gives clear, practical advice – often saving you a trip to your GP.

www.nhsdirect.nhs.uk

Mayo Clinic Online

The world-famous medical clinic has an excellent site designed to answer all your questions on major medical health issues, as well as related topics such as sports medicine. It includes a large number of articles and case studies written by respected medical practitioners and scientists, all of which are dated. One of the best of the sites offered by big medical organisations.

www.mayohealth.org

Pharmacy

Advice and medication are both available from this shopping site where you can order from a huge range of branded products including both medicines and other items you would normally buy in a pharmacy.

www.pharmacy2u.co.uk

Stay Healthy

This UK-based site offers information about keeping healthy, preventing illness and preventing any existing illness from becoming worse. It includes such things as healthy lifestyle, well woman/man advice; advice on healthy eating and exercise; preventing heart disease and cancer; advice on stopping smoking and preventing alcohol and drug abuse; accident prevention; immunisation; screening tests and protecting against disease when travelling.

www.patient.co.uk

Surgery Door

Information and advice on health topics provided by health experts.

www.surgerydoor.co.uk

The Site

This web site is your definitive guide to surviving and enjoying modern life. This site is for everyone, although the British person who needs help and advice through his or her bad spells will benefit from their list of contact addresses and support groups. They have a huge database with over 16,000 organisational records along with dozens of factsheets and features on a wide range of subjects.

www.thesite.org.uk

Wired for Health

These sites, provided by the Department of Education and Employment, are designed specifically for use by children of different ages, and help to teach them about the importance of nutrition, exercise, the effects of alcohol and drugs, and much more.

5–7 year olds (Key Stage 1): www.welltown.gov.uk

7–11 year olds (Key Stage 2): www.galaxy-h.gov.uk

12--14 year olds (Key Stage 3): www.lifebytes.gov.uk

14–16 year olds (Key Stage 4): www.mindbodysoul.gov.uk

NUTRITION

We all know good nutrition is essential to good health, but it's easier said than done. Visit these sites for a few tips on how to eat healthily without being bland. For more information on nutritional cooking, see the sites listed under *Cookery and Kitchenware* and *Food*.

Cyberdiet

This well-organised and informative site offers tips on how to reach an ideal weight and how to maintain it through exercise and diet. You can also have a nutritional profile created that calculates your ideal body weight.

www.cyberdiet.com

Healthy Fridge

We all know the temptations that lurk inside the average family fridge. Nowhere is more likely to blow that carefully planned diet than the top shelf full of desserts and fat-laden cheese. This site, with its motto 'Open the door to a healthy heart', aims to help you better organise your fridge for optimum health. This includes handy hints on how to speed-shop so you avoid the temptations while filling your fridge to avoid the need to resort to takeaway food. Fun and informative.

www.healthy-fridge.org

Vitatonic

With so many vitamins and supplements out there, how can you be sure you're taking what's right for *you*? This site offers advice and information before you shop.

www.vitatonic.com

Vitamins Reference Guide

This site gives a general overview followed by specific information on the vitamins that your body needs in order to function properly. Find out about the importance of each vitamin and what the deficiency symptoms are.

www.realtime.net/anr/vitamins.html

You Are What You Eat

Familiarise yourself with the concepts behind nutrition – and you may find you need to change your diet! This brilliant interactive site enables you to compare what you are currently eating with what you should be eating. You can plan your next meal with the food planner, and find out the nutritional value of what you are eating with the online database.

library.advanced.org/11163/gather/cgi-bin/wookie.cgi

Zipvit

This promises to the cheapest mail order vitamins/health supplements in the UK or your money back!

www.zipvit.co.uk

MENTAL HEALTH

There are many aspects to mental health, of which we cover only a few. Some of these sites focus on a particular issue, while others offer an overview of mental health issues and concerns.

Anxiety Disorders

Millions of people suffer from anxiety disorders and the majority are never diagnosed. To find out about each known anxiety disorder, check out the National Institute of Mental Health's Anxiety Disorders Education Program. This American site is in English and Spanish and contains a section for health professionals.

www.nimh.nih.gov/anxiety

Cyber Psychologist

This is psychoanalysis online. Modern psychological technology offers proven solutions to many common problems. The site has a question-and-answer forum, information on depression, stress, phobias, anxiety and addictive behaviours. You can also find advice on how to improve your relationships and get help with career and work issues.

www.cyberpsych.com

Depression Analysis

Put together by New York University, this short, multiple-choice test is machine-graded. Only you will know the results, so why not find out a bit more about yourself.

www.med.nyu.edu/Psych/screens/depres.html

Dreamlife

This personal development web site features online classes by worldwide experts, including several on stress relief, overcoming shyness and confidence-boosting.

www.dreamlife.com

Internet Mental Health

This is a free encyclopedia of mental health information. Internet Mental Health is for anyone who has an interest in mental health – professionals, carers or patients – who wants to learn more about various psychological problems. The site contains information on each of the 50 most common mental disorders and on each of the 65 most common psychiatric medications. There is even an online diagnostic program that can be used to diagnose anxiety disorders, eating disorders, mood disorders, personality disorders and substance-related disorders, as well as lots of links to other related sites.

www.mentalhealth.com

Mental Health Information

For regularly updated online articles and links to other relevant web sites, the Mental Health Net is a must. The disorders and treatment section has information on symptoms, treatment and support groups as well as the links. There is also a professional resource section, which includes research journals and links to job advertisements.

www.cmhc.com

Positive Thinking and Stress Management

This site contains a collection of entertaining and informative free books on stress, stress management, positive thinking, personal development and biofeedback that you can freely download.

www.ozemail.com.au/~vital1/free.htm

Social Anxiety

This is a light-hearted test that aims to help you identify your social anxieties. It only takes a few minutes and will probably tell you what you already knew, but identifying specific character attributes can be useful if you are selecting a career, for example.

www.queendom.com/soc_anx.html

PHYSICAL FITNESS

These sites offer information on how to get and stay physically fit. See also *Sports*.

The Contemporary Exercise Company Personal Fitness

The CECO web site offers personal fitness trainers and services in all the major cities in the UK. CECO trainers can both come to your home, office or gym and guide and motivate you through a programme designed to increase your fitness, or on the web site you will find specialised fitness solutions. Find out your current fitness and get a customised analysis, hints and tips on specific exercises and lots more.

www.ceco.co.uk

Fitness Link

A huge site with magazine-style format, giving information on all sorts of exercise and sports options, with a focus on gym-based activity. Check out their Locker rooms and the interactive 'juice bar' where you can chat to fellow fitness fiends.

www.fitnesslink.com

Fun and Fitness

Find fitness boring? Try this site from Essex-based trainer Andrew Wright, who believes exercise should be fun. It gives information not only on exercise methods, but on muscle groups and nutrition and energy use. It also has a handy list of clubs and organisations that promote health, some of which are so unusual that they may just prompt you into action!

www.fun-and-fitness.com

Health Club Net

This site aims to help you get fit by finding your local health club for you. Over 5,000 are listed, covering the whole of the British Isles – and you don't even have to get off your butt to search!

www.health-club.net

Men's Fitness

An American site in magazine-style format, giving information for both fitness freaks and the less enthusiastic. Workouts and weight training, nutrition and sports. Check out the guide to the fittest and fattest cities in the US – it's bound to make you smile.

www.mensfitness.com

Physical Health

There are four major areas on the site: nutrition, fitness, weight loss and pregnancy. There is a self-analysis section, which is made up of many interactive features designed to help you assess your health and help you improve it. There is information on eating well and working out, together with 'encyclopedias' which are interactive references of hundreds of nutrition and fitness terms. You can use the forums to share and discuss ideas, opinions and solutions about a number of topics concerning personal health as well.

www.phys.com

REFERENCE

Whether you need to look up a specific medical term or just want information on how the body works, these sites should help. Many are ideal for homework research for topics such as biology or health studies.

Human Anatomy Online

There are two ways to use this very informative site: interactive anatomy, where you choose a body system – such as the skeletal system – and click within it for detailed information on specific parts; or through a series of anatomy lessons. It is important to note that both take a while to download due to the size of the application.

www.InnerBody.com

Hyperreal Drugs Archive

This site contains articles that provide details of both the pleasures and pitfalls of using recreational drugs. The Hyperreal Drugs Archive also contains links to other similar sites. It must be noted that the information in this archive is provided for educational purposes only.

www.erowid.org/Psychoactives/Psychoactives.shtml

Intelihealth

Explanations on a range of common health problems, together with advice on treatment.

www.intelihealth.com

Internet Health Library

This is where you can find plenty of health and medical information, as well as online health tips. It works very much like a search engine, with both keyword and directory searches available.

www.health-library.com

Medical Dictionary

Everything you need to know about your medical problem or the medication you have been prescribed to alleviate or cure it. The site is very easy to use and does not take long to load. There is also a good links page to other medical sites on the web.

www.kemc.edu/n.html

Medicinal and Poisonous Plants Database

Here at this site you will find lots of links to other pages on the internet containing information to help you learn about the medicinal and poisonous properties of various plants. The site is aimed more at people who are studying the plants and the effects but it is also a good place to search if you are interested in learning more.

www.wam.umd.edu/~mct/Plants/index.html

The Natural Death Centre

This is a non-profit charitable project which was launched in Britain in 1991 and has three psychotherapists as directors. It aims to support those dying at home and their carers and to help them arrange funerals. It also has as a more general aim of helping improve 'the quality of dying'.

www.worldtrans.org/naturaldeath.html

SPECIFIC CONDITIONS

Many of the reference sites and general health directories have concise information on specific conditions; these, however are sites dedicated to a particular illness, disease or condition, often run by support groups or research organisations. If the condition you are interested in isn't listed, try running a search for it using one of the better-known search engines.

Alcoholism

Alcoholism is not just a social problem, it's a recognised health issue. These helpful and sympathetic sites are provided by Alcoholics Anonymous (AA), the world-wide organisation for those with an alcohol problem, and by Al-Anon and Alateen, who provide help for those who are concerned about another person's drinking. The sites are also available in French and Spanish.

www.aa.org

www.al-anon.org

Alzheimer's

Alzheimer's is a devastating disease that not only robs its sufferers of their independence but also proves a huge burden on their carers. This American site provides help and support, plus information on prevention, diagnosis an dietary aids that may alleviate early symptoms. It also has links to other Alzheimer's sites and resources.

www.alzheimers.com

Autism

This is one of the most complex developmental problems of childhood. It will affect about 4.5 per 10,000 births. This site, provided by the American organisation The Center for the Study of Autism, provides overview materials in four languages, together with resources for autism and for all the related syndromes.

www.autism.org

Breast Cancer

This site offers a 'complete resource for breast health' from doctors and healthcare professionals as well as sufferers. It is an American site, but the information is useful to all. It features a chat facility with a premier oncologist as well as information on prevention, diagnosis, treatment and recurrence, and links to related sites.

www.ibreast.com

Cerebral Palsy (Scope)

This organisation provides help and support for many disabled people, particularly specialising in those with cerebral palsy. Their web site gives information on the disease and the available treatments and has a useful section of printable factsheets, plus other publications that can be ordered by e-mail. It also has fund-raising and events information.

www.scope.org.uk

Deafness (RNID)

This online shop, run by the Royal National Institute for the Deaf, supplies equipment and publications for the deaf and hard of hearing. You can also link from the shop to their main site, which gives news and helpful information on dealing with deafness and hearing problems, including a directory of over 8,000 organisations who provide everything from sign-language classes to technological aids.

www.rnidshop.com

Down's Syndrome

This site, run by the Down's Syndrome Research Foundation, gives you all the information you need on this often misunderstood condition. The foundation provides medical research into the condition and offers help and advice to anyone involved with the care of a Down's sufferer, including help for pregnant women or new parents who have been told there is a chance their baby is affected.

www.dsrf.co.uk

Dyslexia

Dyslexia affects around 10% of the population, to varying degrees. Its sufferers have difficult with tasks connected with reading, writing, spelling, memory and concentration: anything from tying shoelaces to writing neatly. Until recently many of its sufferers were dismissed as stupid or slow learners, but these days more help is available. Find out more at these sites.

www.dyslexia-inst.org.uk

www.bda-dyslexia.org.uk

www.ukonline.co.uk/wdnf

Embarrassing Problems

We all have them – those niggling problems that we feel too shy about or regard as too trivial to discuss with our doctor. This site provides information on a whole range of such issues, from acne to wind, taking in sweaty feet, snoring and personal itching along the way. There is a monthly feature on a particular problem or a health issue that has recently made the headlines.

www.embarrassingproblems.co.uk

Epilepsy

Brought to you by the same people as Alzheimers.com, this site features a similar level of information on epilepsy, a condition often underestimated by those with no experience of it. Learn more about it, the available treatments, and organisations that can help.

www.epilepsy.com

Headaches

The American Medical Association provides a two-pronged site dealing with headaches, which is well worth checking out. The migraine information centre covers all types of headaches, including information on how to tell them apart together with their possible treatments. Physicians can find details of the latest research, together with a literature review.

www.ama-assn.org/special/migraine

Heart Disease

The British Heart Foundation is devoted to heart disease research. At its site you can find useful information on all heart conditions, including a handy list of 'heart terms', as well as preventive advice and details of how you can help support this organisation.

www.bhf.org.uk

Impotence

Two sites here, both UK-based, giving help and information on this often taboo subject. Each offers helpful question-and-answer based information as well as case studies, updates on causes and treatments, and information on what to expect from your doctor.

www.impotence.org.uk

www.impotence-help.co.uk

Male Cancers

For some reason, women's cancers (breast, cervical, etc) seem to get a lot more exposure in the media than men's. The Everyman site aims to redress the balance by providing information and assistance on both testicular and prostate cancers, including information on what the Everyman centre – a UK centre dedicated to male cancer research – is doing about the problem. The second site listed is specific to prostate cancer, and provides no-nonsense information on the disease, its treatment and possible causes.

www.icr.ac.uk/everyman

www.prostate-cancer.org.uk

Parkinson's Disease

This straightforward, text-based site gives valuable information on this debilitating condition, caring for sufferers and where to get help, and includes a useful list of links to related sites.

www.james.parkinsons.org.uk

Repetitive Strain Injury (RSI)

An increasing problem among office workers, particularly those who use computer keyboards on a daily basis, RSI is finally getting the recognition it deserves as a work-induced condition. Find out more at this site, run by sufferers, including useful tips on how to prevent it.

www.rsi-uk.org.uk

Rheumatism

This site provides useful information on the various rheumatic disorders as well as hints on how to find the best treatments, and where to get support. It includes a definitive glossary and list of common medications. Well worth the visit, even if it is rather a long URL.

ourworld.compuserve.com/homepages/ray_armstrong/pat_main.htm

Skin Disorders

This dermatology site features a self-diagnosis section that will help identify any strange or recurrent rashes, plus a lot of information on skin-care and products. You can also seek advice from the dermatologist site operator if you can't work out what's wrong, and there is a handy news section that keeps you up-to-date with any recent advances in treatment or current infectious conditions.

www.dermatologist.co.uk

HISTORY

A wealth of information for homework research as well as the more general 'channels'. Whatever your preferred period of history, you can find all the information you want here.

See also *Children, Genealogy, Government, Politics and Intelligence, Museums, Galleries and Historical Sites, Reference* and *Women's Interests*.

Anne Frank

If you are interested in the story of Anne Frank, you can see a biography, or read excerpts from her diary in Dutch as well as English. You can even visit the Anne Frank House in Amsterdam.

www.annefrank.nl

Biography

This site offers brief biographical information on at least 15,000 people. It is easy to use and search as you can choose from an alphabetical listing or search for a specific name for short biographical entries. They even include small video clips of broadcast shows.

www.biography.com

The British Monarchy

If you want to know more about the British Royal family, visit this, its official home page. It gives details of the current members of the House of Windsor, plus information on each of the palaces and when they can be visited. It also explains the lines of succession, as well as giving a concise history of the Royals through the ages.

www.royal.gov.uk

The Commonwealth War Graves Commission

This site for the commission was established in 1917 and its duties are to mark and maintain the graves of members of the forces of the Commonwealth.

www.cwgc.org

Conquest

This history society concentrates its efforts on the period surrounding the Norman Conquest. It provides useful information, links and images for research on the Battle of Hastings, the signing of Magna Carta and various other events of the period.

www.conquest.pwp.blueyonder.co.uk

Discoverer of the New World?

We first thought that Christopher Columbus discovered the New World, then we started to give Leif Eriksson the credit. It now looks like everyone is wrong yet again. What about the Irish monk Brendan the Navigator, who is believed to have landed in Newfoundland and for whom St Brendan's Island is said to be named? Read all about it and decide for yourself.

www.castletown.com/brendan.htm

Distinguished Women of Past and Present

Search for biographies of distinguished women by name or by field and you can find out all about the most influential female writers, educators, scientists, heads of state, politicians, civil rights crusaders, artists, entertainers and others. It has an extensive list of links to related sites, so whoever you want to research, you should find her here.

www.distinguishedwomen.com

Earthlore

Earthlore concentrates on recounting tales of ancient cultures and the many legacies of our ancestors. It poses such questions as: 'How are we reflected through our cultural heritage?' and 'What are the historical forces which led us to where we are today?' You can explore the great mysteries of history and perhaps find some answers.

www.elore.com/elore.htm

Encyclopaedia Britannica

The world-famous encyclopedia is now available online. It covers more than just history, of course, but its 'History and Humanities' section is full of great ideas for research, and includes an interesting section comparing current issues with historical events. You will need plug-in software for certain features, particularly video clips.

www.britannica.com

Explorers of the World

There are those who dare to challenge the boundaries of space, time, ignorance and science. What kinds of people choose a life of exploration, challenge and discovery? This site will help you find out. Explorers are grouped by category (land, ideas, sky, and art) and there is a useful list of links to other sites for further information.

www.bham.wednet.edu/explore.htm

Exploring Ancient World Cultures

This site gives you the history of the ancient world in a few short pages. To research or read more, each page contains extensive links. Ideal for research on ancient civilisations such as those in Egypt, China, Greece and Rome.

eawc.evansville.edu

Gallery of Achievers

In the Gallery of Achievers, the focus is on individuals whose accomplishments helped to shape the 20th Century.

www.achievement.org/galleryachieve.html

The Great War Web Pages

On this web site you will find articles on various aspects of the First World War. Although the articles mainly relate to the British and Empire involvement on the Western Front, Hellfire Corner is dedicated to the memory of all combatants, in all theatres of the war and from all nations.

www.fylde.demon.co.uk/welcome.htm

Guardian's Egypt

The goal of the site is to present Egypt in an archaeologically responsible light and create the most complete and inclusive Ancient Egypt web site. The main feature is the ongoing cyber-journey to Egypt, which was created to allow people to visit the ancient monuments of Egypt from their own computer. Bring one of the wonders of the world into your home by visiting this historically and pictorially packed site, and embark on a virtual journey of Egyptian magic. Who were the famous pharaohs? How do you translate hieroglyphics? Does the curse of the sphinx exist? Find out here. There's a section for children, some archived news stories and a discussion board. This is a definitive chronology of Egyptian history and the site is still developing.

guardians.net/egypt

The History Channel

As with most TV channels, this one has its own web site. Here you will find a large amount of history-related information, as well as a listings guide and information about the channel itself. It has several related sites, accessible from links on the main page, which are also useful for research.

www.historychannel.com

The History Net

If you want to learn a thing or two about the past, check out this site for the history of the world. Ideal for homework research as it covers almost every historical period and event.

www.thehistorynet.com

History Today

History Today is a monthly general history magazine published in London. It covers all types and periods of history, and the web site includes articles taken from the magazine, as well as some additional material.

www.historytoday.com

Imperial War Museum

This web site brings together all the sites of the various branches of the Imperial War Museum, including the Cabinet War Rooms, and allows you to search them individually or together for information. Find out about the museums themselves (some include a virtual tour) as well as the events they describe. A great site for war research.

www.iwm.org.uk

Medieval History

Netserf is dedicated to bringing you the best of the Middle Ages on the web. Hundreds of links lead you to information on every aspect of this fascinating period of history, ideal for research. The medieval glossary is particularly useful for 'decoding' old documents.

www.netserf.org

Native American

If you are interested in Native American history, then this is the place for you. Here you will find heaps of information plus a large collection of links to other sites that can tell you what you need to know. The links are vast and various and lead to tribal home pages, Native American organisations, government and educational resources and much more.

www.cowboy.net/native

Roman History

According to the Romans, every day should be celebrated for one reason or another. Find out which days belonged to whom at this fun historical site. You can discover the significance of your own birthday using the instruction manual linked from the home page. Each day has an accompanying graphic with an explanation of the significance of the day.

www.clubs.psu.edu/aegsa/rome/romec.html

Spartacus Books

Spartacus is a small educational book publishing company formed by a group of teachers and is committed to providing free resources for the internet community. The books sold here are all to do with history, though the site does contain some good reference pages and lots of good educational links. There are also some online history books which are great for reference. Many of the topics covered on the site are part of the National Curriculum. Note: There is a lot of advertising (to keep the site free-of-charge to users) so you will often need to scroll down to find the links you require.

www.spartacus.schoolnet.co.uk

The Stone Pages

This is the complete guide to the megalithic sites of Europe. It reads and feels like a reference book, with a useful glossary if you're not au fait with the terms, a map section, links to other archaeological resources and an online bookshop. Full of pictures (which can be slow to load), it's an excellent reference point for this subject.

www.stonepages.com

War Links

For those with a political or military interest, this is a useful research tool offering links to hundreds of war-related sites.

links2go.com/topic/War

The War Times Journal

The goal of this site is the quality presentation of articles and archives relating to military history and science. To make it easy to use, the journal is divided into: archives, featuring constantly updated collections of historic dispatches, memoirs and photographs; articles, interviews and commentary about battles, people, technology and tactics; war and games, featuring online board and miniature war-gaming resources, and an online store.

www.wtj.com

World War One

For an extensive account of the Great War, this is the site to look at. Its pages contain information on the people, places, and events that comprised one of the worst calamities of modern history. This is an evolving project and new material is being added on a constant basis. If the topic you are looking for is not here, check for it again at a later date or use the many links to similar sites.

www.worldwar1.com

HOBBIES

We couldn't hope to cover all hobbies here (some people's hobbies may be unmentionable!) but here are some sites for popular pastimes, plus a few general hobby sites from which you might be able to find more information on a particular activity. If your speciality isn't listed, try using a search engine to find more information, or check the index of this book to see whether your hobby may be covered in another category (for example, *Cookery* or *Games and Gaming*).

About Hobbies

Part of the huge About portal, which has channels for everything from business to baby care, the Hobbies section is particularly extensive and covers almost all the activities you can think of. There is a wide selection of chat rooms and newsletters, as well as a choice of nearly 100 crafts, pastimes and collections to select from. An ideal starting place for information on any hobby.

www.about.com/hobbies

2Busy Stitching

Learn here all about needlework and its history as well as details such as reference to all the different stitches. Check out the designs and the designers and find links to other needlework sites and chat rooms, plus there's a stitchers' post office, a bulletin board and a game room.

www.2busystitching.com

British Royal Mint

The fascinating story of how Britain's coins have been minted for more than 1,000 years. The Mint, a government agency based in South Wales, is responsible for making coins for the UK and 100 other countries. All the information is available here. There is even a coin club which you can join if you wish.

www.royalmint.com

Complete Crafts

This UK-based site offers details not only of craft supply retailers but also of craft fairs, co-operatives and clubs and an enviable selection of bulletin boards. Its layout is a bit confusing, and it is not always easy to pick out the link you require, but it's worth persevering as this is a very comprehensive guide to crafts.

www.completecrafts.com

Country Walks

Created by the Ministry of Agriculture, Fisheries and Food, this interesting site gives you a vast selection of country walks throughout the UK, with details of what you will find along the route, and maps so you don't get lost!

www.countrywalks.org.uk

Craftworks

The web site for this American magazine has a lot of useful information and lots of projects that you can view online or print off for later use. Its Kids section has some fun, easy-to-make projects for children of all ages, using familiar household items or craft materials easily obtainable from your local store.

www.craftworksmag.com

Diamond Cutters

A site specifically created for gem wholesalers, Diamond Cutters is a good read for anyone wishing to know more about this stone. It has a concise tutorial on diamonds, which will leave you knowing just as much as the experts do when you have read it. Also well worth checking out are the sections on the history and science behind this gem. Read it and dream!

www.diamondcutters.com

Hobbies-Plus

This online store stocks materials, books and gifts for all sorts of hobbies, from model aircraft to cartoons and teddy bears. It is well presented with few intrusive adverts and you can order all goods online for delivery within 14 days. A simple site with no frills but an awful lot of products.

www.hobbies-plus.co.uk

Hobbycraft

This site is operated by the Hobbycraft store chain, which boasts over 40,000 hobby-related products, materials and books. Unfortunately you cannot yet order any of them online. However, this is a really useful site as it contains a lot of hobby-related information, including details of the craft workshops held at all their stores, step-by-step craft projects for you to print off and do yourself, an enviable list of links to related sites, and a recently-added online chat facility where you can post queries or get together with like-minded enthusiasts.

www.hobbycraft.co.uk

Juggling

This site, from the Juggling Information Service, brings together loads of information and advice on how to juggle, where to meet other jugglers and links to other juggling sites. Ideal for the beginner or enthusiast alike.

www.juggling.org

Kasparov Chess

Created by world champion Gary Kasparov, this is an excellent site for anyone interested in the game, and includes online games as well as news, lessons and information.

www.kasparovchess.com

Photography Information

Fed up with cutting the heads off all your subjects? Do you always have your finger over the lens just as you take the picture? If so, then Kodak's Photography Information Menu is just for you, containing an online tutorial and a guide to better pictures with an informative introduction to photography and covers everything to do with the lens, from what is in front of it to what is behind it, as well as the workings of a dark room.

www.kodak.com/US/en/nav/takingPics.shtml

Stamp Centre

Stamp collectors should check out this London-based site, which claims to be the biggest stamp centre in England. As well as containing information on stamps, particularly on first-day covers and special issues, it also allows you to bid and buy online. The site is still under construction, so further features should be added soon.

www.stamp-centre.co.uk

Stanley Gibbons

One of the best-known names in stamp collecting offers one of the best sites on the web for those interested in philately. Stamps, albums and everything else the stamp collector could need are available to buy online.

www.stanleygibbons.com

Subbuteo World

Subbuteo, or table football, has a very dedicated following, and this site celebrates all that is good about this miniature sport. Find out the history of the game, where to buy and trade players, where to meet opponents and how to start your own league.

www.subbuteo-world.co.uk

The Webville and Hypertext Railroad Company

This is not a real railroad but a collection of information and links for railroad enthusiasts. The most interesting stuff is in the main yard section. Here you can find out what railroad signals mean, see diagrams of real railroad yards, and even read railroad ghost stories.

www.spikesys.com/webville.html

Winsor and Newton

One of the most famous names in art materials, this company has an excellent web site for anyone interested in painting, whether as a beginner or expert. The site includes many helpful sections, including hints and tips on watercolour, oil, acrylic and pastel techniques, a technical question and answer area, and a creative encyclopedia of ideas, to mention but a few. A very well-designed and helpful site.

www.winsorandnewton.com

HOME IMPROVEMENTS AND INTERIOR DESIGN

These sites offer inspiration to the artistically challenged and great resources for those looking for that particular style of wallpaper, that Regency chair or ideas for a new bathroom. Also see *Antiques and Collectibles* and *DIY and Home Maintenance*.

BATHROOMS

From the antique to the strictly modern, you can find all the baths and showers you want on the web. Here are a few of the best sites to browse in order to find the style you want.

Catchpole and Rye

Antique and period bathrooms from this UK-based company. The site includes advice on choosing and designing a bathroom, as well as a range of their current products.

www.catchpolerye.co.uk

Dolphin Bathrooms

This company offers a wide range of bathroom solutions, including walk-in baths for those of less mobility.

www.dolphinbathrooms.com

BEDS

There are no end of bed manufacturers on the web: here are some of our favourites offering beds in various styles.

Amazing Emporium

Over 500 styles of bed are on offer from this London-based company, so you're bound to find one that suits you.

www.amazingemporium.com

Cannock Beds

This company, which developed from a manufacturer of gates and railings, offers a wide range of wrought-iron bedsteads and headboards.

www.cannockbeds.co.uk

Island Bed Company

Solid mahogany beds and furniture at reasonable prices.

www.island-bed-co.com

Moriarti's

Short of space, or need added storage? Check out this site, which features cabin-style and storage beds in solid pine.

www.moriartis.co.uk

Victorian Dreams

If you really want to splash out on a romantic bed, try this site. Antique and antique-style beds in an assortment of styles: site contents will vary depending on what is available.

www.victorian-dreams.co.uk

BUILDERS AND DESIGNERS

These sites offer to help you find the professionals you need to make your interior design dreams a reality.

Home Pro

This is a portal at which you can find an appropriate professional to work on your home. You submit details of the project you need completed (for example, install a new bathroom) and they will advise registered organisations in your area of your requirement so they can contact you with a quote. All the professionals are rated and inspected by the site. You can also browse their catalogues of information to get ideas for your new designs.

www.homepro.com

Improveline

A useful site to help you with your design and decoration, including extensive home improvements and advice on choosing a builder. You can also search for an approved local tradesman if you don't fancy doing the job yourself.

www.improveline.com

FIREPLACES

Need to replace that 1950s-style horror with something more tasteful? Try these sites.

Fireplace Shop

This site offers a wide range of Victorian-style fireplaces and inset gas or electric fires at excellent prices, with delivery nationwide.

www.fireplaceshop.co.uk

Marble Hill Fireplaces

If you fancy something really special, check out this site for some beautiful antique and replica styles in marble and natural stone.

www.marblehill.co.uk

FLOORING

Carpet, wood or tiles – what's your preference? Check the latest designs out at these sites.

BC Ceramics

This tile manufacturer offers a wide range for any purpose, and actively encourages you to use tiles throughout your home – as they often do on the continent. You can view the styles online or download their full brochure to peruse at your leisure.

www.bcceramics.co.uk

Carpet Online

All the carpet you'll ever need, from the bargain end-of-roll to the high-quality Axminster. Plus hints and tips on measuring, fitting and maintaining carpets, and a whole host of other useful information for the DIY carpet fitter.

www.carpet-online.co.uk

Carpet Tiles

A very versatile flooring solution for home and office alike. Find out more and browse the available styles at this site, a sister site to Carpet Online.

www.carpettile.co.uk

Ceramic Tile Distributors

Trying to match an existing tile, or looking for a particular pattern? This site will probably help. It has a wide range of tiles for all purposes, and will deliver anywhere in the UK. Prices are shown together with a list of suppliers and distributors.

www.ceramic-tile-distributors.co.uk

Wood Floors

Wooden floors bring style and warmth to any home; laminate flooring provides a similar look with the benefits of being easy to install and clean. This company offers all you need to transform your floors, all at trade prices, and delivered free the next day, anywhere in the UK. No hanging about there then!

www.wood-floor.co.uk

INTERIOR DESIGN

These sites offer hints and tips on design, and are often based on glossy magazines. Most also include advertisements and sometimes classified listings of sources and suppliers.

Interiors and Sources

This online version of *Interiors & Sources* magazine brings to you the best of the commercial and residential design and architecture fields. It gives in-depth trend analyses, opinion pieces, case histories, product specification guidelines and reviews, plus the profiles of some of the designers and architects. Get all the features from the magazine and back issues here but do not expect to see lots of pictures!

www.isdesignet.com

World of Interiors

This is the online version of the magazine *World of Interiors*. The site features all the articles from the publication plus a searchable catalogue of all the top names in British interior design from antique dealers and furniture makers to lighting consultants and fabric designers.

www.worldofinteriors.co.uk

SOFT FURNISHINGS

Interior Design and Decoration Village

If you prefer to wander round a virtual showroom to choose your fabrics and soft furnishings, then this is the site to visit and buy online.

www.iddv.com

Linen, Lace and Patchwork

This site offers a wide range of traditional and modern-style cushions, throws, quilts, tablecloths, towels and curtains. You can view all goods online, including measurements, and use their e-mail order form to request them if you live in the UK. A full online shopping facility should be available shortly.

www.llph.co.uk

Rosebys

A familiar name from the high street, Rosebys offers a wide range of affordable linens and accessories for bed, bath and living rooms, and you can view all their items online. You will soon be able to order online as well – see site for details – but meanwhile can use their handy store finder to locate your nearest branch. You will need the Flash 4 plug-in to view the site.

www.rosebys.co.uk

OTHER

Handmade Tiles

For a really personal finish to your tiling, check out this site. Royce Wood Tiles is a family business that offers only handmade tiles, for use on their own or as highlights to more general tiling schemes. Some fabulous designs.

www.tilesrus.com

Ironwork

Jim Lawrence offers traditional ironwork to embellish your home, from light fitments to curtain poles and door furniture.

www.jim-lawrence.co.uk

HOMEWORK RESEARCH AND REVISION

The net has revolutionised homework for all ages, giving access to almost unlimited resources of information at the touch of a few buttons. But sometimes finding what you need can take longer than expected, particularly with the temptation to follow links endlessly – until you end up on a totally different subject! Many of the sites listed under other categories in this book provide information ideal for school and college projects, while those listed below are dedicated to homework research and revision, often pointing you to information directly related to the topics covered by the National Curriculum. When preparing a project, cast your net as wide as possible: remember that you can often find useful nuggets of information on other sites that will gain you those extra few marks. Never copy information directly into your homework unless you are identifying it as a quote – this would be plagiarism – but rather use the information you find to create your own version.

If you are revising for exams, many of the sites provide sample Q&As or test papers, or summaries of the topics you need to know.

See also specific subjects, for example, for biology or health studies research, see the sites listed under *Health, Fitness and Nutrition*; for English Literature see those under *Books*; for History those under *History* and also those under *Museums, Galleries and Historical Sites*.

BBC Bitesize and BBC Education

The BBC has long been at the forefront of education in Britain, and the Bitesize service aims to help students to revise for GCSE and other exams. As part of an integrated revision strategy encompassing TV, books and the internet, it provides handy 'bite-sized' revision sessions to get your children ahead in the exam race. The second site is a more general education site, giving details of the BBC programmes that support the National Curriculum, and related information to help with homework.

www.bbc.co.uk/revision

www.bbc.co.uk/education

GCSE Answers

This site aims to help students preparing for GCSE exams, in particular maths and English. It provides suggested questions and answers, tutorials on specific topics and links to many other helpful sites.

www.gcse.com

Homework Elephant

This site is a valuable resource for both children and mature students – and even for teachers. It helps you find answers to questions and problems and information you need for homework or research. As it is a UK site, it is appropriate to the National Curriculum and its various Key Stages.

www.homeworkelephant.co.uk

Homework High

This site, provided by Channel Four, provides help for students aged up to 16 on a range of National Curriculum subjects. You can submit questions to their experts (all professional teachers), chat online with other students, or visit their library to peruse questions previously asked by others. Click on the 'Get Help' link to find out how before you start.

www.homeworkhigh.com

KidsClick

More than just homework here, so don't get side-tracked, but it is a really great site for all things school-related.

www.kidsclick.com

Kidslink Educational

This UK-based site consists of pages for each subject, listing related sites that are useful for homework research. Rather a lot of ads, which are off-putting but keep the site free for users.

www.dstarkey.freeserve.co.uk/index.htm

Research It

Not so much a homework site as a useful resource for tools – dictionaries, searchers, converters and the like – Research It and its companion sites offer help with all sorts of study and research and are ideal to keep by you while finishing that assignment.

www.itools.com/research-it

SAM Learning

This site – the only educational site supported by the National Association of Head Teachers – offers information on all major exams, broken down by subject and then topic. It offers explanations and sample questions – with drag and drop so you can complete the answers – to help you revise. Some of the information designed for use by schools (rather than at home by students) is only available by paid subscription.

www.samlearning.co.uk

S-Cool

This new site offers interactive study aids for many GCSE, A and AS-level subjects, plus discussion groups to help stimulate debate and encourage learning.

www.s-cool.co.uk

Study Web

Although American, this site covers all subjects in the National Curriculum, providing handy hints and more than 100,000 links to related sites – so you should be able to find all the information you need to complete that project. It also has a 'study buddy' section that provides useful tools such as dictionaries, measurement converters and maps.

www.studyweb.com

INTERNET

These sections provide helpful information on the internet and direct you to sites designed to help you build your own web site, surf more safely, or which provide search facilities. For other internet-related sites, and details of newsgroups, e-mail and other related topics, see *Computers and Software*.

GENERAL INTERNET HELP

1,001 Best Internet Tips

If you need help, here you have it. The internet doesn't come with a manual but you're in luck: *PC Computing's* exclusive guide to the 1,001 best web tips gives you the top net speed-up tricks, undocumented secrets and loads of insider information. This site is guaranteed to make you an instant internet expert.

www.zdnet.com/pccomp/besttips

4 the Net

All kinds of useful information and services for your surfing activities: free e-mail, a guest book, web tools, statistics and lots more.

www.4thenet.co.uk

E-mail Directories

If you've forgotten someone's e-mail address, how can you find it? Not always easy – there is no comprehensive 'directory' in which you can reliably find details in the same way as a telephone book. However, you can choose to have your address listed in one or more of the following directories, in case anyone wants to find you. Many

ISPs provide a similar service for their own subscribers, in which you can search for fellow members. You can choose which of your details you want to reveal to others.

www.infospace.com

www.whowhere.lycos.com

people.yahoo.com

members@netscape.com

192.com

Internet Help Desk

This is a free guide which is designed to help both beginners and advanced internet users. It has guides to e-mail, 'netiquette' and browsers.

w3.one.net/~alward

Learn the Net

Learn the Net is a web-based tutorial for internet novices and a continuing source of educational and technical assistance for all users. It was originally created as a publication of Paradesa Media. The English site went online in April 1996, followed by the French, German, Spanish and Italian editions. It has subsequently become a publication of Michael Lerner Productions.

www.learnthenet.com

Microsoft Internet Guide

If you are new to the net then this site is a great starting point for you. The site is clearly written with loads of advice for everyone. It starts with an explanation of the basics of using the internet and takes you right through to how to create your own web site.

www.microsoft.com/insider/internet/default.htm

Webopedia

If you find new jargon you cannot understand, go to this site for good definitions and explanations of the latest web-related terminology.

www.webopedia.com

What Is?

This site offers the quickest way to get reliable definitions for internet, computer and telecommunications jargon.

www.whatis.com

ISPS AND FREE E-MAIL SITES

These sites are home to (or list) some of the most reputable service providers, or provide an online e-mail service which you can access from around the world. Some also offer web hosting, for those of you who wish to create your own web site.

Bigfoot

Bigfoot is a really good site which not only offers free e-mail for life, but also offers one of the largest search engines. The second address below is UK-specific. It is also available in several other languages, accessible from the main homepage.

bigfoot.com

uk.bigfoot.com

Cybercafé Search Engine

This is a site for people who need their fix of the internet while away on business or holiday and do not have the luxury of a portable computer. The database at this site contains listings of 1,537 cybercafés in 89 countries. You can search for a cybercafé by name or by a city.

www.cybercaptive.com

The Directory

This site provides a listing of recommended ISPs world-wide. An excellent way to find a new provider if you are changing location, or even if not.

www.thedirectory.org

Free Web Space

At this site you can use a simple search for free hosts. You can also view the complete list of free personal web space providers available on the internet. There are also special pages if you want free hosting for your business site or a non-profit organisation or your game site. There is also a page for special interest-free hosts.

www.freewebspace.net

Freeserve

If you are UK-based and have not already found this service provider, take a look at its web site. It offers a good level of service with various payment plans, including unlimited free access for a monthly fee, unlimited off-peak access (lower fee) or pay-per-call access for no monthly fee. It also has an extensive, easy-to-navigate web site including a speedy search facility.

www.freeserve.com

Hotmail

One of the most famous and widely-used e-mail services, Hotmail is provided by Microsoft, the largest software vendor in the world. It is easy to use and very reliable, and has a handy inbox protector feature, which helps to eliminate junk mail (spam). Signup is free, but you will need a connection to the internet – one reason why this is often used in shared facilities such as internet cafés and libraries. The site is available in a variety of languages and can be accessed from anywhere in the world.

www.hotmail.com

Mail2Web

This handy service allows you to pick up your e-mail from anyone's computer, no matter who your service provider is. You simply enter your e-mail address and password on their front page (you may also require your server details, but not for most of the major ISPs) and Mail2Web connects to your ISP's server to download your mail.

www.mail2web.com

Twigger

Similar to the Mail2Web service described above.

www.twigger.com

UK and Ireland ISPs

This site provides a review of all the currently-operating ISPs and OSPs in the UK and Ireland.

www.ispreview.co.uk

Web Box

One of the first and best web-based universal e-mail clients was MailStartPlus. Now relaunched under the Web Box banner, this site gives you all the features and benefits you have come to expect from a well-made e-mail program, with the added advantage of being accessible any time you find yourself on the internet. The best part is that you get all these advantages and services free of charge.

webbox.com

NEWSGROUPS AND BBS

These sites are not newsgroups or bulletin boards in themselves, but provide information on these services and where to obtain them.

Boardwatch

Boardwatch is the most respected and established magazine for bulletin board users. It gives details on new BBS and how to access them. View its latest content at this site, now part of ISPworld.com

www.boardwatch.com

Bulletin Boards

This American site hosts bulletin boards and is a good source of information if you are thinking of joining a BBS or creating your own. It shows some great sample bulletin boards and explains how to access and use them. You can even set up your own bulletin board following their instructions (there is a monthly fee).

www.bulletinboards.com

Deja News

Deja News is a great starting point for joining in with a debate and for taking part in a discussion on almost any topic that comes to mind. Discussions take place in newsgroups or Usenet groups, which normally require you to download and access a newsreader program. The Deja News web site allows you to access newsgroups easily from the web and is well worth looking into.

www.dejanews.com

The Directory BBS listings

This site is great for information on both Telnet and dial-in bulletin boards (read the site pages for details of the differences), as well as ISP and web-hosting companies.

www.thedirectory.org/diamond/bbslists.htm

Easy News

Easy News automatically decodes and indexes the binary files found in Usenet newsgroups. If a binary file is posted to any newsgroup, Easy News will catalogue it into an easy-to-navigate thumbnail index. They browse through all the newsgroups to bring you the newsgroups that contain binary files such as AVIs, MPEGs, MP3s, ZIPs and JPEGs. The unfortunate part is that you have to subscribe to this service, though you can get a free three-day trial. If you do download a lot of binary files from the newsgroups, then it is worth it.

www.easynews.com

Liszt

This is a well-established site offering information on hundreds of newsgroups, BBS and chat rooms. You can search for the names of groups related to a particular topic and then access these using your regular newsreader software.

www.liszt.com

SECURITY AND PROTECTION

These sites provide site verification or safe-surfing products, to make the internet safer for children and adults alike. For information on more basic computer security (including virus protection) see Chapter 9: *Protect yourself from internet problems* and the web sites listed in *Computers and Software: Security*.

The Adult Check System

This adult verification system is the largest of its kind in the world. It has been designed to prevent minors from accessing information of an adult nature. There are over 45,000 participating sites and the service is available in seven languages, including Chinese and Japanese.

www.adultcheck.com

The Adult Pass

Created by internet specialists as a response to US government censorship, this verification service restricts minors from accessing adult-oriented sites. You must have a valid credit card number to be verified as an adult.

www.adultpass.com

American Links Up (Netparents)

America Links Up: A Kids Online Teach-In is a public awareness and education campaign sponsored by a coalition of non-profit organisations, education groups, and companies concerned with providing children with a safe and rewarding experience online. This site contains a number of valuable resources for parents and kids. Although it is an American site, much of the information is valid wherever you happen to live.

www.netparents.org

Consumer's Association

This site includes a list of all the companies who have joined its Which? WebTrader Scheme for consumer protection and gives details of the protection it offers anyone who has suffered a problem with a registered trader.

www.which.net/webtrader/wt5.html

Cyberangels International

This organisation, claiming to be the largest net safety group in the world, monitors the net for various types of undesirable content and works with police and other interested parties to remove such sites from the web. It offers a variety of filtering services and is the ideal site to visit if you are concerned about what you or your children could encounter while surfing.

www.cyberangels.org

Cyber Patrol

Cyber Patrol is a good way to manage children's computer use and safety on the internet. You can create different filtering criteria for your children according to their age and needs; supervise your children's internet access; regulate time spent online; and protect your child from sites you determine to be objectionable. Children have the opportunity to explore the internet safely and have a positive learning experience. At the site you can download a trial version of the software for use at home, work or school.

www.cyberpatrol.com

Family Internet

Discover web sites for the family to enjoy together or individually, including software to control web site access.

familyinternet.about.com

Internet Lifeguard

This site offers you a collection of tips and resources for safer internet surfing. It includes a library of filtering software, a parent/child agreement and online basics.

www.safesurf.com/lifegard.htm

Internet Watch Federation

The IWF was launched to address the problem of illegal material on the internet, with particular reference to child pornography. All users of the internet are encouraged to report potentially illegal material. Note, though, that the IWF is concerned with the law, not personal taste or morality, and can only act on material that could be prosecuted under UK legislation.

www.iwf.org.uk

Kid Safety

An easy-to-follow tutorial for kids on internet safety with step-by-step instructions on how children should behave online.

www.ou.edu/oupd/kidsafe/inet.htm

Net Nanny

Net Nanny filtering software for your PC protects children from the dangers from the internet from standard e-mail, chat programs and newsgroups. Net Nanny offers you the necessary tools to ensure safety and peace of mind while on your PC and allows you not to worry about access to inappropriate material, to prevent the threat of cyber strangers and deny the misuse of personal information. You can download a trial version of the software from their site.

www.netnanny.com

The Recreational Software Advisory Council

The RSAC is an independent, non-profit US organisation that helps parents to make informed decisions about electronic media by means of an open, objective content-advisory system. The RSAC system provides consumers with information about the level of sex, nudity, violence and offensive language (vulgar or hate-motivated) in software games and web sites. Here at their site you can find out about them and how they work, their rating system and how to use it, and register your own web site to be rated.

www.icra.org

SafeSurf

The original and best rating system on the net, designed to weed out undesirable content by allowing site owners to rate their site according to a number of criteria. The whole system is explained here, and they also offer specialised internet filtering and a number of related services.

www.safesurf.com

Surfer Beware

It is widely assumed that unless you explicitly give away personal information, your anonymity remains when you surf the web. Unfortunately this is not true and to find out just how much information you are giving away, visit this site. It has been put together by the Electronic Privacy Information Centre and is well worth checking out before you decide to visit those sites of an adult nature!

www.epic.org/reports/surfer-beware.html

SEARCH ENGINES

Search engines do the hard part of searching the web for you. They all differ in how you input the search criteria and also in their look and content. There are many to choose from, and you will soon find the one that suits you best.

For more information on search engines and how to use them, see *Chapter 6: Searching for information*.

About.com

Calling itself 'The Human Internet', this search engine offers an entry-point to a whole range of linked sites with information from news updates to maps of Finland.

www.about.com

All the Web

This searcher claims to be able to reference 200 million web pages.

alltheweb.com

Alta Vista

The AltaVista search service helps you find documents on the web. To tell the search service what you are looking for, simply type in key words, phrases or questions in the search box. The search service responds by giving you a list of all the web pages in the index that relate to those topics. The most relevant content will appear at the top of the list.

www.altavista.com

Ask Jeeves

This is a search engine with a difference. You ask a question in plain English and Jeeves will give you the answer. It is a mix of human and automation, and there is no need to mess about with multiple keywords, operators and phrases like with most traditional search engines. Ask Jeeves is also linked to major search engines like Yahoo, Alta Vista, Infoseek and Webcrawler and gives you their answers too.

www.askjeeves.com

Deja News

This engine searches newsgroups rather than the web. It is exceptionally good for accessing old articles and for finding the right newsgroup for your needs.

www.dejanews.com

Excite

This is a popular and efficient search engine with a reasonable reference index.

www.excite.com

GoTo

This site offers you the chance to 'simply type what you are looking for and GoTo it': giving you easy access to sites if you don't know their URL.

www.goto.com

Hotbot

This is an easy-to-use search engine with useful search options that can be tuned to your own needs. The site is well known for its accurate and thorough keyword searches.

www.hotbot.com

Infoseek

At Infoseek you can search the web, newsgroups, and various web FAQs. The web search is quite fast but its database is not as big as many others available, so you will receive fewer results.

www.infoseek.com

Ixquick

This service uses a slightly different approach in that it searches 14 other search engines and gives you the best options on the subject you are looking for.

www.ixquick.com

LookSmart

Looksmart organises the web for you like no other site can, as it is three powerful internet tools in one. Explore speeds you through familiar categories to help you pinpoint web sites faster and more easily. Search will search its listings for sites first, then use Alta Vista to find what you want. Personalise allows you to choose your own favourite shopping, software and news sources and will provide you the top links from your own home area based on this information

www.looksmart.com

Lycos

This search engine offers you the usual customisable keyword search, together with a range of web guides to browse. The first address is the main US engine; the second the UK version.

www.lycos.com

www.lycos.co.uk

Real Names

This engine is one of the fastest ways to search the web. You can use Real Names addresses in Alta Vista, LookSmart, Inktomi and GO Network. All you need to do is to type a name, brand or company in the Real Names locator box and it takes you to the exact site, or to a list of companies that match your query.

www.centraal.com

Regional Directories

Nearly every country has its own web directory purely for itself. At this site you will find a comprehensive list of country-specific web directories. Not totally exhaustive, but it is a good place to start.

www.edirectory.com

Search Engine Watch

This is not a search engine itself but a very good and useful resource about search engines for both beginners and the more experienced. Here you can find out how to use all the popular and largest search engines available on the web. Or if you are trying to get your site listed at the top of the search engine databases, this will tell you all you need to know.

www.searchenginewatch.com

Webcrawler

This search engine is actually owned by Excite but has its own unique user interface. The search engine itself is mainly directed towards news, so it is a good place to look for stories about what is currently going on in the world.

webcrawler.com

UK Plus

This site is a friendly, sensible guide to the web designed to help you find what you want, quickly and easily. Although it concentrates on UK web sites of all kinds, there are also many from all over the world.

www.ukplus.co.uk

Yahoo

The original and the biggest search engine of them all. It is very easy to use and it is also available for individual countries (just replace the .com with .uk, .fr and so on). Yahoo is now more of a community than just a plain search engine, offering you free e-mail access and free web space, plus the chance to search in other engines for the same keyword if your search fails to bring results.

www.yahoo.com

WEB SITE DESIGN AND HOSTING

These sites offer advice and help with creating your own web site, or somewhere to put it.

Domain Names

There are hundreds of companies out there offering *domain names* (the name of a site, such as www.domainname.com), some free, some terrifically expensive. If you have a particular name in mind for your site, visit one of the listed registrar companies to see whether the site is still available: if not you will be directed to the site for the company that owns it. If it is available, you can usually purchase it online.

www.register.com

Free Web Space

This site offers the largest searchable list of free or cut-price web space providers on the net. Just enter the maximum you wish to pay and the amount of space you need, and it will present you with a list of options.

www.freewebspace.net

Javascript Source

This site provides free javascript code to plug in to your site, allowing you to provide utilities like calculators, calendars and forms with ease.

javascript.internet.com

Net Resources

A huge range of computer-related products is available from this site, all available for you to download free of charge. So if you find yourself missing a file or DLL in your computer set-up then the chances are that you can find it on this site. It also offers loads of free cut-and-paste Java scripts for the web designers out there, and a wide range of anti-hacker tools.

www.uforesources.com

Webmonkey

The Webmonkey site offers a vast resource for web developers, whether novice or experienced. Pick up tips for best design, tools to help you create pages, and links to sites providing plug-ins and free graphics.

www.webmonkey.com

Web Developer's Virtual Library

This site provides not only web authoring resources, but also free tutorials. Some of the content is a bit 'techie' but most is easily understandable at any level.

www.stars.com

LAW

Need a lawyer? Or just need to know your rights or how the system works? These sites will help with most basic legal problems or offer advice on legal procedure. Some are less serious. If you are seeking specific advice, remember to look for a site based in your own country, as laws do vary from one country to another.

ACAS

The Advisory, Conciliation and Arbitration Service mediates in industrial disputes and promotes good employer-employee relations. Its site offers general information, press releases, local offices and a book list.

www.acas.org.uk

Active Most Wanted and Criminal Investigations

This site is a compendium of fugitive listings. Check out the FBI's top 10 most wanted on the war criminal directory. The site also has information on the US State Department's Anti-terrorism Unit.

www.activemostwanted.com

Advertising Law

This site has been established by a US law firm which specialises in US advertising law, consumer protection, anti-trust and trade association law. They have a long history of assisting clients regarding advertising and marketing law issues. The site has links to other internet advertising, marketing and consumer law sites. From time to time, links to articles, press releases and other related materials are added.

www.advertisinglaw.com/home.html

Consumer Law

Many consumer organisations offer consumers assistance by providing guidance on how to resolve disputes without the need to hire a lawyer or to initiate a legal proceeding. Although most organisations will not take action on behalf of individual consumers, they may provide you with contact information, education activities or publications. This site contains links to these organisations. It is mainly American but it does contain some useful international links.

consumer.pub.findlaw.com/congen/index.html

Dumb Laws

An entertaining and thought-provoking, if not altogether useful, site about stupid laws that should have found their way off the statute books of various countries. It's a sobering thought that in some cases the law really is an ass!

www.dumblaws.com

Staff Relations

This site claims to help employers stay on the right side of employment law. Information on some topics is provided free of charge, or for a fixed annual fee you can get unlimited advice on employment and personnel legal issues, templates for employment documents for your type of business, optional insurance against legal costs and employment tribunal awards, representation at employment tribunals, and access to their free information pages.

www.staffrelations.co.uk

Find Law

This is one of the leading web portals focused on law and government. It provides access to a growing online library of legal resources for legal professionals, consumers and small businesses. At this site you will find lots of different features such as web search utilities, cases and codes, legal news and more.

www.findlaw.com

Law4today

This magazine-style site promises to help you find the right lawyer for your case, as well as offering legal advice and tips on a wide selection of topics, including the likely cost of different types of legal transaction (such as conveyancing). An interesting read even if you haven't got a lawsuit pending.

www.law4today.com

Law Net

The Law Net site offers lots of information on law to internet users and is sponsored by attorneys and vendors of legal services and products in America. It is a good resource for searching for specific laws and attorneys who specialise in specific areas of law, There is also an online forum available for the discussion of legal issues. This site is one of the longest-running sites dedicated to law so it has an exhaustive array of resources.

www.law.net

Law on the Web

A UK solicitor built this award-winning web site, which aims to demystify the law and explains basic legal procedures as well as how to find a lawyer and the likely cost. You can also e-mail the owner for advice on legal issues.

www.lawontheweb.co.uk

The 'Lectric Law Library

The library's goal is to allow you to find and access law-related information and products that you want or need – easily and free. There is a lot of material for legal professionals, business people and formal and informal students of the law, but mostly the site has things that just about everyone could find interesting or helpful at some stage.

www.lectlaw.com

Legal Pad Junior

This site provides kids and teens with an area in which they can express themselves using either message boards, chats or newsletters produced by adults for kids. Legal Pad For Kids hosts Kids Who Care for kids aged 6-12 and 2B Heard for kids aged 13-17. It is designed to encourage positive attitudes and active participation in learning how the law and good character affect our lives both today and in the future.

www.legalpadjr.com

Organised Crime

This site contains all the information that you need to find out about organised crime. This site will fascinate conspiracy lovers, worry the fearful and leave law-abiding citizens wondering what's gone wrong.

www.alternatives.com/crime

Police Officers Directory

A directory containing more than 1,500 police bureaux, together with law libraries and special operations branches. You can also use it to find out what investigative tools are used in the process of solving any crime, and information on wanted criminals and hate groups.

www.officer.com

UK Legal Resources

This site is the portal to legal resources in the UK and Ireland. It is regularly updated and you will find that it has been split into four areas. It gives details of free legal information to individuals and also to companies. There is information for solicitors and barristers plus information from the current issue of the *International Newsletter for Lawyers*.

www.venables.co.uk

MOTORCYCLES

Biker heaven! The web is full of sites for motorcycle fans, from manufacturers, biker organisations, race organisers and motorcycle magazines. If you're a fan of the two-wheeled lifestyle, check these out. See also *Motoring* and *Sports*.

Aprilia

This site from the Italian manufacturer of scooters and motorcycles offers photos and a technical chart for each model. Also available on the site is racing information and news in Italian, German, Spanish, Dutch and English.

www.aprilia.com

Bennetts

This is a site for the motorbike enthusiast as it offers information on biking events, insurance, motorcycle clubs, security devices, news, tips and special offers.

www.bennetts.co.uk

Bike Net

A motorcycling e-zine mostly dedicated to road use rather than racing, the range and speed of the news here is excellent, and the site is a must for all motorcyclists. They say they 'have brought together the world's top suppliers of bikes and gear to help you find what you need' and as a result, you will find that the site contains a large and extensive classified advertisement section.

www.bikenet.com

BMF Riderspace

This is the web site of the British Motorcyclists' Federation, Britain's largest rider group. The organisation states that its job is 'to protect and promote road-riders' interests so no matter what you ride, there is bound to be something here for you'.

www.bmf.co.uk

Carl Fogarty's Site

Never one to hide his light under a bushel, three-times world champion Carl Fogarty, recently retired from racing due to injury, has his own site celebrating all things Foggy. Read up on his achievements, view his fan mail, or read his no-holds-barred opinions on everything and everyone involved in racing.

www.carlfogarty.net

Ducati

There is a lot to see and do at this web site from the motorcycling equivalent of Ferrari: exclusive shots from their model range, technical designs, model year previews and more. You can also search for your local dealer by selecting your country from the map. The site is also available in Italian.

www.ducati.com

Harley Davidson

The site has been created to provide a forum for enthusiasts so that they are able to chat to Harley Davidson directly and find out what it means to be part of the Harley family. Whether you are a Harley rider, future Harley owner, or just want to experience the Harley lifestyle and culture, check out this site, which also includes an archive of Harley photographs and videos.

www.hd-stamford.com

Honda

Find out about Honda's range of motorcycles, including all touring, off-road, racing, sport, and custom motorcycles, plus scooters and all-terrain vehicles, and get information about the Honda Riders' Club.

www.hondamotorcycle.com/index.html

Isle of Man TT

The Isle of Man TT has truly become a festival of motorcycle sport, with over 40,000 fans travelling to the island for those two special weeks every year. This site contains a photo gallery and gives details of the various social events, races and results, news and the history of the TT races. Rider Steve Hislop also provides the site with an excellent guide to the course. During TT fortnight, the Manx Radio site provides streamed commentary on all races.

www.iomtt.com

www.radiott.com

Kawasaki
Motorcycles as well as jet-ski watercraft, all-terrain vehicles, utility vehicles, and portable generators are just some of the unique consumer products that have made the Kawasaki brand a household name around the world. Learn more about Kawasaki by checking out this site. Here you can find information on the history of Kawasaki and its products, view industry links, get free brochures and copies of the *Good Times* magazine, or find out about job vacancies within Kawasaki.

www.kawasaki.com

ManxBiker
A free-to-use site giving information on road racing, trials and motocross as held in the Isle of Man and elsewhere. Check out the schedules for Irish and Manx road races, keep up to date with the latest changes in rules, dates and riders, or scan their listings for bikes, parts and bike gear for sale.

www.manxbiker.co.uk

Motorcycle Consumer News
Motorcycle Consumer News magazine is an American magazine, concentrating on US bikes. The site includes sample articles and sections from the monthly print version of the magazine, plus an events calendar and used bike value guide. If you like what you find here, consider subscribing to the magazine, which ships world-wide.

www.mcnews.com

Motor Cycle News
All bike fans will know of *MCN*, the UK's number one motorcycling magazine. This is the online version, including all the usual magazine

features, the *MCN* directory and what's on guide, plus a number of chat boards and links to related sites.

www.motorcyclenews.com

Motorcycle Safety Foundation

This organisation is American so all the information concerning courses are for the Americas. However, the site also contains a lot of information that is applicable to motorcyclists all around the world. For example, it has sections concerning protective clothing, riding safety and helmet information.

www.msf-usa.org

Motorcycle Web Index

If you are looking for information on motorcycles, then this is one place for you to start. Here you will find links to many different sites on motorcycling covering magazines, movies, dealers, fan pages, safety and insurance, with links, newsgroups and mailing lists.

sepnet.com/cycle

Old Bike Mart

If you're into older bikes, need parts for a restoration project or just want to meet like-minded riders, check out this site. It has a large classified section, plus info on projects, events and other related sites.

www.oldbikemart.co.uk

Piaggio

For over 50 years Piaggio have been making scooters. Whether you are into scooter nostalgia or simply want a run-around that is able to weave its way through the rush-hour traffic, find out everything about the Vespa scooter and others here.

www.piaggio.com

Suzuki

It all started in 1930 when Suzuki developed the first cotton loom works in Japan. In 1940 Suzuki put an engine on to a bicycle and thus developed the motorcycle principle. Since then Suzuki has been at the forefront of design and technology in the worlds of two-wheel racing, commuting and off-road. Find out more about the company and its products, which include automobiles and marine 'mean' machines too!

www.suzuki.com

www.suzuki.co.uk

Triumph

At the official site, check out Triumph's classic, sports and touring ranges as well as details of accessories, clothing and dealers. Go on a tour of the Triumph factory, which is situated on the outskirts of Hinckley in Leicestershire. Find out what the Riders' Association of Triumph has to offer. RAT is the worldwide club for owners of modern Triumphs and is run by the factory, from the factory. It is a direct link to Triumph and offers a range of services including a quality colour magazine, a package of exclusive discount arrangements and an extensive international events programme.

www.triumph.co.uk

Used Motorcycle Evaluation Guide

This is a web page that contains a very good resource for the second-hand bike buyer. The document contains practically everything you need to look out for when buying a used motorcycle, with pictures, parts-based breakdowns and links. This is an American-based site.

www.clarity.net/~adam/buying-bike.html

Used Motorcycle Guide Online

This is a UK-based guide which provides reports on Honda, Kawasaki, Suzuki and Yamaha motorcycles and contains information on motorcycle faults, data, comments and UK prices.

umgweb.com

Yamaha

The Yamaha Motor Corporation began operating in 1955. It is a major part of the entire Yamaha group but is a separately managed business entity from the Yamaha Corporation. The Yamaha Motor Corporation produces not only motorcycles but also snow mobiles, golf carts, outboard engines and water vehicles. Yamaha is the second largest manufacturer of motorcycles in the world and at this site you can get information on all its models.

www.yamahausa.com

MOTORING

If four wheels are more your style, you're in the right place. Whether you're planning a trip, looking for a new model or an old banger, want the latest fuel prices or just want to know how it all works, these sites should help.

For motorsport, see the relevant section under *Sport*. For insurance and finance options, see *Finance and Insurance*.

AA

With everything from hotel and insurance recommendations to warnings of road works and information on fuel prices, the AA site aims to help you get the best out of your motoring.

www.theaa.co.uk

Audi

The official site in German or English lists everything you may want to know about Audi cars and the Audi company.

www.audi.com

Autobytel

This site makes buying a car easy in America, Sweden, Canada and the UK. Here they give you point-and-click access to as much information as you want in order to make your car-buying decision. Once you're ready to buy, you specify the make, model and other relevant information for the car or truck you wish to purchase. You submit this information online. Then they connect you to the Autobytel.com manager at an accredited dealership near you. The manager finds you exactly what you asked for and offers it to you at a low price. You go to the dealership, and if you like what you see, you buy the vehicle at the agreed price.

www.autobytel.com

Auto Trader

Britain's biggest showroom for new and used cars plus information on insurance, finance and other related topics. There are helping-hand features, advertising, a buyers' guide and bookshop. If you want to find a dealer, get an insurance quote, hire or lease a car, you'll find help here. The site can also take you to France, Ireland, Italy, the Netherlands, Norway and South Africa.

www.autotrader.co.uk

Automotive Advice

If you have got a problem with your car, van or truck, Dave Benoit, a certified auto mechanic with over 25 years' experience, may be able to help you. However, Dave is American, and therefore may be unable to give advice on certain models. It is worth giving him a try though.

members.home.net/daveandlois

BMW

The official web site of BMW is available in either German or English. Like many other car companies, you can find out about all the models in their various ranges as well as the company itself. They have a vast library area where you can download all the information on their models. The site serves BMW cars and motorcycles.

www.bmw.com

Bristol Street

Buying cars online is becoming more popular, so this group of dealers has created its own web site so that you can do just that. An easy-to-navigate site, it still has the dealer link for peace of mind.

www.bristolstreet.co.uk

Carnoisseur

Very modern, blokey site for a company selling alloy wheels, flash accessories for cars with special offers, online ordering and details of shops throughout the UK. Almost trade prices.

www.carnoisseur.com

Carsource

If you want to buy a new or used car, need information on dealers, what's new on the market or insurance, take a look at this site. There's also a useful search service so that you can find exactly what you want.

www.carsource.co.uk

Car Talk

This excellent magazine-style site featuring model reports gives answers to problems and advice on car maintenance. Go to the good 'carma' zone too where you can either help others or share your problems. On a light-hearted note, why not find out if you are a good match for your car? If you turn out to be incompatible you can then see which cars their 'car-o-scope' recommends for you.

cartalk.cars.com

Cars DIY

This web site has been developed with the car DIY enthusiast in mind. As you browse, you will hopefully gain more knowledge and understanding of the car and how it works. They have tried to cover as much on the topic as possible without going into ridiculous amounts of detail, but if you have specific problems, you can send them the information and they will help you to rectify the problem as quickly and cheaply as possible.

www.carsdiy.co.uk

Chevrolet

At this site you again will find all the information you will ever need about the Chevrolet range and the dealers in the group in America. Here is also a link available to GM motors, the company that owns the Chevrolet group. Also includes current special offers.

www.chevrolet.com

Classic Car Directory

This is a superb resource for classic car enthusiasts. With an A-Z listing of all classic car companies and clubs, plus a parts and services directory, price guide, and diary of events around the UK.

www.classic-car-directory.com

Classic Motor Monthly

This is the web version of the newspaper for all classic car enthusiasts. The site gives all the news and a selection of features, coupled with an archive, hints and tips and details of veteran, vintage and classic automobile events, plus spares and services.

www.classicmotor.co.uk

Ford

This is the official web site of the famous Ford motor company. From this site you can access countries' own individual web sites around the world, everywhere they sell Ford cars, by using the find-your-dealer feature. You can also find out all the information you want about the Ford motor company itself from cars to careers, design and technology. Also available is information on the other car manufacturers within the Ford group: Volvo, Mazda, Lincoln, Mercury, Jaguar, Land Rover and Aston Martin.

www.ford.com

Mercedes-Benz

This is the official site of the German car manufacturer where you will find all the information you need about Mercedes cars.

www.mercedes-benz.com

MG Enthusiasts

You can tell by this site alone that there are lots of proud MG owners out there and if you are one of them, or you would like to know what makes this car so appealing to so many, look no further. The site contains every conceivable detail on every MG ever made, and lists of cars for sale in countries all around the world. You will also find details of world-wide clubs and services here, too.

www.mgcars.org.uk

No Risk: Used Car Buying

Thinking of buying a used car? If so, then you would do well to check out this site first. It tells you what to look out for so that you can give those dodgy dealers and their cars a miss!

www.goodasnew.com

Opel/Vauxhall

For anyone interested in Opel cars and services, this is their official web site, full of information. Here you can take a compact, informative tour of the complete Opel showroom or choose quick access to your country's national site. Also available (on the Opel in Europe page) is a route planner and good links through the site.

www.opel.com

Parkers Online

The Parkers Car Price Guide Online has information on buying second-hand, new and used cars, as well as advice on car insurance and finance, reviews and news on new cars. The 'car chooser' option is very useful and unique to this site.

www.parkers.co.uk

Peugeot

Peugeot's official site is written in French but is available in English as well. Pages list all the models and options available for the Peugeot range in the relevant country, plus fun things such as screensavers and wallpaper.

www.peugeot.com

Porsche

From the main site you choose either a site in English on an EU server or American server, or the site in German. Also available is a virtual in-depth tour of the factory or you can even locate your local Porsche club anywhere in the world.

www.porsche.com

Rolls Royce and Bentley

This is a very good and informative site from the manufacturers of the most exclusive hand-built cars in the world. The site has two sides: one that deals with only Rolls Royce and the other which is Bentley cars.

www.rolls-royceandbentley.co.uk

Scions of Lucas

This is an index of comprehensive British car marque web sites. From the site you can see that there is a large, vibrant group of British car enthusiasts drawn from all over the world and that the major interest is vintage cars. The site contains links to all British car manufacturers as well.

www.team.net/sol/solwebs.html

Speed Trap Registry

This is the site if you are planning a tour in your car and do not want to be caught speeding. The site lists speed traps all over the world, though because it is run by an American there is a bias towards the states of America. You can use their form to add any speed traps that are not listed and even find out about unmarked police vehicles in your area, the scanners available for the motorist and if they are legal where you live.

www.speedtrap.com

Swift

The Swift Group is one of the world's leading manufacturers of touring caravans and both coach-built and hi-top motor homes. This is essentially a corporate web site, but you can use it to browse Swift's current range of vehicles and to request a full brochure.

www.swiftleisure.co.uk

Toyota

At the official site of Toyota you can use the international directory to get the world-wide listing of Toyota sites. If you were to link to the Toyota Motor Corporation in Japan, you could take a tour of the virtual factory, or pass the time at their automobile museum and catch up on all the latest news and information about Japan's leading car company.

www.toyota.com

Volvo

From the official site you can access information and dealers around the world for all the machines that Volvo make. Here you can find information on anything from cars, trucks, buses, to plant machinery and marine and aero engines that are produced by Volvo.

www.volvo.com

Women Motorist

Whatever some people say, women drivers are, in fact, safer than men! Although this site is designed specifically for the female driver, it would be of interest to anyone since it is designed to contain information on all kinds of related topics from buying or selling a car through to general car maintenance, all explained in straightforward language. The site is also very easy to navigate. One very good part of the site is the safety section, which is full of useful information.

www.womanmotorist.com

MOTORSPORT

See *Sport: Motorsport*.

MUSEUMS, GALLERIES AND HISTORICAL SITES

Whether you're after a good day out or information on a particular artefact, these sites can probably help. Most of the larger museums and attractions have their own site, so if the one you want isn't listed here, try using a search engine to find what you need. See also *Art* and *Entertainment*.

24-Hour Museum

The 24-Hour Museum is the UK gateway to museums, galleries and heritage attractions. It is quality controlled, which means that only museums and galleries registered with the Museums and Galleries Commission – or non-profit-making galleries, historic houses and heritage attractions – are included on this site.

www.24hourmuseum.org.uk

Beaulieu and the National Motor Museum

Set in the grounds of beautiful Beaulieu Palace House, the National Motor Museum is a celebration of motors old and new, ideal for all ages. Visit its main exhibits here and take a tour of Palace House, as well as the beautiful Beaulieu Abbey and the village itself. You can also find out what's on in the coming months, and search its archives for information on a specific model.

www.beaulieu.co.uk

The British Museum

British Museum press, gifts, shopping and the British Museum traveller are the main sections on this site, which aims to support and build the reputation of the museum throughout the world. Online ordering of gifts and replicas is included, as well as what's new at the museum, and details of its tour programme.

www.britishmuseum.co.uk

Central Intelligence Museum

This site contains pictures and details of different types of spy equipment. The objects shown on this site have been made according to technical descriptions and/or schematic drawings of equipment allegedly produced by the Central Intelligence Agency's Office of Technical Services. The site is neither endorsed by nor associated with the Central Intelligence Agency of the United States of America!

www.acmenet.net/~dna

KidsNet

If you want to take the kids for an educational or fun day out but don't know where to go, check out this site. You can list museums, galleries, stately homes and all sorts of other attractions by area, and the information given includes such vital details as price range, whether access is suitable for wheelchairs and buggies, and opening times. You can even print a route map and directions from your starting point to the place you want to visit.

www.kidsnet.org.uk

Leeds Castle

This is a very good site on Leeds Castle in Kent, England, but it is graphics-intensive and could take a while to load. Once it does though you will be able to look all around the castle and find out about all the different shows and events that are going on there throughout the year. The site also offers excellent travel directions and information on admission prices.

www.leeds-castle.co.uk

The Louvre

This is the online site of the world-famous Louvre Museum in Paris. At this site you can take a look at the collections they have on show, read the history of the Louvre and you can even take a virtual tour of the museum. There is all the information you need at this site to make your visit easy. You can even purchase your entry tickets online. The site itself is available in French, English, Spanish and Japanese.

www.louvre.fr

Museums Around the World

This site is a directory of web services connected with museums around the world. The museums listed are categorised by country/continent.

www.icom.org/vlmp/world.html

The National Gallery

This site includes details of the Gallery's collections, events and exhibitions, including a selection of its most stunning works. A great site to visit if you are planning a trip to the Gallery, as its online floor plan will help to ensure you get to see the areas you want.

www.nationalgallery.org.uk

The Natural History Museum

This is the official site of the Natural History Museum in London, England. The site contains science galleries, museum history, details of services and scientific research, visitor information and links to hosted sites. It is well worth a visit to this site, especially if you are planning a visit to the museum itself.

www.nhm.ac.uk

The National Railway Museum

Based in York, this museum is an award-winner that covers everything rail-oriented from Stephenson's *Rocket* to the latest technology. Its web site provides a great introduction to this hands-on interactive attraction and also has a great research section for homework projects if you need more information.

www.nrm.org.uk

The Science Museum

Visitor information, exhibition details, collections, research and commercial information are all included on this fascinating site, which features some QuickTime movies and online experiments. There are links to the National Museum for Science and Industry Home Page and sites for the National Museum of Photography, Film and Television and the National Railway Museum.

www.sciencemuseum.org.uk

The Tate Galleries

Now including the new Tate Modern, this site provides a guide to all the Tate Galleries around the UK, including a wealth of information on the artists whose collections are featured. Check out the site before you visit to see what's on, whose works are featured where and some of the items to look out for. You can also book for their talks and workshops.

www.tate.org.uk

The Victoria and Albert Museum

Collections, education and research, what's on, membership, art library, features, views and newsroom are all elements of this excellent site created by the London fine-art museum. Their various collections include prints, china and glass, costumes, metalwork and sculpture. The site also gives details of opening hours and general information about the museum.

www.vam.ac.uk

Westminster Abbey

As well as being a functioning Anglican church, Westminster Abbey is also a major tourist attraction where tours, concerts and coronations are held. This site lists the schedules of services and events, gives you a tour around the abbey, offers samples of the organ music played there, and provides the history of the abbey and who is buried there.

www.westminster-abbey.org

MUSIC

Whatever your taste in music, you can find it on the web. Whether you are looking for details on your favourite band, trying to track down an old LP or the score for a favourite track, or researching a particular composer, it is all there. These sites cover many styles, so don't expect them all to be to your taste!

See also *Entertainment, Fun, Films, Television, Video and DVD*, and *Radio and Broadcasting*.

Addicted To Noise

If alternative rock is your kind of music, then this is the site for you. It has monthly news and reviews, the majority of which are on the alternative rock music scene.

www.addict.com

All Music Guide

A huge music database in which you will find most of the popular genres. Despite its large size, it gives sufficient critiques, is well researched and is comprehensive, making it easy to use. On the site you will find biographies, keyword crosslinks, reviews and ratings, together with an online ordering service.

www.allmusic.com

Audio Review

If you want to know more than the manufacturers are telling you about the latest audio equipment, check it out here. All audio equipment has been reviewed by end users on this site. However, it must be remembered that some opinions can be quite extreme! Once you have taken this into account, verify what you have read by looking at the links page.

www.audioreview.com

Audiostreet

This is an online sales site for music, DVDs, games, CDs and gifts, as well as a source of music news, charts and information. Prices include VAT and free delivery in the UK.

www.audiostreet.co.uk

A-UK

Calling itself the Useful Knowledge Company, you can use this site to order guides on learning to play a range of musical instruments.

www.a-uk.co.uk

CDDirect

This is the place to buy your CD players, PlayStations, Nintendos and DVD players as well as the CDs, DVDs and games to play on them.

www.cddirect.co.uk

CD Now

CD Now offers approximately 500,000 CDs, cassettes, vinyl albums, music videos, laserdiscs, DVDs, movies, T-shirts, mini-discs and other music-related items. Clips are available to listen to or watch using both RealPlayer and mpeg files. CD Now also ships world-wide and has various bases over Europe to make the delivery time quicker. The site is available in English, French, Dutch, Japanese, Portuguese, Spanish, Italian and German.

www.cdnow.com

Classical MIDI Archives

Search this database of over 11,000 MIDI files of mostly classical music. Software for playing MIDI files is also available. Download up to 100 MIDI files per day from here.

www.prs.net/midi.html

Classical Net

Classical Net provides a point of entry into a wide array of information files about classical music – over 5,500 files at Classical Net and over 3,800 links to other classical music web sites. The site also includes a repertoire list, reviews and articles, a CD-buying guide and a database of composers.

classical.efront.s4r.com

Crotchet Web Store

A site dedicated to classical music, jazz, film soundtracks and world music, and for over 40 years it has been successfully mailing sounds around the world. It has a main classical department and 12 specialist departments: audio books, baroque, chamber, classical home, historical, jazz, Naxos, orchestral, soundtracks, vocal, Warner and World Music.

www.crotchet.co.uk

The Dailywav

Every weekday this site brings you yet another TV or film sound sample that you can listen to or download. It will even do the occasional 'grab bag' at the weekend. So now there is no excuse for driving everyone crazy by playing the same tune!

www.dailywav.com

Dotmusic

Check out this site for up-to-the-minute music news, UK charts, reviews, interviews and gossip.

www.dotmusic.com

Dusty Groove

For all lovers of soul, jazz, funk, Brazilian and Latin music, Dusty Groove has it all on vinyl and CD.

www.dustygroove.com

Freebase Internet Magazine

Get all the reviews, charts and gig guides at this site, where you can check out audio samples of up-and-coming, currently unsigned bands. You can even visit the chat room and make your thoughts and comments known to others.

www.freebase.com

Harmony Central

Harmony Central is an attempt to bring together many of the music-related items that can be found on the internet. The site hopes to make it much easier for musicians to find useful things quickly and easily, as well as provide some useful services. There are plenty of links here to equipment, software, bands, as well as ads for musicians and a good auction service.

www.harmony-central.com

HMV

The web site for the high street music store, you can buy CDs, videos and PC games direct from HMV.

www.hmv.co.uk

Live Concerts

If you have missed gigs that you really would have liked to have gone to, this site is for you. It offers live and archived webcasts of concerts, covering all kinds of music, so you can see your favourite singer or band perform 'live' after all! You can also visit the listening post to hear an exclusive album before it is officially released.

www.liveconcerts.com

Moving Music

Moving Music specialises in superb-quality, low-cost, mail-order music cassettes and CDs, special interest videos, children's videos and feature films. World-wide delivery, with an excellent reputation.

www.movingmusic.co.uk

Music for free

Here you'll find hours of music and all for free. Don't scoff at the bands listed in its archives. They may seem obscure today but you will end up knowing some of them very well quite soon.

www.mp3.com

MTV

The MTV site is certainly not as fast-paced as the TV programme – in fact it is slow – but that is not surprising considering the size of its content. It holds a huge amount of information and has plenty of chat rooms. So have patience with it and check out the A-Z of bands, news, charts, video clips, interviews and reviews.

www.mtv.com

Music at 101

This site offers music, videos, games and books at discount prices, as well as reviews, information on new releases and recommendations. The site has over 1.6 million titles in its catalogue.

www.101cd.com

Musicnewswire

If you want to know what is happening on the music scene, this site will give you all the information you need.

www.musicnewswire.com

New Musical Express

This well-respected musical paper has its own web site where you can read articles and find all sorts of information on what is going on in the music business.

www.nme.com

OperaBase

This site is now working in partnership with Opera America. You can get venue/booking/season details for 700 opera houses and festivals, schedules for thousands of singers and powerful opera-performance search tools. There are mouse-sensitive maps, reviews from leading newspapers, hundreds of links to opera resources and timelines of composers and works. Available in seven languages.

operabase.com

OperaGlass

This fine resource is an opera information server. Here you can get detailed information, including performance histories, synopses, libretti, discographies, pictures and more on any of a small but rapidly growing number of operas. It also has a fair-sized list of links for international opera listings.

rick.stanford.edu/opera/main.html

Opera Schedule Server

The Opera Schedule Server has been set up to serve opera-lovers in the internet community. There is a constant demand for information about the schedules of different opera companies, and this server will try to satisfy that demand. Search by city, title, artist or composer.

www.fsz.bme.hu/opera/main.html

Second Sounds

If you have been trying to get hold of that CD you wished you had bought years ago, it could be on the database of this online store.

www.secondsounds.com

Ultimate Band List

If a band is not on the list of the Ultimate Band List site, it does not exist! For links to all your favourite bands, look no further than this site which is part of the ARTISTdirect network.

www.ubl.com

Virtual Opera House

A light-hearted introduction to opera. Meet the singers, composers and conductors, listen to some sound clips, read some synopses and anecdotes – and perhaps by the end of the performance you may be curious enough to venture closer to real opera.

users.lia.net/dlever/main.asp

NATURE AND THE EARTH

For all things nature-related, check out the sites listed under *Animals, Environment and Nature, Gardens and Gardening* and *Geography*. For information on nature-related holidays, see *Travel and Holidays*.

NEW AGE

Whatever your New Age interest, and there are many, you can find more about it on the web. From tarot to fairy rings, crystal healing to palmistry, it is all there. See also *Astrology* and *Health, Fitness and Nutrition: Alternative and Complementary Medicine*.

Aeclectic Tarot

If you are a lover of the tarot cards, check this site out. It features over 250 different designs of tarot cards as well as digital tarots. If you are new to the tarot, you can find out all you need here: just click on their 'Frequently Asked Questions' section.

www.aeclectic.net/tarot

Alexander Technique

This site aims to provide a systematic guide to all Alexander Technique information and resources and contains links to several related sites, including Alternative, New Age and Complementary Health.

www.alexandertechnique.com

Biorhythms Site

The principle behind biorhythms is that our lives are affected by three primary cycles: physical, emotional and intellectual. These cycles start at a mid-point when we are born, then go up and down at different rates throughout our life. It is believed that people can improve the quality of their lives by monitoring their biorhythms and acting accordingly. This site enables you to create your own biorhythm chart to conduct your own investigation into this theory.

www.facade.com/attraction/biorhythm

Cassandra Eason

This New Age site by the well-known author contains stories about customs and superstitions, psychic experiences and magical rituals. A reader-friendly site that is informative and contains actual experiences to give beginners an overview of divination and other related topics without being weird.

www.cassandraeason.co.uk

The Center for the New Age

This is the site for a New Age community in Arizona. Find out all about New Age living and what it encompasses, chat online with community members, and visit their online store for New Age books and accessories. Some areas of the site are a little intense – it can be rather a cult-like experience so is best avoided by impressionable youngsters.

www.sedonaonline.com

Ceridwen's Cauldron

This site tells all about pagan living, beliefs, heroes and rituals, and even gives pagan recipes. It also features chat and message boards. Worth a visit if only to find out more about this ancient religion.

www.cauldron.org.uk

ConsciousNet

A US-based site with stacks of information, articles, book reviews and features on a range of New Age subjects, sometimes with a political bias but interesting nonetheless.

www.consciousnet.com

Crystalinks

An online encyclopedia of information on everything from aboriginal spirituality to werewolves. Entries are fairly brief but informative.

www.crystalinks.com

Feng Shui Society

Talk to the consultants at the Feng Shui Society and find out how to live in harmony with the energies around you.

www.fengshuisociety.org.uk

Glastonbury

Everyone has heard of the Glastonbury Festival, but do you know why it is held there? Find out all about Glastonbury's ancient and New Age links at this informative site.

www.isle-of-avalon.co.uk

Goddesses

Goddess site of the organisation celebrating the goddess in all her forms. Open to men and women, it offers a calendar of goddesses of every day of the year, with information on their focus.

www.fellowshipofisis.com

New Age

Another US-based site, but a good starting point for New Age research in that it has an extensive web-links index for mind, body and spirit topics, as well as articles and a catalogue of products.

www.accessnewage.com

Palmistry

An excellent site if you are interested in palmistry, with new and updated information to download.

www.edcampbell.com

The Palmistry Center

Find out how you can learn more about yourself through a personal palmistry and astrology reading. Home-study courses on palmistry are being developed from this web site created by the Palmistry Center of Quebec.

www.palmistry.com

Rebel Angel

Information, lists of practitioners, books and products to inspire and stimulate those with an interest in magic. Lots of articles to read and products for sale.

www.spellbound-online.co.uk

NEWS

If you want the most up-to-date information on current affairs, or merely the latest headlines, add these sites to your list of favourites.

BBC News Online

From its TV, radio and world services, this site provides access to all the BBC's news services.

www.bbc.co.uk/news

CNN

CNN Interactive is updated 24 hours a day, seven days a week, so you have the latest US and world news and other related topics.

www.cnn.com

Crayon

Crayon is a tool for managing news sources on the internet. You can create a customised news page that contains links to the daily information you are most interested in, which are updated daily. All you do is click to retrieve the story.

www.crayon.net

Drudge Report

Look here and get sensational news hot off the net and not off the press! Drudge is well known for leaking stories by free bulletin and beating all the major press at releasing the headlines (although some are definitely suspect!). You can also find many of the best news sources on the net through the top page of this site.

www.drudgereport.com

The Guardian

The online version of the UK daily newspaper.

www.guardian.co.uk

Megastar

An online newspaper with up-to-date news and sports reports. Select your areas of interest from the contents list and read the latest news from around the world.

www.megastar.co.uk

The Mirror

These two sites relate to the sister daily *Mirror* and *Sunday Mirror* UK newspapers.

www.mirror.co.uk

www.sundaymirror.co.uk

MSNBC

This is the home of the American news giant MSNBC. Because it is American there is a bias towards American news, but there are international news stories as well. Before you use this site you will need to download a small piece of software for the news menu but it works well once that has been done.

www.msnbc.com

NewsTrawler

Database search for news stories featured in various newspapers and magazines and found by country or topic.

www.newstrawler.com/nt/nt_home.html

Oneworld

Many users think this is the best newspaper on the web.

www.oneworld.net

Sky News

For all the latest news and current affairs, check out this site for 24-hour news coverage from around the world.

www2.sky.com/news

Sports news

This web site is brought to you from CNN as a joint venture with the magazine *Sports Illustrated*. It has all the news and scores for over a dozen sports as well as in-depth coverage of events, fantasy games, discussion areas and complete team and player statistics.

www.cnnsi.com

The Daily Telegraph

All the latest news and information from the web site of the UK national daily broadsheet.

www.telegraph.co.uk

The Times

If you want to read *The Times* and *The Sunday Times* newspapers, why not read them on the net? The internet editions are updated daily at about 2 a.m. London time with virtually the complete content of the printed edition. There are direct links to all the sections and there is also easy access to back issues and those challenging crosswords!

www.the-times.co.uk

www.sunday-times.co.uk

The Voice of America

You can listen to audio clips or read the text of international, regional and US news in 53 languages to an estimated weekly audience of 91 million. It is 'on the air' 24 hours a day, seven days a week, and has been tailored to provide news and information to each region of the world during its prime listening hours.

www.voa.gov

USA Today

This site gives you all the day's news, sport, money, life and weather in the USA.

www.usatoday.com

ORGANISATIONS AND ASSOCIATIONS

Of course, there are many organisations, social groups and other associations that feature on the web, but many have restricted appeal. The following are useful to us all in one way or another. If the one you want is not listed, use a search engine to find it, typing the organisation's name (for example, Action Aid). See also *Charities*. Some women's organisations are listed under *Women's Interests*.

Citizen's Advice Bureaux

Need help understanding your rights, your entitlement to benefits, or have a problem with debt, housing or tax? The Citizen's Advice Bureaux are there to help. Visit their web site to find out more about the services they offer, get details of your local offices or how you can become a CAB volunteer. Select the 'AdviceGuide' link to view their comprehensive guide to your rights.

www.nacab.org.uk

Consumers' Association

This site puts all the resources and research of the Which? organisation (the Consumers' Association) at your fingertips. If you have a problem with a trader, or simply want to check out the best buys, visit this site first.

www.which.net

Neighbourhood Watch

Useful tips on beating crime, together with all the information you need if you are already a Neighbourhood Watch member or would like to set up a scheme.

www.nwatch.org.uk

Rospa

This site, from the Royal Society for the Prevention of Accidents, covers safety in all areas, including the road, home, at work, around water and in leisure facilities and play areas. Find out what you need to be aware of and how you can minimise risks, as well as how to report and deal with hazards.

www.rospa.org.uk

Timebank

Ever had the feeling you should do more for others, but don't know where to start? Timebank is the answer. It allows you to share your skills – and we are all good at something, no matter how obscure – with others who need help. Whether it be helping with a community gardening project, teaching the basics of reading to young children, or giving a local charity tips on how best to present itself, whatever your particular skill, someone needs you to share it. Find out how at this web site: all it takes is a little time. If you're still uncertain, visit their Stories section to see how others have helped.

www.timebank.org.uk

PARENTING

Nobody knows how hard it can be to be a parent, or how rewarding – except other parents. When you need inspiration, advice, guidance on the baffling world of your child's education, or just some light relief, check out these sites.

See also *Children, Pregnancy and Childbirth, Relationships and Dating* and *Teenagers*.

Adoption

This site contains useful help, information and guidance on all aspects of adoption. It is home to the world's largest online searchable registry of hopeful adoptive parents. The registry allows birth mothers to find adoptive parents with specific characteristics. On the other hand, if you are searching for a lost birth relative, the Reunion Registry is there to help. The person you are searching for might already be looking for you. Just register and add your details.

www.adoption.com

Advisory Centre for Education

This web site offers information to parents on all educational issues – not just what your child is learning, but how to handle bullying, admissions policies, homework and special needs. They offer free telephone support but the site can answer a lot of your questions, particularly through their discussion list, at which you can view questions posed by other parents and add your own.

www.ace-ed.org.uk

ChildCare

This site is for anyone who is involved in looking after children or looking for childcare in the UK. It is full of useful information with advice for parents, suggestions for children's activities, useful addresses and a directory of childcare agencies in the London area. If you are thinking of working in the field of childcare, it also has guides on being a nanny or childminder.

www.childcare-info.co.uk

ChildCare Link

This site is provided by the government and includes a comprehensive listing of childcare facilities around the country – just enter your postcode to find out what's registered and available in your area. It includes helpful details of what each type of childcare can offer, and how each is regulated. Well worth a visit if you are considering making use of such a facility.

www.childcarelink.gov.uk

Generation Gap

If you are a parent, you have probably visited that gap more than once with your teenager. For an insight into your adolescent's state of mind, visit Spank! The Magazine of Youth Culture. Find out what worries them (school bullying, exams, etc.) and about the things that bother you (body-piercing). It's an essential read for every parent.

www.spankmag.com

Gingerbread

Gingerbread is the leading support organisation for lone-parent families in England and Wales. Its site is a valuable resource which provides information about the organisation, including how it can help you and how you can help it. A reply service enables you to locate the Gingerbread group nearest your home.

www.gingerbread.org.uk

Idea Box

All sorts of ideas and activities for toddlers and kids to keep them occupied are available here. The guides are very easy for parents, teachers and children to understand and complete. Grown-ups may also find things here they had forgotten since they themselves were young. Great for playgroup holidays.

www.theideabox.com

Kids' Health

Kids' Health, sponsored by the Nemours Foundation, is a good place to get some help and advice on children's health. Parents can find information on safety and infections, children can find an explanation of feelings and a games room and real teens tell their stories.

kidshealth.org/index2.html

Moms' Network Exchange

This site is full of resources for mothers who are working from home. It is a good place to share tips, ideas, seek advice and communicate with other home-working mothers. The site includes things such as a business survival kit, products and services resources, a classified section and more.

www.momsnetwork.com

National Centre for Fathering

The NCFF provides helpful information on all aspects of fathering. For men who are about to become fathers, the site consists of humorous scenarios to complement its down-to-earth, practical advice. For people who have not been in contact with their fathers for a while, the site also includes suggestions for getting back in touch.

www.fathers.com

National Centre for Missing and Exploited Children

The NCMEC spearheads efforts to locate and recover missing children and raises public awareness about ways to prevent child abduction, molestation and sexual exploitation. It is a private, non-profit-making organisation and this is its official site. It is good for parents to be aware that it exists, and it is the place for anyone to contact if they can be of help with any leads.

www.missingkids.org

National Family and Parenting Institute

The NFPI is a newly launched charity that aims to make society more family-friendly, and promote both the well-being of families and the issues that surround parenting today. Find out more at its web site.

www.nfpi.org

Natural Parenting

This UK site offers information on alternative parenting at all levels and all ages. If you are concerned about modern approaches to parenting, or the eagerness of medical practitioners to stuff your child full of chemicals, visit this site for a no-nonsense guide to responsible, nurturing and respectful parenting.

www.natural-parenting.com

Parent Club

This not-for-profit site is a one-stop shop for anyone with children, giving information on all sorts of topics including the latest kids' fashions, where to go on holiday or for a day out, or get good deals on toys and books. Regularly updated, so a great source of information when the school holidays are dragging on a bit.

www.parentclub.co.uk

Parentline Plus

Parentline Plus is a charity dedicated to helping anyone who is parenting a child, whether biological, adoptive, step- or foster parents, carers or grandparents, even professional helpers such as childminders, in whatever circumstances. It offers advice and help on a wide range of issues, backed up by a freephone helpline. It runs courses on parenting and innovative projects for both parent and child.

www.parentlineplus.org.uk

Parents' Centre

This site is provided by the Department for Education and Employment (DfEE) and gives information specifically targeted at parents and carers regarding the National Curriculum, its Key Stages and schools in general. If you want to help your child with schoolwork, this is the place to start.

www.parents.dfee.gov.uk

Parents Information Network

PIN is an independent organisation established in 1994 to provide information and advice to parents about the role of computers in their children's education. It works in partnership with schools to help parents to develop an understanding of the relationship between computers and learning so that they can become more effective supporters of their children's education. The PIN web site provides information on how to make the most of ICT at home, from evaluations of educational software to advice on filtering unwanted internet material.

www.pin.org.uk

Parents' Place

This site is not your normal web site as it allows parents to connect, communicate and celebrate the adventures of child-rearing through the use of bulletin boards and chats. You can find your speciality here whether you are interested in talking about women's health, child development, your daily pet peeves, school work, discipline or family-related politics.

www.parentsplace.com

Parent Soup

This site contains regularly updated articles, advice pages and discussion boards. Good online advice and support for all parents.

www.parentsoup.com

Sure Start

Sure Start is a new strategy by the government to help children under four to prepare for school. It includes health services, early learning and childcare, and parent support. Check out the web site for further information.

www.surestart.gov.uk

UK Parents

This is a general meeting place where you can find information, exchange experiences and chat with other mothers at the same stage of pregnancy or with children about the same age as your own. There is information and advice for dads, too.

www.ukparents.co.uk

Urbia

This is a family-oriented online 'community', with an online magazine designed to help parents work with their kids to help them through school, whether learning to read or revising for those all-important GCSEs.

www.urbia.co.uk

PREGNANCY AND CHILDBIRTH

Whatever you need to know about pregnancy, childbirth or those early months with baby, you can find it on the web: personal experiences, professional advice, suggestions for names and nurseries. Most of the general *Health, Fitness and Nutrition* sites include a section on pregnancy and childbirth; these are more specific. See also *Parenting*.

Babies of our Youth

This site is aimed directly at teenagers and deals with all issues surrounding teenage pregnancy and parenthood. It is written by a young single mother, and pulls no punches. Topics include preventing pregnancy, what to do if you find out you are pregnant, bringing up baby and support services, with sections for grandparents and true stories from other teenage parents of their experiences.

www.parentingyouths.com

BabyNames

The perfect site to help you name the new addition to your family. Here you will find the most extensive, ethnically diverse names database online. You can search the database by name or meaning, or go to one of their unique names lists.

www.babynames.com

BabyTime

This site is an internet resource for pregnancy, birth and childcare. Here you will find everything you need – from the first signs of pregnancy to what to pack in your labour bag – to help you have a well-informed pregnancy. Be sure to check their comprehensive list of pregnancy terms as well.

www.clicked.com/babytime

Babyworld

This is an online magazine full of practical advice for new parents. The site covers everything from trying to conceive to what to do once the baby has arrived.

www.babyworld.co.uk

Online Birth Center

If you're pregnant, planning a pregnancy, or know someone who is, you will find lots of interesting information on this American site. Do remember, though, that things are not always treated the same way in the UK. Here you can learn about pregnancy, birth, home birth, midwifery and breastfeeding. You'll also find a variety of general health resources, including alternatives to the Western approach to medicine.

www.moonlily.com/obc/

Pampers Institute

The Pampers Institute provides a forum for child health and development experts to give parents information, guidance and support in caring for their infants and toddlers. In an effort to inspire the loyalty of Pampers customers by providing this valuable resource, the information is presented in a way that is cross-cultural, sensitive and appropriate to the diversity of families everywhere.

www.pampers.com

Pregnancy Calendar

Once you have a baby on the way, visit the Interactive Pregnancy Calendar. Enter the approximate day of conception (the site has instructions for estimating it) and get a customised calendar that gives a day-by-day account of your baby's development. If you know someone who has a baby on the way, why not create a calendar for them? You will also be able to pick up parenting tips and links to other information sites as well as talk to other people in various chat groups.

www.pregnancycalendar.com

Ultrasound Procedures and Pregnancy

For parents-to-be who want to know more about the ultrasound procedure, the Obstetric Ultrasound Page is the site to visit. It gives a complete explanation of the procedure, why it is used and what can be learned from it. There is also an ultrasound gallery showing foetuses at various stages of development.

www.ob-ultrasound.net

PROPERTY

Fed up with the endless trail around estate agents to find your dream home? Why not let your fingers find your new pad? More and more estate agencies are active on the web, and there are also several alternatives – sites that are dedicated to selling homes directly for the owner for a fixed fee (often much less than agency commission). In addition, there are several sites that offer information on buying, selling and renting property. For holiday properties, see *Travel and Holidays*.

08004homes

More than 100,000 properties are advertised on this site, with a database of mortgages and finance, regular news and features related to the property market, such as house-buying advice and neighbourhood guides.

www.08004homes.com

Assertahome

A huge range of properties from a collection of agents with a search facility which is very much area-based. If you find something you like, you can then e-mail the relevant agent from the site.

www.assertahome.com

Buy-to-let

All sorts of advice on raising finance, the best type of property to buy and how to renovate and furnish properties for letting.

www.buy-to-let.com

Find-a-Property

This useful site offers more than just property listings; it includes the latest news on the property market and issues affecting it (including a category for 'unusual' property stories), guides to the areas it covers, and categorised searches. Many of the big agencies list their properties with this site. Worth a visit, if only to browse.

www.find-a-property.co.uk

Hometrack

Is it time to sell? Or time to buy? Where is the best place for likely gains in value? Homebuying has become more than a question of somewhere to live; these days it's all to do with good investment. This site promises to be 'your independent guide to property prices and trends in the UK', so if you are concerned about the value of your house, visit this site first. It also offers valuable information on the processes of buying and selling property, and guides to conveyancing and mortgages, including several pitfalls to watch out for.

www.hometrack.co.uk

House Web

House Web is a comprehensive resource for buying, selling, renting and exchanging properties. It includes guides and extensive links to other property-related web sites. House Web also contains a glossary of terms used in the property market, e.g. APR (annual percentage rate), disbursements, and MIG (mortgage indemnity guarantee).

www.houseweb.co.uk

Loot

Property to let and buy throughout the UK, including student accommodation. Largely London-based but does include other parts of the UK as well.

www.loot.com

National Property Register

This site has all the usual listings, plus links to other related sites. It covers the whole of the UK plus Ireland. Fill in its buyer's registration form to get all information on suitable, available properties from all its associated estate agents in the area of your choice.

www.national-property-register.co.uk

Pavilions of Splendour

If you have the funds, and fancy something a little different, visit this site. It covers listed buildings, follies and all sorts of fancy properties throughout the UK. It also provides helpful information on buying, selling and renovating listed and heritage properties.

www.heritage.co.uk

Property Auctions

This is an internet property auction site for the UK. There are other sites covering Australia, Hong Kong, Scandinavia and the US. If you have a property to sell, using this facility enables you to reach thousands of buyers – not only in the UK but also world-wide! If you are looking for a property to buy, you can receive free catalogues of properties within your desired area by e-mail.

www.propertyfind.co.uk

Property Broker

An excellent database for those wanting to buy or sell their home in the London-M25 area. You can view properties without registering, or you can advertise your own property, including a photograph, for a reasonable fee.

www.propertybroker.co.uk

Property Sight

Details from a large number of estate agents are included on this site and are updated daily. Key in your requirements by region and specific details to see a range of appropriate properties. You can then contact the relevant agent.

www.property-sight.co.uk

Smart New Homes

As you might expect, this site deals exclusively with newly built properties, and features developments from many of the UK's biggest house builders, as well as some smaller, localised companies. If you fancy a new home, give it a try.

www.smartnewhomes.com

UK Property Sales

This is rather a misnomer, as the site covers property in Ireland and further afield as well as the UK. It's a basic, no-nonsense site with property listings supplied by the owners, usually including a photograph and basic dimensions. It's a cheap way to advertise your home for sale (£39 for up to three months) but you are only permitted 100 words of description, so you need to either have a very small home or be very succinct!

www.ukpropertysales.com

Underoneroof

This site does just what it promises, bringing property information from estate agents together with information on everything from mortgages and finance to removal firms under one roof.

www.underoneroof.com

Up My Street

Up My Street is the first web site for Europe that helps you find the latest published statistics about where you live today, or might live tomorrow. It also carries direct links to a wide variety of useful local services.

www.upmystreet.com

RADIO AND BROADCASTING

So did video kill the radio star? It seems not. Radio is alive and kicking and flourishing on the web, where you can listen to your favourite shows via your computer's sound card and plug-in software such as RealPlayer. Many radio stations offer you the chance to replay archived shows, so you no longer need to worry about being home in time for *The Archers*.

If transmitting rather than receiving is your personal pleasure, you will find many discussion groups and sites dedicated to ham, CB and other radio genres. A few are listed here, but it is also worth trying newsgroups under rec.radio if you have access to a newsreader.

Broadcast.com

The Broadcast.com web sites, now part of the Yahoo!Events network, offer a large and comprehensive selection of programming, including sports, talk and music radio, television, business events, full-length CDs, news, commentary and full-length audio books, serving an average of over 1.1 million unique users per day. The site broadcasts on the internet 24 hours a day, seven days a week.

www.broadcast.com

BRS Radio-Directory

A comprehensive directory of international radio stations on the web.

www.radio-directory.com

e-Ham

'Home of ham radio on the internet'. This site is full of information about ham radio, its enthusiasts, clubs, resources and equipment. As expected it is an American site, but most of the information applies wherever you are based.

www.e-ham.net

G7KPF UK

This site offers a listing of over 1,000 UK-based amateur radio resources and sites.

www.users.zetnet.co.uk/kama/hamlinks.htm

HRO Ham Radio Outlet

This massive store for radio hams is US-based but will ship goods anywhere in the world. It has an extensive catalogue of products, plus lists of used gear for sale, and all your ordering can be done online.

www.hamradio.com

Knights CB

This store has been voted the top CB retailer by readers of *Citizen's Band Magazine*. It offers a wide range of equipment, including second-hand, and gives details of the latest changes in the law governing CB transmissions as well as links to CB newsgroups.

www.users.zetnet.co.uk/knightscb

Net Radio

Net Radio is an internet-based online music source that provides more than 120 unique music channels. You can listen to music that has been programmed and also purchase the music that you hear on this site. In addition to this, Net Radio provides dozens of audio information channels from country music news and jazz notes to sports and celebrity news.

www.netradio.net

Radio Now

This site gives you a list of almost 300 radio stations in the UK with their frequencies.

www.radionow.co.uk

Radio Sonicnet

Do you ever wish you could change the music that is played on the radio? If so, then tune into this site. You can now have your very own radio station and decide what is played on it!

radio.sonicnet.com

Radio Tuner

From Real.com, the home of audio plug-ins, this site allows you to find and tune into your favourite radio station and listen in real time across the web. It lists 2,500 stations and you needn't worry about interference: one of the beauties of web-based radio is that you can pick it up wherever you happen to be! So at last you can listen to country music in Cantonese, if you really want to...

www.real.com/tuner

REFERENCE

These sites offer a simpler way to look for what you want, rather than relying on a search engine. Many are encyclopedia-style databases of articles, facts and information: others concentrate on a specific topic or offer a specific service, such as translation.

See also *Books* and individual subjects.

The Active Mind

This excellent site offers theories and information on the more earthly mysteries, such as the lost city of Atlantis, Nostradamus, Stonehenge and Bigfoot.

www.activemind.com

AltaVista Translations

At this site, translate text between English and French, German, Italian, Portuguese and Spanish. It is fast and you can even use it to translate web pages.

babelfish.altavista.digital.com

Bartleby

This site is a comprehensive web reference publisher and features a searchable database of pre-20th-century quotations. It also contains chronological and alphabetical listings of hundreds of major contributors.

www.bartleby.com

Biographical Dictionary

This is a free, general-purpose source of biographical information on more than 28,000 notable men and women. It is searchable by name, year of birth or death, positions held, professions, literary and artistic works, achievements and other keywords.

www.s9.com/biography

Brewer's Phrase and Fable

This classic work of reference has been described as 'a browser's joy'. The dictionary is extensively cross-referenced, which makes it ideal for the hypertext environment of the internet. This first hypertext edition is taken from Dr Brewer's substantially revised and extended edition of 1894. Either browse or search this site, it is both useful and very appealing.

www.bibliomania.com/Reference/PhraseAndFable/index.html

Calculators Online

Calculator.com gives you free access to online calculators that help you to solve problems and answer questions in the home, office and school. There are calculators for finance, business, science, cooking, hobbies and health. Whether you want to solve problems, satisfy your curiosity or just have fun, there are calculators to suit every need.

www.calculator.com

Central and Eastern European Languages

If on your travels you are heading for an Eastern European country, then this site is a must – unless you already speak the language. Here you will find basic phrases and pronunciation in 14 different languages.

www.cusd.claremont.edu/~tkroll/EastEur/index.html

Dead People Server

If you are wondering whether a famous actor, musician, film star or politician is still alive, look here to see if their name is listed! This is part of the Frequently-updated Web Sites site.

dpsinfo.com

Dictionary

A web dictionary including links to foreign language dictionaries, advice on correct grammar and style and a section for translating text and web pages.

www.dictionary.com

Dictionary of English Slang

A unique dictionary of slang and colloquialisms used in the UK, which is updated every month. It is both useful for the student who has been taught textbook English, and for anyone who finds themselves wondering what the latest terms being used actually mean – wicked!

www.peevish.co.uk/slang

Encyclopedia

Encyclopedia.com is one of the internet's premier free encyclopedias. This site offers you an extraordinary amount of information. There are more than 14,000 articles from the third edition of *The Concise Columbia Electronic Encyclopedia*, which have been assembled to provide free, quick and useful information on almost any topic. The entries are short, so you can check facts quickly, though each one has extensive cross-references.

encyclopedia.com

Encyclopaedia Britannica Online

The Encyclopaedia Britannica is the world's most comprehensive reference product and has been since its first publication in 1768. Encyclopaedia Britannica Online includes the complete encyclopedia as well as *Merriam-Webster's Collegiate Dictionary* and the *Britannica Book of the Year*. You will also find an internet directory with more than 130,000 links to web sites that have been selected, rated and reviewed by Britannica editors.

www.eb.com

Encyclopedia Mythica

This is an encyclopedia on mythology, folklore, legends and more. It contains over 5,700 definitions of gods and goddesses, supernatural beings, legendary creatures and monsters from all over the world. The site has a search facility that allows you to locate key subjects and the bibliography lists the sources consulted. You can even make your own contributions and the site is fairly regularly updated.

www.pantheon.org/mythica

International Dialling Codes

Look up international dialling codes in a telephone directory, or check them out at this site. You will find a list of dialling codes for most countries in the world.

www.eventsworldwide.com/i-codes.htm

Knowhere

Whether you are thinking of moving or want to visit another area of the UK on holiday, this site will give you the low-down on the town or area of your choice.

www.knowhere.co.uk

Languages

For anything you need to know about languages – from dictionaries to tuition – this site is a starting point listing a huge range of internet sources from lessons to dictionaries.

www.june29.com/HLP

Language Translator

This site is handy for people who correspond with others around the world. Here you can copy some text and translate it to a foreign language. Also you can even translate foreign language web pages by placing the address in the web page address box.

translator.go.com

List of Lists

This is one of the largest directories of special-interest group e-mail lists (also known as listservs) available on the internet. To submit updates for the description of an existing mailing list or to add a new entry for the list, you can use the list submission form. This list is the SF-lovers' mailing list and you are able to search for a list by subject or content.

catalog.com/vivian

Liszt

A directory of mailing lists, newsgroups, chat lines to browse and find those of interest to you.

www.liszt.com

Mega Converter

Mega Converter.com, now with Mega Converter 2, is an ever-growing set of weights, measures and units conversion/calculation modules which allow users to discover things like how many seconds old they are, the difference between a gallon in the USA and a gallon in the UK, how many nanometers to an inch, and much more. For just about anything you can think of, Mega Converter can show you its equivalent. There is a ton (that's 4,540,000 carats) of modules available now and many more on the way.

www.megaconverter.com

Merriam-Webster

Search Merriam-Webster Online for the word you need defining. You will find that the site is quick to respond and the definitions are concise and helpful. However, it must be remembered that it does have a bias towards American spelling and usage.

www.m-w.com

OneLook

There are a number of good dictionaries on the internet, and people who use dictionaries regularly tend to have a favourite. This page is intended to make the process of finding the right dictionary quick and painless. The purpose is to encourage people to use internet glossaries and dictionaries by searching over 660 dictionaries at the same time for the word you seek. The One Look dictionaries page provides two approaches to finding definitions for a word. You can either search the site indexes for the word you seek or link directly to a dictionary page.

www.onelook.com

Online Writing Lab

At this site you can learn more about grammar and punctuation as well as presentations and internet resources.

owl.english.purdue.edu/writers/by-topic.html

Postcodes Online

Whether you have an address but not the postcode or know the postcode but not the address, you need look no further than this site. It consists of Royal Mail's postcode-finder and address-finder services.

www.royalmail.co.uk/paf

Public Record Office

The Public Record Office and Family Records Centre offer an online catalogue of files as well as useful information related to records that can be ordered up for providing on a specific date to save time doing the research when you go there.

publicrecord.com

The Quotations Page

This page was originally developed as a catalogue of quotation resources on the internet; it has since evolved into a large-scale quotation site with many original resources. It now consists of many thousands of quotations and is updated daily. It is searchable and you will find that site users are also invited to contribute their own favourite quotations.

www.quotationspage.com/

Reference Desk

A huge site offering a compilation of reference sources from dictionaries and phone books to information on government and religion.

www.refdesk.com

Roget's Thesaurus

Now you can browse the thesaurus through the six broad categories into which Mr Roget classified the entire vocabulary of the English language, or you can browse through the alphabetical index of headwords.

www.thesaurus.com

Scoot

This site is an internet version of *Yellow Pages*, although the latter has its own site as well. It contains a free directory of all businesses and gives you other information such as local cinema listings. To use Scoot, simply enter the type of business being searched for together with the area or location, then press the Scoot button. After a few seconds, you will have a list of all the services in your area, including all telephone numbers and addresses.

www.scoot2.co.uk

Sign Language Dictionary

This is a site on which you can learn all you need to do sign language. All you have to do is to watch the sign language gestures and learn!

dww.deafworldweb.org/asl/

Spelling Test

At this site you can test yourself and learn some techniques to improve your spelling.

www.sentex.net/~mmcadams/spelling.html

Telephone Directories on the Web

Telephone Directories on the Web is a really comprehensive and useful index of online phone books. It has links to Yellow Pages, White Pages, business directories, e-mail addresses and fax listings from all around the world.

www.teldir.com

Time 100

This is where *Time* magazine features the people who are considered to be the most influential of the 20th Century. Categories of influence include leaders and revolutionaries, artists and entertainers, and scientists and thinkers.

www.time.com/time/time100

UK Dialling Codes

If you need to know the dialling code for any city or town in the UK, look it up here.

www.brainstorm.co.uk/utils/std-codes.html

UK Legal Resources

This site is the portal to legal resources in the UK and Ireland. It is regularly updated and you will find that it has been split into four areas. It gives details of free legal information to individuals and also to companies. There is information for solicitors and barristers plus information from the current issue of the *International Newsletter for Lawyers*.

www.venables.co.uk

UK Passports

All the information you require to find out how to obtain a passport, qualifications, visa details and so on.

www.ukpa.gov.uk

UKstate

This site is a mass of information on all aspects of the legislation and government of the UK, with all kinds of useful reference material that relates to you, your home and your business.

www.ukstate.com/portal.asp

World Clock

At this site you can select among several selections of cities in the world to locate the time. There are two different views: full will display all the cities/places known to the world clock; standard will show the large/important cities all over the world. Then there are a number of continental versions, each showing all cities for a particular continent for a more in-depth view. There are versions for Africa, North/Latin America, South America, Asia, Europe and Australia and the Pacific Islands.

www.timeanddate.com/worldclock

World's Bank Holidays

Do you find yourself trying to contact somebody abroad but cannot get in touch with them? Do you find yourself travelling halfway around the world to do business when the company you are visiting has closed for the week? Ensure that this does not continue to happen by looking up world-wide bank holidays and feast days here.

www.national-holidays.com

World Wide Words

This site is an archive of words and phrases that have not yet reached most dictionaries. There are indexes of topical words, weird words and turns of phrase. Find out where words and phrases come from as well as what they mean, and why they are the way they are now.

www.quinion.demon.co.uk/words

Xrefer

By bringing together reference works from the world's major publishers in one place on the net, this is an excellent place to start researching almost anything. Great for resolving those family arguments about who said or did what.

www.xrefer.com

RELATIONSHIPS AND DATING

This section covers all sorts of relationship issues, from finding a partner to resolving difficulties with family and loved ones, including gay and lesbian issues and advice to teenage broken hearts – so don't expect them all to be of particular interest to you!

Adolescent Adulthood

Aimed at teenagers, but recommended reading for all ages, this site is full of teen angst and tips on flirting, dating and dumping.

www.adolescentadulthood.com

Berkeley Sweetingham

An upmarket introduction service based in Mayfair, so ideal for London-based readers with a taste for the better things in life.

www.berkeley-sweetingham.com

CareZone

This is an information resource site for parents and children who have been affected by divorce. It provides contact addresses and extensive recommended reading lists. It is aimed at helping people break through the isolation and vulnerability they may feel after separation or divorce. It provides a means of trying to understand and accept all that has happened in a positive and forward-looking way.

www.dudley-gateway.co.uk/cz/czindex.htm

Condom Country

Buy condoms, books and sex aids at this mail-order site. Condom Country believes in personal choice and personal privacy. It provides high-quality products to people all around the world. Customer information is confidential and will never be given to any other organisation for any purpose. The electronic and physical mailing lists only include those people who have specifically asked to be on them.

www.condom.com

Dating Fun

Many of the dating sites are far too serious. Try this one for size: it offers tips on how to make your dates more fun, as well as great ice-breaking lines and put-downs. You can even check your compatibility with your date using its 'romantic astrology' section.

www.datingfun.com

Dinner Dates

This dating service with a difference offers you the chance to meet people at organised lunches, functions and events, rather than individually over a wilting carnation. Events are held nationwide and include theatre, sports and holidays, plus dining experiences from the informal to the black-tie ball.

www.dinnerdates.com

Divorce Central

This is a useful site full of resources for people who are divorced or in the process of divorcing. It contains information, support and discussions on the different issues surrounding divorce.

www.divorcecentral.com

Gender and Sexuality

This site publishes texts which address gender and gay studies, with a particular focus on discussions of sex, gender, sexual identity and sexuality in cultural practices. You will see that the broad-ranging set of links to essays includes eclectic titles as well as the more conventional topics.

eserver.org/gender

Match

A leader in online personals, match-making and dating, this site offers a fun and safe environment to meet other single people and has a privacy guarantee. It caters for straight or gay men and women who are looking for romantic relationships or just a casual date. You have to pay to register, but a free trial is on offer if you are not convinced that it will be of use to you. It is an American site but has many UK members, although many seem to be somewhat out of date.

www.match.com

Matchmaker

This is the leading online community enabling connections between people with similar interests and needs. If you are looking for a lifetime lover, a weekend workout partner or a local wine connoisseur, Matchmaker is the place to meet all types of people across the world.

They have a register of over 2.6 million members from the US, Australia, Brazil, Canada, Ireland, England and Singapore.

www.matchmaker.com

Natural Friends

Another dating site, this time offering 'unbeatable value introductions'.

www.natural-friends.com

OutRage!

OutRage! campaigns on behalf of the gay and lesbian community with the aim of eliminating homophobia. It is a forum for non-violent protest, which uses imaginative, witty and shocking tactics to provoke debate and promote awareness.

www.outrage.cygnet.co.uk

Pink Passport

This site aims to be the number one guide to the best gay and lesbian hotels, clubs, bars, restaurants, gyms and saunas around the world. It certainly is extensive and very impressive.

www.pinkpassport.com

Relate

Relate can help you whether or not you are married and whatever your age, race, personal beliefs, sexual orientation or social background. It offers guidance and counselling for those in troubled relationships of any kind and gives contact details for Relate services around Britain and information on what you can expect.

www.relate.org.uk

SecretAdmirer

A fun, free service, this has already matched up plenty of couples throughout the world. Secret Admirer helps you start a relationship with someone you already know and like, and also offers romantic gifts to help love on its way.

www.secretadmirer.com

Stonewall

Stonewall is the national civil rights group working for legal equality and social justice for lesbians, gay men and bisexuals. The web site provides a series of free fact sheets covering all issues facing the gay and lesbian community. There is also information about ongoing campaigns, as well as general advice. A mailing list is available for those who want to keep up-to-date with Stonewall's activities.

www.stonewall.org.uk

Straight Answers

This site is a guide on how to answer questions about gay life and change anti-gay attitudes. Although written with a gay audience in mind, Straight Answers is open to anybody. This US-based site has been extremely well conceived.

www.sipu.com/sa/index.html

RELIGION

Whether you want divine inspiration or religious information, you can find it online. Many of the more mainstream religions have information pages on the web, as well as some extremely dubious cults. Here are some of the more useful, informative sites we have found. For New Age religion, see *New Age*.

About Islam and Muslims

This British-based resource gives information about the different aspects of Islam. An English translation of the Koran has been included, together with an interesting series of articles on popular misconceptions about Islam.

www.unn.ac.uk/societies/islamic

About Religion

Another part of the giant About directory, this one gives a selection of links to sites on all sorts of religions and religious studies. Great for research.

www.academicinfo.net/religindex.html

The Bible Gateway

The Bible Gateway is a front page of a script that would create HTML versions of Bible chapters. Not only will it display the page but it will display the page in German, Swedish, Latin, French, Spanish, Portuguese, Italian, Tagálog, Norwegian or Arabic.

bible.gospelcom.net

Bible Magazine

This site contains the online version of *The Bible Magazine*, although to read the magazine you have to subscribe. However, there is a good database listing of all previous magazines and articles for sale. The site does contain downloadable sample files of the magazine.

www.biblemagazine.com

Boddhisattva Centre

This Buddhist retreat in Brighton is open to all, and gives information on Buddhism, mediation and retreats. A well-designed site which provides a great introduction to this religion, without pressure, to the accompaniment of soothing music.

www.bodhisattva.co.uk

British Humanist Association

'Humanism is an approach to life based on reason and our common humanity, recognising that moral values are properly founded on human nature and experience alone.' The site gives the association's principles and advice on non-religious ceremonies.

www.humanism.org.uk

Buddhist Information Network

While identified as an Eastern religion, Buddhism has quite a following in the West where its more open-ended teachings appeal to many people. Find all you need to know about the many aspects of the Buddhist faith.

www.buddhanet.net

Catholic Online Saints and Angels

Information on all the Catholic saints, allowing you to scroll through an alphabetical listing or to use the 'saint search' facility. You can also search for answers to your questions about angels.

saints.catholic.org/index.shtml

Church of England

The official site of the Church of England gives contact details, news, details of daily services, and articles on the Church's views. Find out about the organisation of the Church of England, its history, liturgy and relations with other denominations.

www.cofe.anglican.org

Cult Information Centre

The Cult Information Centre is an educational charity that provides vital information on mind-control cults. It is a London-based centre, but for security reasons the office location will never be made public. The site includes a guide to detecting cult recruiters and a list of things you should or should not do with regard to communicating with friends or relatives who have joined a cult. The Cult Information Centre also provides a list of contact addresses and web links.

www.cultinformation.org.uk

Hinduism Online

The Hinduism Online web site is created and maintained by the monks of the Saiva Siddhanta Theological Seminary at Kauai's Hindu monastery on the island of Kauai in the Hawaiian islands. This web site is a public service of Himalayan Academy to make available the timeless truths of the Sanatana Dharma, the Hindu religion, to the people of the world.

www.hinduismtoday.kauai.hi.us/ashram

The Holy See

This is the official site of the Vatican and has been written in six languages. Find out everything about the Vatican City State: its library, secret archives and museums and, of course, the Pope himself.

www.vatican.va

Introduction to Hinduism

There are over 700 million Hindus, mainly in Bharat, India and Nepal. Hinduism is referred to as Sanatana Dharma, the eternal faith, and is not strictly a religion. It is based on the practice of Dharma, the code of life. It is quite a complicated faith, however, so have patience as you use this site as a gateway to understanding the Hindu gods!

www.geocities.com/RodeoDrive/1415/indexd.html

Jewish Holy Days

This site is a guide to the Jewish high holy days. It contains explanations of the days as well as recipes, prayers and quizzes. It also has an ask-the-rabbi section if you have any other questions that have not already been answered. The site has been split into two areas, one geared for adults and one aimed at children.

www.vjholidays.com

Jewish Magazine

This is a major Jewish information resource on the web, containing articles by Jewish authors on Jewish and Israeli topics and the contents of the magazine change monthly. Over 200 articles of varied Jewish interest are in the archive area alone for this site. The site also contains a good links page to all other Jewish sites on the internet, as well as giving you the chance to get your magazine sent to your e-mail address at the beginning of the month.

www.jewishmag.co.il

Maven

This 'Jewish Portal' is a web directory and search engine that covers all aspects of Judaism plus Jewish and Israeli culture. It also includes the option to subscribe to *Maven Announce*, the free, weekly newsletter, and have it sent to your e-mail mailbox.

www.maven.co.il

Nida'ul Islam internet magazine

Nida'ul Islam is a bi-monthly magazine published in over 60 pages in both the Arabic and English languages. An independent magazine, it will provide you with news, regular articles on the political sphere, articles on youth, Islamic economics, women, special reports and other topics of interest.

www.islam.org.au

Patel's Corner Shop

This very professional-looking site displays Muslim prayer times, Arab news, and other information. A useful insight to the world of Islam.

www.patelscornershop.com

Rabbi Scheinerman's Pages

This is a lively, colourful site provided by Rabbi Amy Scheinerman, which clearly explains all aspects of Judaism in terms even a young child can understand. A good source of information for projects, or simply for finding out more about this ancient and flourishing religion.

www.scheinerman.net/judaism

Rastafarianism

Find out more about the Rasta lifestyle, beliefs, Haile Selassie and the Lion of Jah at this simple one-page web site. It also has links to other Rastafarian sites.

www.aspects.net/~nick/religion.htm

Shambhala Sun

This is another religious magazine published on paper each month, from which samples are put on the internet. You can subscribe from this site to the magazine. The magazine is inspired by Buddhism and the world's great contemplative traditions, and aims to bring compassion and insight to the arts, politics, relationships, social issues, livelihood, and all aspects of life in the modern world.

www.shambhalasun.com

SCIENCE

These sites are useful not only to students also but to the rest of us as well: some are highly technical while others are simply fun and informative. Science doesn't have to be boring!

See also *History,* and *Environment and Nature*. For anatomy/ biology, see under *Health, Fitness and Nutrition*.

4,000 Years of Women in Science

This site comprises biographies of women who have made a major contribution to scientific thought or discovery.

www.astr.ua.edu/4000ws/4000WS.html

About Rainbows

It is a shame that there are no pots of gold at the end of the rainbow, but nevertheless it is still well worth looking out for them. Visit About Rainbows and learn why they occur and how they are formed.

www.unidata.ucar.edu/staff/blynds/rnbw.html

Cells Alive!

See for yourself what different cells, viruses, bacteria and crystals look like under very powerful microscopes. Find out about the techniques that are used for cell imaging and research here too.

www.cellsalive.com

Chemical Elements.com

This site includes a detailed version of the periodic table and links to additional information. It is easy to use and there are different ways to view the table, which helps make this a useful reference site for any chemist or student of chemistry.

www.chemicalelements.com

Chem4Kids

Chemistry is the study of matter and the changes that take place with that matter, and since matter comprises everything we can touch, see, feel or smell, it is an important, albeit often neglected, area of learning for some people. This site is easy to navigate via its site map and search engine, and includes a drop-down glossary of terms. Chem4Kids also includes data on atoms, elements and matter, as well as biographies of famous chemists.

www.chem4kids.com/

Conchologist's Information Network

Everything you ever wanted to know about shells and the mysterious creatures that live inside them can be found here. At this site all levels of interest are covered and there is even a specific children's section. There is also plenty of information about the Conchologist's Information Network organisation as well.

erato.acnatsci.org/conchnet

Desert Life

Learn about the desert environment and the unique characteristics that define the beautiful arid and semi-arid landscapes of the American South-west. The site begins with a general introduction to the complex and delicate desert ecosystems, including a discussion of the role humans play in the changing desert environment.

www.desertusa.com/life.html

EurekAlert

The latest scientific inventions are featured on this site so you can be the first to break the news about tomorrow's world.

www.eurekalert.org

Extreme Science

This extensive portal gives answers to almost any science poser you can throw at it! Up-to-the-minute details on the latest advances as well as historical facts. An excellent resource for homework.

www.extremescience.com

A Guided Tour of the Visible Human

The Visible Human Project consists of some 18,000 digitised sections of the body. The animations and images in this tour demonstrate the planes of section, and how the two-dimensional images provide a unique means of studying the three-dimensional anatomy of the human body.

www.madsci.org/~lynn/VH/

The Heart

From the moment it begins beating until the moment it stops, the human heart works tirelessly. In an average lifetime, the heart actually beats more than two and a half billion times. There has always been an air of mystery surrounding the heart, and even though modern technology has removed much of that mystery, there still remains an air of fascination and curiosity. Explore the heart at this site. Discover the complexities of its development and structure. Follow the blood through the blood vessels. Wander through the web-like body systems. Learn how to monitor your heart's health and ensure that it remains in peak condition. Look back at the history of heart science.

www.fi.edu/biosci/heart.html

History of the Light Microscope

The microscope has become one of the most recognisable symbols of science. This site covers the early history of the microscope, starting with use of a simple lens in ancient times, to the first compound microscope developed in about 1590, up to the microscopes of the 19th century.

www.utmem.edu/personal/thjones/hist/hist_mic.htm

HowStuffWorks

Do you find yourself wondering how things work, or do you need to find out for that school project? If you do, then pay a visit to this site straight away. It contains a huge collection of articles on the numerous technologies and is divided into topics such as engines, around the house and electronics. A new article is added each week. So don't take the appliances you use every day for granted any more!

www.howstuffworks.com

How Things Work

If you find yourself wanting to ask someone 'How does this work?' then do so. A physicist at the University of Virginia has designed this site as a call-in program on the web. Simply go to this site and ask it anything. All the questions are archived, so scroll through to find the answers you need.

howthingswork.virginia.edu

Interactive Frog Dissection

The Interactive Frog Dissection was designed for use in high school biology classrooms as an online tutorial. However, anyone can take part and so if you are not squeamish, why not have a go? The site will help you to learn the anatomy of frogs and give you a better understanding of the anatomy of vertebrate animals in general, including humans.

curry.edschool.virginia.edu/go/frog

National Science Foundation

The NSF is an independent US Government agency responsible for promoting science and engineering through programmes that invest over $3.3 billion per year in almost 20,000 research and education projects in science and engineering. On their web site is a huge listing of online scientific resources. It should be one of the first places you look for any information needed on scientific problems.

www.nsf.gov

Nova Online

Nova is an American television company that makes science programmes for the US and the world. Men, women and children of all ages explore the science behind the headlines, along the way demystifying science and technology. On its web site you can view written information about all the programmes it has made and the content of these programmes, watch small video clips from previous shows and even purchase videos. The site is full of resources for all on a vast range of topics.

www.pbs.org/wgbh/nova

Pretty Strange Patents

This site displays the most bizarre inventions from around the world. The site's descriptions also come with diagrams showing you how the inventions really work – or in some cases don't.

soundreach.simplenet.com/psp

Robots4U

This site offers kits for kids to make robots, perform scientific and electronic experiments and build their own projects. They have a wide range of items on offer, all orderable from their secure online shop, to suit from age four upwards. If you're a fan of the BBC's programme *Robot Wars* you will find some of the house robots here, as they were designed by the owners of this site.

www.robots4u.com

Science and Mathematics Education Resources

This site contains news and information on a range of scientific subjects, has links to other sites and lists suppliers of equipment and software. The physics section contains a page called Physics Biographies, with biographies of all the great physicists, a comprehensive history of physics, a full list of Nobel Prize winners since 1901 and much more.

www-hpcc.astro.washington.edu/scied

Science, Technology and Medical Biographical Dictionary

This is a useful, searchable index of hundreds of figures from the history of science and technology, linking to brief biographical information. A good reference site for science projects and an interesting read.

www.asap.unimelb.edu.au/hstm/hstm_bio.htm

Spy gadgets

High-tech spy gadgets – a fact not fiction. The Central Intelligence Museum claims to have produced models of actual spy hardware and you can examine them online. They might not be items you can add to your shopping list, but keep dreaming!

www.acmenet.net/~dna

Telescope Makers

Ever wanted to build your own telescope but don't know where to begin? Look up the Amateur Telescope Makers' page for help. The site contains sections on design, mechanics and optics and lets you choose the type of telescope you are interested in. Once you have done this, you can see detailed plans to help you on your way to creating your own equipment.

www.atmpage.com

SEARCH ENGINES

See *Internet: Search Engines*.

SENIOR CITIZENS

The internet isn't only for the young! Whatever age you are, you can find information, entertainment and support within its pages. These sites are aimed at, or written by, those of advancing years, mostly with a view to promoting the benefits of being retired. For information on age-related health conditions, see also *Health, Fitness and Nutrition*.

British Geriatrics Society

This professional organisation brings together doctors, scientists and others involved in geriatric medicine and age-related health, providing qualified opinion and useful links to other sites on this topic.

www.bgs.org.uk

Care Homes

A database site containing information on nursing homes and residential care homes in the UK.

www.carehomes.co.uk/index.htm

CenNet

'New Horizons for the Over-50s' is how this site describes itself. Put together by a group of over-50s who realised the appeal of the web to this age group, it includes sections on lifestyle, entertainment, wellbeing, home and garden, finance, travel, and a discussion room. Well worth a visit, whatever your level of web expertise.

www.cennet.co.uk

Fifty On

This recent addition to the web is aimed at, obviously, those aged 50-plus. But this doesn't restrict it to the retired: one of its main aims is to provide information on job and career opportunities and retraining, ideal for those who've been made redundant. It also offers information on travel, leisure and health. A clear and useful web site which should go from strength to strength.

www.fiftyon.co.uk

The Oldie

Richard Ingrams, who for 23 years was the editor of *Private Eye* magazine, launched *The Oldie* magazine in 1992. He founded the magazine because he was alarmed that the media was sidelining good writers and journalists simply because of their age. This humorous magazine provides cartoons, regularly updated articles and ample opportunity to subscribe to the paper version.

www.theoldie.co.uk

Peter Gopfert's 60+ Pages

Here's proof that just because you're an OAP doesn't mean you can't run a web site! Peter's pages offer a wide range of information, humour and suggested sites for seniors. A page giving details of free software distributors is included, as well as other pages for computer buffs.

www.gopfert.freeserve.co.uk

Retirement Residential and Care Home Search

Retirement Home Search UK claims to be the definitive resource for information about homes for the elderly. Whether you are looking for a retirement home, a residential home, or a nursing home it will be listed here. Information is given for people who prefer to stay in their own homes too, and there is a great list of related sites.

www.retirementhome.co.uk

Retirement Matters

A lively, friendly site for the retired and the about-to-be retired. Everything from health and travel to pets and pen pals, with useful 'essential guides' to such things as retirement abroad, plus links to helpful related web sites.

www.retirementmatters.co.uk

Retirement Resorts

If you've ever fancied retiring to the sun, and want to be with like-minded individuals of similar age, try this American site. It gives information on retirement resorts in the US and Spain, described as 'senior communities that have distinguished themselves by providing exemplary services and amenities to their community members, as well as access to quality on-site healthcare services'.

www.retirementresorts.com

The Retirement Site

Information for those who are about to enter the world of retirement, whether voluntarily at retirement age or as the result of redundancy. The site is useful both for employers and for their retiring employees, and covers such issues as social security, tax, and financial planning as well as offering seminars on approaching retirement.

www.the-retirement-site.co.uk

Saga

Saga pioneered the idea of providing holidays exclusively for mature travellers some 45 years ago. Today they are the leaders in the field, with offices in Britain, the US and Australia, and they are associated with much more than holidays. Saga provides an increasing range of services for people aged 50 and over, including their acclaimed magazine, as well as financial and insurance services.

www.saga.co.uk

Senior One Source

Describing itself as 'the ONE referral source for older adults', this American site has an extensive list of links to sites for seniors and includes travel, health and lifestyle advice.

www.senioronesource.com

Seniors Information Resource Centre

Don't be put off by the title as this is a fairly useful resource with a broad range of categories for you to explore. It is the only search directory exclusively for the over-50 age group. Not all the sites here are exclusively for the elderly but the best sites are labelled 'senior friendly'.

www.seniorssearch.com

Stannah Stairlifts

Most of us have heard of this company from their TV adverts. They are one of the best-known manufacturers in their field, offering products that provide independence and mobility to those too elderly or infirm to manage the stairs unaided. Their site contains full details of their product range and advice and support for existing users.

www.stannah.co.uk/stairlifts

Third Age

The site states that the Third Age is 'a time of life characterised by happiness, freedom and learning. A life stage following youth and preceding old age'. This is 'a web site where like-minded people find intelligent conversations and useful tools'. So, in order to find out what to do in your best years yet, look no further. There are sections devoted to family, health, living, money, news, technology, romance and work. There are also daily jokes, comics, crosswords and word games, as well as regular articles and chats.

www.thirdage.com

Twilight Years

The Twilight Years has been created for anyone needing information relating to elderly services. It aims to provide all the information you'll ever need in the quickest and easiest way possible without leaving your chair! From health tips to holidays, gardening to funeral plans, it's all here.

www.twilightyears.co.uk

Vavo

This site, aimed at anyone over 45, claims to 'redefine the internet generation'. It's basically an online community and covers almost any subject or interest you can imagine without throwing your age in your face.

www.vavo.com

SHOPPING

The net is a shopper's paradise: no more trudging round in the rain only to find that little black dress isn't available in your size. Listed below are some of the more established and general shopping sites: you'll also find that many specialist sites either have links to sales outlets or you can buy online from those sites, so if you are looking for specialist items, check out the relevant subject pages (for example, for sports equipment and clothing, see *Sport*).

Remember that if you buy goods from a site outside your own country, you will have to pay import taxes and probably shipping charges too, which may outweigh the benefit of lower prices.

American Priceline

Priceline.com is a revolutionary new buying service where you can save money by naming your own price for the things you need in America. The way that this does it is that you submit a bid for the price you are prepared to pay, and they pass it on to the relevant company. You can name your own price for home mortgages, home equity loans, mortgage refinancing, even new cars and trucks!

www.priceline.com

Argos

The well-known UK catalogue store sells almost everything from trainers to tents. Browse or search for specific products. There's a useful finder, help guide, order forms and services details.

www.argos.co.uk

Best of British

Fashion, accessories, interiors, cosmetics, hampers and everything British, which you can purchase online. There are special offers and a good keyword system of searching for the item you want.

www.thebestofbritish.com

Bigsave

With a range of over 7,000 products and promises of up to 70% off high street prices, it's not surprising that this is a popular site for products and services from clothes to electrical goods. Online purchasing, direct delivery and full guarantees.

www.bigsave.com

Boots

Beauty products and a wide range of other products stocked by the high street chain and now available online. It also includes pictures of various make-up looks and descriptions of the products needed to achieve them.

www.boots.co.uk

Carphone Warehouse

This company was established to give impartial advice to help you make the best decision on the phone that is right for your needs. The web site works on the same principle, and adds a special deal online every day.

www.carphonewarehouse.com

Catalog Mart

The Catalog Mart is the easiest, fastest and most direct way to receive just about any catalogue offered in the US today. It offers more than 10,000 catalogues in over 800 topics that are free of charge with no obligation. Just choose your product categories and fill out the electronic order form.

catalog.savvy.com

Check a Price

For all kinds of product prices, from CDs to cars, you can key in what you need to buy and the search engine will offer comparative prices from various online sources.

www.checkaprice.com

Comet

The electrical retailer has this online sales service for all kinds of kitchen, household, entertainment and personal-care products.

www.comet.co.uk

Contacts Direct

Making savings through low overheads and direct supply, Contacts Direct can pass those savings on to its customers and supply designer glasses, sunglasses and contact lenses at considerable discounts.

www.contacts-direct.co.uk

Daltons

Daltons Weekly has been published for many years, listing properties, holidays and other items for sale. Now the magazine is online with good database-search facilities.

www.daltons.co.uk

Exchange and Mart

The site for the well-known magazine in which you can buy everything from cars to can openers, book holidays and find jobs.

www.ixm.co.uk

Fat Face

Another online store, you'll find clothes and accessories for sale on this site, with some useful discounts on offer.

www.fatface.co.uk

Figleaves

For a wide range of brand names in women's lingerie and hosiery and men's underwear, take a look at this site. Delivery is easy and free.

www.figleaves.co.uk

FragranceNet

FragranceNet is a great way to buy your favourite fragrances because you can make savings of up to 60 per cent off the retail price! Even if you do not have a favourite fragrance, you may be able to decide on a scent by reading the description given. Do you like floral or fruity scents, or do you prefer an oriental, musky note? Whatever your taste, this site will have a fragrance for you.

www.fragrancenet.com

FreeShop

FreeShop is the place to subscribe to hundreds of magazines and to try before you buy on the internet. Shoppers can browse through nearly 20 popular-interest categories for access to free samples and risk-free magazine trial issues. The site has a shopping assistant that compares prices across the internet, making it easy to find the best value available.

www.freeshop.com

Harrods

This is the web site of the world's most famous store. Need we say more?

www.harrods.co.uk

Innovations

Following the success of its mail-order catalogue containing unusual household, DIY, gardening and gift items, this site now offers the online equivalent.

www.innovations.co.uk

Jungle

Now familiar to most people because of TV advertising, Jungle offers computer equipment, games, CDs, videos and DVDs for sale online.

www.jungle.com

Kays

An easy site to use, this is the online Kays catalogue, which includes fashion, household wares and a whole range of other items for sale. Key in what you want to see, the price, size and colour, and it will give you a list of matching items. Select the ones you want to view and drop your final choices into a shopping bag.

www.kaysnet.com

Lastminute

At this easy-to-use site, snap up the latest bargains in travel, entertainment and holidays. Get help in choosing the perfect gift in the presents section or find short-term accommodation from flats and houses to country mansions and castles. You can even purchase items from auctions. Registration is free and even though you may not always find something to buy, it is definitely worth checking out this site if you are interested in obtaining last-minute flight or concert tickets.

www.lastminute.com

Loot

On this site you can search the advertisements for a whole range of goods from sports equipment to household items. Search for what you want, and they will supply the full details of the advertised products.

www.loot.com

Organic shopping

Organic clothes and bedding as well as food, with a 10-day delivery on clothes, check out this site for all your environmentally friendly needs. The site is easy to navigate although it has no pictures.

www.organicsdirect.co.uk

QED

All kinds of electrical goods are on sale here, but the site is especially good for household electrical products such as washing machines, as well as both gas and electric cookers. There is also a good range of telephone equipment.

www.qed-uk.com

QVC

QVC, The Shopping Channel, prides itself on having an interactive relationship with its customers, listening to what they say, learning what they want and delivering it quickly and efficiently. On their web site you will find all the products offered on the TV show. Ordering online is available or by telephone if you wish.

www.qvcuk.com

Retail Link

Not so much a site in itself, but a link to the sites of dozens of leading UK high street shops, offering information on their products and, in many cases, the opportunity to buy online.

www.retail.co.uk

Scotch Corner

Set up by a part of Scotch Corner, the high street store, this site provides information on the correct tartans and everything you could possibly need to know about Scottish highland dress. Some items can be delivered in a few days; other items, such as kilts, are made to order and so take about six weeks.

www.highland-dress.co.uk

Shops On the Net

This is a resource site aimed at advertising and reviewing the sites that are selling on the internet, and giving awards to those that have a good retail environment. Shops on the Net is operated by NetCommerce Ltd, a multi-faceted organisation providing commercial internet services in the United Kingdom and Europe.

www.shopsonthenet.com

ShopSmart

An easy way to find the best shopping sites, ShopSmart offers a selection of the top 1,000 online shopping sites with the facility to compare prices between the different sources.

www.shopsmart.com

Sony Online

This site gives news, previews, support and information on Sony's movie and TV merchandise, computing and accessories, music and consumer products. It has an online shop and also a store locator facility. You can even play games online at this site.

www.sony.com

Ticketmaster

Visit this site and you will be able to book all your seats for plays, shows, rock concerts, exhibitions and sporting events being held all over the UK. You are also able to buy tickets for shows in other countries such as America, Australia and Canada online using the appropriate Ticketmaster sites, accessible from the UK site.

www.ticketmaster.co.uk

Top Shop

A good range of clothes, especially for the younger set, from the familiar British high street chain. Payment is by credit card so you have to be over 18.

www.tops.co.uk

Unbeatable

Photographic and electrical goods at the entertainment end of the market are available for sale online. A very wide range of goods is available at competitive prices.

www.unbeatable.co.uk

U Shop U Give

This shopping site allows you to dedicate a percentage of the cost (their profit) to one of several charities. A great way to shop online and help others at the same time.

www.ushopugive.com

Value Direct

With a good search system, this is an online store for household appliances such as televisions. Free UK mainland delivery.

www.value-direct.co.uk

Vegetarian Leather

Fake leather clothes such as shoes, jackets, gloves and coats for sale online with delivery in about a week. Prices compare favourably with the real thing.

www.vegetarian-shoes.co.uk

The Virtual Mall

This is the UK's only real-life internet shopping mall. The site contains links to 120 of the leading high street and internet shops in one place. The only difference is that this mall is open 24 hours a day, 365 days a year. The site contains four floors at the moment and it is always increasing. Every floor has a mall directory to help you find a specific store, or specific type of store.

www.thevirtualmall.co.uk

SPORT

Whatever your sport, you can find out more about it on the web. From mainstream sports to the truly bizarre, all you need in terms of instruction, equipment and information can be found here. Whether you're an armchair-based commentator or an active dynamic, get physical at these sites. Some fitness sites can also be found under *Health, Fitness and Nutrition*.

ADVENTURE AND EXTREME SPORTS

Adventure Racing

This sport, encompassing several punishing disciplines, is particularly big in America, which hosts several prestigious races each year. The Four Winds site covers one of the most popular, and gives links to other sites on related races. At their site you can sign up to take part or follow the progress while the race is on.

www.4windsadventure.com

Aerial Sports Club

The mad members of the aerial sports club will do anything that involves falling or flying, including bungee, free-fall and cliff-climbing. Visit this site if you need an adrenaline rush: don't expect tuition though, this is for the serious dangerous sports fan.

www.aerial.org

Choose Sport

This site covers over 100 adventure sports, from rock climbing to paragliding. You can search for activities taking place in a particular area, or for adventure holidays and accommodation. Each week they feature a different sport, so visit regularly. They also have an online store.

www.choosesport.com

Explore

The site's content covers an in-depth look at a variety of extreme sports including biking, snowboarding, climbing, water sports and many more. The site asks visitors to share their experiences to make it as interactive as possible.

www.explore.com

Street Luge

This has to be one of the maddest sports of all time. Developed from the ice-based speed sport, street luge involves lying on an elongated skateboard and propelling yourself down a track (often paved private roads) at extreme speed and rather close to the ground. If this sounds like you, try this site for more information on when and where to try it.

www.streetluge.co.uk

AMERICAN FOOTBALL

Gridiron

This is the site for the British American Football Association (BAFA)'s British Senior league, covering all major American Football games in the UK. It gives stats, fixture lists, player bios and much more. It also has links to sites for individual clubs.

www.gridironuk.com

Gridiron England

This is the site of the official England team and gives details of its fixtures, team news and updates, previous games etc.

www.gridironengland.co.uk

The Official NFL Site

This site offers informative profiles on each of the thousands of players in the NFL together with individual club pages. It also offers you stats, a video and a very good news service. With terrific graphics, animations, games, countless surprises and bags of attitude and fun, it will appeal to everyone who is a footie fan.

www.nfl.com

ANGLING

Fish and Fly

This site covers the UK and Europe, giving up to date news and weather for fly-fishers as well as techniques, details of suppliers and suitable sites. It also has an online store for supplies.

www.fishandfly.co.uk

Go Fish

This UK-based site provides information on fisheries, clubs, techniques, even fishing holidays, and you can submit pictures of your finest catch for their gallery.

www.go-fish.co.uk

Where To Fish

This site claims to be the world's largest online fishing information service. At this site you will find more than 3,000 pages of daily updated information covering fishing locations in the UK and abroad, both at sea and on land. There is also a wide range of articles covering all aspects of fishing. Users of the site can add their own fishing information.

www.where-to-fish.com

ATHLETICS

Athletics Links

This site lists details of other athletics sites, with links. A good starting place for information on any track and field sport.

members.nbci.com/athletilinks/index.htm

International Amateur Athletics Federation

This is the official site of the IAAF. Here you can find out about all the current news, stats and results. The sport section gives the history, landmarks and required qualities in each event. From legends to the latest scientific advances and last season's major events, this has everything, including video interviews and coaching tips for the budding athlete.

www.iaaf.org

Nuff Respect

This site, owned by Linford Christie, gives information (some rather tongue-in-cheek) on famous athletes, offers the chance to bid for memorabilia or purchase signed photos, and provides links to other athletics sites.

www.nuff-respect.co.uk

Running Tracks

With maps, address, telephone and fax numbers for all the running tracks in the UK, this is an invaluable site for athletes.

www.runtrackdir.com

UK Athletics

This is the official site of UK Athletics, the sport's governing body, and gives up-to-date information on fixtures, results, entrants and their rankings. You can also shop for official team goods online.

www.uk-athletics.com

AUSTRALIAN RULES FOOTBALL

Australian Football League

This official site contains everything you could possibly want to know about the Australian Football League with news, views and highlights plus information on forthcoming matches.

www.afl.com.au

Real Footy

This magazine-style site gives all the latest news on the AFL season, including match reports and interviews with the stars.

www.realfooty.com.au

BASEBALL

Baseball Tips and Drills

If you need to improve your game, or if you've been co-opted into coaching the Little League, here's all the information you need.

www.eteamz.com/baseball/instruction/tips

The Official Site of Major League Baseball

This site is really for the true baseball fan as it has no glossary or 'idiot's guide'. It is very informative with detailed team sections, history, masses of multimedia and stats. A section for kids offers profiles, interviews and interactive games.

www.mlb.com

BASKETBALL

Britball

This site covers the English, Scottish and Irish basketball scenes, and is well-designed with useful information and e-mail newsletter service. It also has information on European games and profiles of up-and-coming players.

www.britball.com

Hoops

This site offers comprehensive coverage of the UK basketball scene, including clubs, leagues and fixtures, plus where to buy clothing and equipment and where to watch the games.

www.hoops.co.uk

National Basketball Association

This is the official site of the NBA. It contains all the information you could possibly want on the game and its teams and players. For the news, history, statistics and schedules plus special features and the online NBA store, look no further.

www.nba.com

BOXING

Boxing.com

The complete low-down on boxing. Find out the schedules, ranking and results and add your own opinions to the site.

www.boxing.com

Boxing Records

Need to settle an argument over who beat whom? Go to this site. It claims to have details of over 26,000 fighters and their fights. You have to pay to access some of the records, but information on current fighters is free. It also has an online store and several forums, plus interviews.

www.boxing-records.com

House of Boxing

This American site claims to be 'the home of boxers on the net'. It certainly has a lot of information on all the big events, reports of previous bouts and interviews with the contenders, plus an online boxing gift store that stocks books, videos, games and DVDs. It also covers women's boxing.

www.houseofboxing.com

CRICKET

CricInfo

CricInfo provides detailed cricket information, including live scores for international matches free of charge to cricket fans around the world. CricInfo promotes interest in cricket worldwide through building and maintaining the largest and, at times, the most popular cricket database on the internet. It has mirror sites in the UK, the USA, India, Australia and South Africa.

www.cricket.org

CricketLine

Up-to-date information on current match scores, both international and domestic.

www.cricketline.com

CYCLING

BikeMagic

The UK's premier net resource for bikers (of the non-motorised kind). This site covers mountain biking, racing and general street biking, with details of events, news, and thousands of product reviews.

www.bikemagic.co.uk

Tour de France

Keep up with the 21-day race around France from the comfort of your own home! The site has profiles of the riders, the route, the rules, videos of the race and merchandise for sale. During the race, the site is updated daily.

www.letour.com

Procycling

This is the magazine for all cycling enthusiasts, whether participants or mere spectators. It provides up-to-the-minute reports on all cycling events, plus archived information. The site is not particularly extensive because they want you to buy the magazine, but when an event is on it provides the best news coverage.

www.procycling.com

Trail Break

If mountain biking is your thing, check out this site for details of biking holidays and events, Whether you're new to the sport and want to know how to get the most out of it or you've been riding forever and you're looking for somewhere that you haven't ridden yet, there's something in the Trail Break calendar for you.

www.trailbreak.co.uk

WWW Bicycle Repair Shop

This site offers advice on bike repairs, both for mountain bikes and road-going bikes. Click on the appropriate part of the bike in the picture on the left, and select the most appropriate description from the list to view a step-by-step guide to what you'll need and how to complete the repair. The site also features tool guides, product reviews and links to other cycling sites. It is run by an American so some of the terms may be unfamiliar to non-US cyclists.

www.bicyclerepairshop.com

FITNESS AND BODYBUILDING

See also *Health, Fitness and Nutrition: Physical Fitness*.

Gymworld-On-Line

This company delivers fitness equipment to your door, so if you can't make it to your local gym, why not set up your own? Their site gives details of their full range of equipment, and they offer daily deliveries across the UK.

www.gymworld.co.uk

The Fitness Guide

This American site is aimed at bodybuilders, and gives information on training, nutrition and supplements, as well as the latest news from the industry.

www.thefitnessguide.com

The Fitness League

The Fitness League, a well-established nationwide exercise network, sponsored by Sport England and Sport Scotland, teaches low impact, rhythmic exercise to music. Its exercise regime is based on encouraging correct posture which releases the body's potential for good health. Its site gives details of the classes and how to train to be a fitness instructor, and you can search for the trainer and class nearest to you.

www.thefitnessleague.com

Virtually In Shape

This claims to be 'a complete on-line source for exercise, nutrition, and any other health and fitness needs'. It includes an exercise section, describing the correct use of free weights and nautilus to increase muscle strength and of treadmills, exercise bikes, stair steppers etc to lose weight and stay healthy. The nutrition program provides information on healthy diets, and strategies for safe weight loss. To use the site regularly you will need to join up and pay a fee, but you can take a tour for free first to see whether you think it's worthwhile. You can also use several of the other facilities for free, for example to calculate your Body Mass Index to see whether you are overweight or not.

www.virtuallyinshape.com

FOOTBALL (SOCCER)

Arsenal

News, results, ticket information, diaries and all kinds of other information about this major UK football club.

www.arsenal.co.uk

Football365

At this site you will find the most comprehensive, exciting and funniest football site on the web. The site is run by football fans who are dedicated to bringing you a view of the game that combines knowledge and passion. They have the latest news, interesting features, opinions, match reports, interviews and football humour, together with plenty of avenues for input.

www.football365.com

Football Nationwide

A wealth of information on football for the enthusiast, plus plenty of links to the financial services of Nationwide, the football sponsor.

www.football.nationwide.co.uk

FootballNews

This is the place for the sporting statistician as it contains every kind of result or table you could think of throughout the range of soccer leagues in the UK.

www.footballnews.co.uk

Manchester United Football Club

This site is about England's premier football club, Manchester United. You will find the latest news, information on players, matches, fixtures, results, goals and more.

www.manutd.com

Soccernet

A complete guide to the new season's fixtures and a forum for you to chat to other fans.

www.soccernet.com/index.html

Teamtalk

This site is one of the UK's leading independent football news and reports services, producing news, results, statistics and reports on 59 top club and national teams. It also provides up-to-the-minute audio news and match reports for all 59 league teams.

www.teamtalk.com

When Saturday Comes

See for yourself just how good the site really is! Now accessed through its partner site, onetouchfootball.com, there is for example the football pub guide that gives details of top pub venues for important matches, and the famous player alert section where the almost inconspicuous activities of past and present players are noted. You can also add your own views.

www.dottwo.com/onetouch/

GENERAL SPORTS SITES

CBS SportsLine

Check out this site for the news, views, fixtures and scores on all US sports. It gives fast facts on the standings, schedules, statistics, teams and players.

www.sportsline.com

International Blind Sports Association

This site is available in either English or Spanish and contains a regularly updated news section plus an impressive and wide range of articles and features. Best of all is the colossal database. It has brief profiles and sporting records of hundreds of athletes and clear, accessible guides to 14 disciplines.

www.ibsa.es

Sky Sports

This site has a rolling sports news service which gives you all the latest sports news and scores 24 hours a day, seven days a week, 52 weeks a year. Find out what is happening in the world of soccer, cricket, rugby, boxing, golf, tennis, NFL and motor racing.

www.skysports.com

Sports.com

An online sports store together with news and information on sports, especially football.

www.sports.com

Sportal

A magazine for all mainstream sports, this is the UK version of Sportal, which is available in various languages and for various countries. It covers news, events, betting and shopping.

www.sportal.co.uk

UK Sports Guide

This site gives information on all the UK's favourite sports, plus several that are becoming popular. It lists other sites by their sport and grades them according to their content, saving you a lot of searching around for the best sites.

www.uksportsguide.co.uk

GOLF

GolfAgent

GolfAgent enables internet users to book tee times at a wide range of golf courses. Reservations are all online, using SSL credit card encryption methods for security and ease. When tee times are booked online, the golfer's details appear on the club's system as if the person had telephoned the club and they had taken the booking themselves.

www.golfagent.com

Golf in Europe

GolfEurope is a commercial web site with a mission to be the definitive reference point for European golf on the internet, and to offer golfers a genuinely valuable information resource free of charge. On the site is a course directory containing every club in Britain and Europe. Other sections include an almanac and golf tuition to provide the golfer with a host of valuable reference information.

www.golfeurope.com

Golf Today

Home news, travel, golf questions and answers, this is the site of the premier golf magazine, a mine of information for anyone interested in the sport.

www.golftoday.co.uk

GolfWeb

A major golf web site, this is committed to providing 'everything golf on the world-wide web'. GolfWeb offers something for everyone with an interest in golf, from the latest professional and amateur tournament scores and news to extensive golf course information and an online pro shop. GolfWeb's auxiliary sites are GolfWeb Japan and GolfWeb Europe.

www.golfweb.com

Worldgolf

A brave name, but this site more than lives up to it. There's exhaustive, up-to-date tour results, plus archived stats and majors sections. But this site excels for the player rather than the spectator, with hundreds of recommended courses from over 30 countries, club-choosing tips, fitness, rules and endless advice. Discover the joys of the Texas wedgie in the dictionary and learn the art of yelling 'Fore!' in Joey West's humour section. And if you're really, really good – or lucky! – you can always join the hole-in-one register.

www.worldgolf.com

Professional Golfers' Association European Tour

This is the official web site of the PGA European golf tour. It gives details of events, players, ranking and sponsors, as well as all the latest news.

www.europeantour.com

ICE HOCKEY

National Ice Hockey League

An American site which contains everything you need to know about the National Ice Hockey League. It has non-stop news, photos, video highlights, articles, encyclopedic Winter Olympic details and features ranging from match previews to the features on old players file. They also broadcast live commentary on every league game.

www.nhl.com

MOTORSPORT

For motorcycle racing and motocross, see also *Motorcycling*.

Autosport

The online site for the premier motor racing magazine. You can subscribe here, or read articles on all aspects of motor racing.

www.autosport.com

Crash.net

This recent addition to the web covers all major motorsport events around the globe, from Indycar to the RAC rally, speedway to superbikes. A one-stop shop for motorsport fans: well worth a visit.

www.crash.net

Formula One

A must for all F1 fans, this site provides commentary on the current season plus bios and interviews, statistics and archive footage. You can buy tickets and merchandise online.

www.formula1.com

Motorsport international

Motorsport International provides news, results, race reports and other information about all types of motorsports – from Formula One and road racing to stock cars, from midgets to rallies, and from dragsters to touring cars – through the internet and through a digest-format mailing list.

www.motorsport.com

Racer

Racer.com is the online news and commentary service of *Racer* magazine. This is a monthly American publication. Stories are augmented by news of the latest motor racing developments, along with an easy-reading summary of important race results and a complete day-by-day listing of all live and taped television motorsports events for the month.

www.racer.com

RUGBY

International Rugby Football Board

The International Rugby Board (IRB), with its headquarters in Dublin, Ireland, is the world governing and law-making body for the game of rugby union. The board was founded in 1886. This is the official site and contains information about the board and the game itself, together with links to other relevant sites.

www.irfb.com

Planet Rugby

The ultimate resource for international rugby union, this site includes ranking, tournaments, an interactive chat room, fixtures and an interesting archive.

www.planetrugby.com

Rugby Club

At this site you can find details on every aspect of the playing side of the game: the results, the fixtures and a comprehensive guide to the clubs and their players. The Allied Dunbar League tables are updated within a couple of hours of the end of matches. There is also the subscriber club where supporters can register to be sent pre-match information by e-mail on the club of their choice.

www.rugbyclub.co.uk

Rugby Mail

This is a Daily Mail site designed to keep sports fans up to date with the latest news on current tournaments and players.

www.rugbymail.co.uk

Rugby Scrum

Up-to-the minute news, results and comments on the international game of rugby union. The site gives information on the tests, tours and tournaments and has links to other similar sites.

www.scrum.com

World of Rugby League

Whether you are a fan of rugby league or simply wonder why 26 men should want to play such a rough game, check out this site. Statistics, news and scores are posted on the World of Rugby League site after each game.

www.rleague.com

SAILING

Banks Sails

Banks designs and makes sails but its web site includes reports and results from the world of sailing and expert sailing tips.

www.banks.co.uk

International Sailing Federation

With daily news updates, a weekly newsletter and an exhaustive fixture and results service, this official site gives you all you need to know about ocean racing. There's thorough coverage of the big races and more than 700 regattas listed in their global calendar, together with lots of features and editorials. With its varied content and fleet of photos, the site is entertaining as well as hugely informative.

www.sailing.org

Semaphone World Sailing

This magazine covers all aspects of sailing, yacht racing and even boat building and has a huge list of links to related sites around the globe. Whatever you need to know about your boat or the ongoing race season, you can find it here.

www.semaphore.co.uk/sailing

Sunsail

If you fancy a sailing holiday, whether to learn how to sail or merely to sit back while others crew your craft, this is the place to go. Sunsail offer holidays in the UK, Europe and further afield, ranging from one-day charters to two-week flotilla cruises.

www.sunsail.co.uk

UK Sailing Academy

This non-profit organisation exists to promote sailing and sailing instruction within the UK, both for competitive and for leisure purposes. Its site provides information on training at various levels, as well as competitions and events. Useful if you are starting out, need additional training or are thinking of becoming a sail instructor.

www.uk-sail.org.uk

SKIING AND SNOW SPORTS

GORP Skiing and Snow Sports

This page covers all you need for downhill and cross-country skiing, as well as other snow sports such as snowboarding and snowmobiling. There are trail maps of American skiing areas, regional ski area guides, and the all-important equipment pages. A good resource if you are planning a skiing break in America.

www.gorp.com/gorp/activity/skiing.htm

SkiCentral

This is a search and index site for skiers and snowboarders. Ski Central is designed as the primary gateway for accessing ski and snow sport-related sites. Use this free service to find information related to these sports quickly and easily on the internet.

www.skicentral.com

Winter Sports Foundation

This site is both fun and very informative. The site's home page features an image map of a cartoon winter resort. Click on the area of the map for further information on that sport. Guided by one of the top names, each section features history, news, description and how to get involved. You can send questions to internationals in the resort's town hall or even share stories with other enthusiasts of winter sports.

www.wintersports.org

SNOOKER

Embassy World Snooker

At this site you won't just find information about the World Championships but also details of other ranking tournaments, match reports, a review of last year's season, a hall of fame and player profiles. You can also test your snooker knowledge with a trivia quiz, pick up some tips on trick shots from John Virgo and find out how snooker is televised. A comprehensive and very informative site for all snooker fans.

www.embassysnooker.com

Snooker

With great graphics, good display, interesting information and right up-to-date text, this site has everything for the enthusiast.

www.stud.ifi.uio.no/~hermunda/Snooker

SPORTS EQUIPMENT AND CLOTHING

Can-Am

This company supplies equipment and clothing for all ice and skate-based sports, such as ice hockey and in-line skating. Delivery is generally within two days but you will need to pay extra for p&p.

www.can-am.co.uk

Fitness Peak

Fitness Peak offers exercise and fitness equipment for the UK and Europe. The site's comprehensive list includes exercise bikes, rowing machines, treadmills, steppers, multi-gyms and more. Delivery is free within mainland UK.

www.fitnesspeak.co.uk

HI-TEC Sports Online

Find a huge collection of sports footwear from the UK-based stockist here for you to buy online. The web site also includes news, sports-related games and Real Video to keep you on the run.

www.hi-tecsports.com

Kitbag

For all kinds of sports equipment, this site offers a good range for online purchases and free delivery.

www.kitbag.com

Mike's Sports World

This site covers a huge number of sports and provides equipment and clothing for them all! It also provides links to the manufacturers' web sites for further information on the products offered. You can't order online but they will quote prices by e-mail and they do deliver.

www.mikessportsworld.co.uk

Outdoor Megastore

This is a massive on-line outdoor equipment discount warehouse for many of Europe's leading outdoor suppliers. Outdoor gear can be supplied for skiing, walking, climbing, caravanning and camping and orders can be shipped to anywhere in the world.

www.outdoormegastore.co.uk

Sportsmart

This online store provides branded sports clothing, footwear and equipment at reasonable prices. Spend over £40 and delivery is free.

www.sportsmart.co.uk

SURFING AND SEA SPORTS

Adventure Surf Unlimited

Adventure Surf Unlimited is designed to serve as an introduction to the sport in a exciting holiday package. If you have ever dreamed of the ultimate adventure surf trip but lack the know-how and equipment, then ASU will supply it all for you. It provides all inclusive surf camp/excursions to some of the best surfing in North America.

www.adventuresurf.com

OceanBlue

This site is dedicated to all aspects of sea sports, as well as information about the best beaches in America, and environmental concerns for the oceans of the world. The site is split into three sections: the island earth pages aim to promote the well-being of the planet; the sea sports pages cover the world of ocean-based sports; the best beaches pages are devoted mainly to American beaches.

www.oceanblue.com

World Surfing

This site is a must for all surfers. It gives links sorted by region, which cover all aspects of the sport. Find out how to forecast waves or where to buy equipment and go on holiday. Read the surf reports or watch the action through the large number of surfcams.

www.goan.com/surflink.html

TENNIS

Association of Tennis Professionals

This is the official men's tennis tour site. It is attractive and fun, and is much more than just a fund of information. Here you will find up-to-the-minute news, player, tournament and ranking details, or head for the Acerace Quiz for quick-fire trivia questions against the clock, or Pick the Champ where you can back your favourites for forthcoming championships. The site also includes excellent magazine features and a notice board for you to find that doubles partner.

www.atptennis.com

International Tennis Federation

Claiming to be the most authoritative database on tennis on the net, there certainly seems to be a vast range of information collected here. Rules, champions, news, players, results are all covered in this ITF site.

www.itftennis.com

Tennis

From the most recent tournament reports to topical feature articles, this first-rate site leaves few bases uncovered. Though the design may be bland there's latest news, rankings, Grand Slam sections, a free monthly newsletter and endless magazine features. You can improve your skills with the tip of the week, organise that tennis holiday in the travel pages and give your mind and body a workout in the fitness section.

www.tennis.com

WALKING AND HIKING

British Walking Federation

The British Walking Federation (IVV) organises, through its clubs, non-competitive events designed for people of all ages and abilities. Participants walk at their own pace and receive awards for their personal achievement. You don't have to be a member of a club to take part – all you need to do is go to an event and register and take the opportunity to have fun, make friends and improve your own personal fitness. Whether you're thinking of taking up walking, or are a seasoned trekker already, visit their web site for more information.

www.bwf-ivv.org.uk

Country Walks

Created by the Ministry of Agriculture, Fisheries and Food, this interesting site gives you a vast selection of country walks throughout the UK, with details of what you will find along the route, and maps so you don't get lost!

www.countrywalks.org.uk

Sherpa Walking Holidays

This Middlesex-based group offers walking holidays for all abilities, from gentle rambles to full-on hikes, in various locations around the world. Some are guided group tours, others independent self-guided walks (where they provide the directions, accommodation, baggage handling and so on, and you do the walking). They also offer cycling trips.

www.sherpa-walking-holidays.co.uk

Trailwalk

This site contains lots of helpful information on walking, rambling, trekking and hiking, and what to wear while you're doing it! Great for the beginner who needs to know what level of protective clothing is required for a particular trip. You can link from their site to recommended retailers of clothing, footwear and equipment.

www.trailwalk.com

Walking Britain

This authoritative guide, comprising over 1,000 pages, gives information on recommended walks and hikes throughout Britain, and includes an online shop for suitable walking equipment, guides to accommodation and weather, plus links to other sites. The site is updated weekly and is currently expanding to cover walks in Ireland and other places.

www.walkingbritain.co.uk

WRESTLING

British Amateur Wrestling Association

BAWA's web site gives information on UK wrestling in general, including regional clubs and local events as well as the bigger competitions. You can browse the galleries for high quality action pictures; read up-to-date results of national competitions or discover how you can become a member of the BAWA and support the growth of this sport.

www.homeusers.prestel.co.uk/bawa

Wrestling.com

Watch your favourite wrestlers being punched, smacked and thrown around. Then think just how glad you are it is not you in the ring!

www.wrestling.com

STRANGE AND UNUSUAL

These unusual, weird or intriguing sites don't fit neatly into any of our other categories. Try them out for size when you fancy something a little different. See also *Fun*.

Abandoned Missile Base VR Tour

This presentation will take you on a full tour of a decommissioned, abandoned underground missile complex. The site was opened many years ago by explorers and vandals, and in fact the technology therein was nearly obsolete by the time the bases were completed in 1963, so there's little 'secret' about it beyond the location of the sites revealed here.

trigger.org/silo

Because-We-Can

This somewhat anarchic site is run by a group of so-called 'ethical hackers' who flag up security issues with other web sites. It contains some very useful information on what to avoid, how not to get ripped off and how to protect yourself.

www.because-we-can.com

The Camelot Project

The main menu lists Arthurian characters, symbols and sites. You can move from any highlighted element to a sub-menu of basic information, texts, images and a bibliography.

www.ub.rug.nl/camelot/

Chinese Language

A dictionary of Chinese characters on the first site and, at the second, the chance to have your name transliterated into Chinese.

www.chinalanguage.com/CCDICT/index.html

www.chinalanguage.com/cgi-bin/name.pl

Conspiracies

Conspiracy theories seem to pop up all over the place. Are they true? Check out these sites to see what certain people may or may not be up to!

www.conspire.com

www.mt.net/~watcher

Infamous Exploding Whale

There has been a story floating around the net for years about a beached whale that was blown up (exploded, not inflated) for lack of a better way to be rid of it. Many people thought it was an urban legend – but it is true! See for yourself exactly what happened at this site – if you are not too squeamish.

www.perp.com/whale

Linky and Dinky

This pair will send you a weekly e-mail containing their pick of the top internet sites: some useful, others just bizarre.

www.linkydinky.com

Search for Extraterrestrial Intelligence

Are we alone in the universe? That is the question being asked at the SETI Institute. At this site you can see the effort that is currently being made to detect evidence of technological civilisations that may exist elsewhere in the universe, particularly in our galaxy. There are potentially billions of locations outside our solar system that may host life. Find out more about it all here.

www.seti-inst.edu

Skyscraper Page

If you like all things tall, check out this page. It is dedicated to the tallest structures in the world, 500 of them to be exact, from radio masts to tower blocks.

www.skyscraperpage.com

The Smoking Gun

See what makes the celebrities shameful. The Smoking Gun brings you exclusive documents that cannot be found anywhere else on the web, using material obtained from government and law enforcement sources, via Freedom of Information requests, and from court files.

www.thesmokinggun.com

Strange Laws

From the obscure to the ridiculous, if there is a strange law out there you can be guaranteed the Strange Laws web site has it! Some of them still apply but most simply give an insight into bygone days.

www.wj.net/rborek/strange.html

Strange Magazine

This is the web site for the American magazine *Strange*. It contains a bizarre collection of tales, myths and other stories from around the world. The web site includes new material never published in the printed magazine, plus features from back issues. Though most of the current magazine is not on this site, you can subscribe to the magazine from the site.

www.strangemag.com

Sturge's List of the Insane and Unusual

Those who think the Web is for weirdos, here is your proof! This site lists a top 100 of the weirdest, maddest web sites. It is updated regularly – each new entry pushes another off – so put it in your favourites. It also lists other lists of unusual sites. Some of the items may be unsuitable for children.

www.concentric.net/~Sturge/unusual.shtml

What's In Your Name?

Some people believe that your name is extremely important because it has a powerful influence on your life. Apart from being the way you identify yourself and how others identify you, an insight into its influence will give you a greater opportunity to enjoy the successes you are capable of achieving. If you want to see what your name says about you, visit this web site. An interesting read.

www.kabalarians.com/gkh/your.htm

TECHNOLOGY

See *Astronomy and Space, Computers and Software, Internet* and *Science*.

TEENAGERS

Teenagers live in a different world to the rest of us, but these sites aim to help them through the angst and torture of life as a misunderstood young adult. Some are quite enlightening for the rest of us to peek at too, but don't tell them that – it'd be too uncool!

More conscientious teenagers who want to concentrate on homework and exams should visit the sites listed under *Homework Research and Revision*.

Babies of our Youth

This site is aimed directly at teenagers and deals with all issues surrounding teenage pregnancy and parenthood. It is written by a young single mother, and pulls no punches. Topics include preventing pregnancy, what to do if you find out you are pregnant, bringing up baby and support services, with sections for grandparents and true stories from other teenage parents of their experiences.

www.parentingyouths.com

Breakup Girl

Are you smarting from a recent break-up? Do you want to wallow in your misery, or wreak shrewd revenge? If so, then this site is for you. There is an advice column where you can ask Breakup Girl everything you need to know about break-ups but were afraid to ask!

www.breakupgirl.oxygen.com

ChickClick

This site lists all the most notable independent girl web sites in one place. Full of news, views and gossip, this might be your thing!

www.chickclick.com

Cyberteens

This site enables you to submit your artwork, musical compositions or writing to a public gallery. It is well worth considering as you may win a prize!

www.cyberteens.com

Gay Teenager

If you're a teenager and worried about being gay – or glad to be gay for that matter – visit this site which tells you all you need to know. Written by a gay teenager, it tells of his worries about 'coming out' as well as giving details on where to get help and support, and who his current idols are.

www.gay-teenager.co.uk

Mykindaplace

A site for teenage girls, this covers many areas including an agony aunt, quizzes, 'real life' stories, music and showbiz.

www.mykindaplace.com

Off The Streets

This site is designed specifically for teenagers by the Bournemouth Youth Service and includes all sorts of cool information, including a guide to the town's best clubs (reputedly among the hottest in Europe!). It also has a homework guide and several chat rooms. Even if you've never been to Bournemouth, it's well worth a look.

www.offthestreets.co.uk

Spank

Spank! Claims to be the 'Magazine of Youth Culture'. It covers all sorts of issues relevant to teenagers today, from school bullying and exams to body-piercing. If you can't find something that interests you, you can even write for them!

www.spankmag.com

Teen Advice Online

Teen Advice Online (TAO) provides support for teenagers. A team of non-professionals, ages 13 and beyond, provide suggestions for your problems so you can get the answers to your questions, and offer the chance to network with other teens around the world.

www.teenadvice.org

Teenage Health Freak

This site, reputedly written by 15-year-old Pete Payne, covers all sorts of health and relationship issues that are of particular interest to teenagers with the help of his friendly doctor, Dr. Ann. You can link directly to Dr. Ann's virtual surgery, which seems to have exclusively teenage patients and provides down-to-earth advice on all sorts of teenage worries and complaints.

www.petepayne.com

Wicked Colors

This is a UK-based site (despite the spelling) covering everything from celebrity gossip and horoscopes to competitions and reviews. Primarily for girls.

www.wickedcolors.co.uk

THEATRE

If you're a fan of the theatre, use the internet to gen up on your favourite shows, check the cast lists, or order tickets, videos or soundtracks. See also *Entertainment, Films, Television, Video and DVD* and *Music*.

The Best of Andrew Lloyd Webber

If you're a fan of the musicals, here's a site for you. Operated by his Really Useful Company, these pages give details of Lloyd Webber's various productions old and new, available recordings and merchandise, and how to licence certain productions if you want to put them on locally. For the real enthusiasts among you, try out the online quiz.

www.reallyuseful.com

National Theatre Online

Britain's National Theatre is online, with a stylish site featuring details of forthcoming productions and events, education programmes, and a history of the theatre itself. You can book tickets online (although not for the first three weeks that they are available) and subscribe to the site for regular updates.

www.nt-online.org

Official London Theatre guide

Plan your trips to see shows in London's West End using this site. You can search by type of performance or by what is new. The site gives descriptions of the shows, including details of how long they last. The only thing you cannot do through the site is book the tickets (see *Entertainment*). However, all the phone numbers you may need are listed here for your use.

www.officiallondontheatre.co.uk

On Broadway

This is a site dedicated to the shows, musicals and history of the Great White Way. Visit Jogle's Broadway page to find listings information for on and off-Broadway shows. As well as all this, you will find a useful cabaret hotline, plus a list of Tony award winners and theatre links to give you further information.

www.on-broadway.com

Playbill Online

The magazine for theatre-goers, *Playbill*, is now available online. On the site you will find all the listings for US and international performances, with lots of industry news, events, feature articles and the chance to purchase tickets for London shows. Also available here is the Playbill Online Club. Playbill Online is dedicated to bringing club members the opportunity to receive discount ticket offers, as well as travel and dining discounts and advantages.

www1.playbill.com/playbill

Royal Shakespeare Company

This is a brilliant site detailing the work of the RSC, including information on performances, productions and booking.

www.rsc.org.uk

Showbizwire

Visit this site for the latest showbiz news and all film, theatre, television, music and video productions. Showbizwire claims to get its information from around 50 major sources.

www.showbizwire.com

Virtual Library Theatre and Drama

On this site you will find links to resources in more than 50 countries for professionals, amateurs, academics and students of all ages to do with theatre and drama. The site and its links are updated daily.

www.vl-theatre.com

UK Theatre Web

This site covers everything from amateur productions to dance, opera and even performances signed for the deaf. It has links to ticket sites and an open discussion forum for all topics theatre-related. Its

Greenroom section has all the gossip plus celebrity birth and death info for every day of the year.

www.uktw.co.uk

What's On Stage

This site covers venues around the UK, from the West End to small local theatres. As well as listing what's on, it provides reviews, recommendations and details of openings and closings. It also features a good list of links to other theatre sites.

www.whatsonstage.com

TOYS AND PLAY

If you're looking for toys to keep the kids amused, or play equipment for your pre-school group, check out these sites. See also *Children*. For computer-based games, see *Games and Gaming*.

Dominoes

This Leicester-based toy retailer has a wide selection of toys and games on offer from its online shop. It specialises in traditional toys and items not stocked by the main retailers, but also has the latest dolls, as well as collectibles, art materials and play equipment. Delivery takes three to ten days.

www.dominoes-highstreet.co.uk

Early Learning Centre

The direct-sale point for the well-known UK high street chain selling educational toys is a great site with a good search engine that allows you to find specific items or a general range.

www.earlylearningcentre.co.uk

Hamleys

The online site of the well-known toy store in London's Regent Street. You can buy a huge range of toys and collectibles to be delivered to your home.

www.hamleys.co.uk

Hasbro

This famous toy-maker has a lively site that includes an online shop stocking all its products. You can also ask questions about any of their products, and get advice on what is suitable for what age. The Daily Smile section has a selection of articles and special features especially for parents and kids, including the latest ideas for themed parties, ways to play and places to go to, plus seasonal features providing recipes, things to make and competitions.

www.hasbro.co.uk

The Hill Toy Company

This company specialises in 'traditional' toys and games, including wooden blocks, dolls houses and dressing up gear, but also offers a wide range of other types of toys, all fully illustrated and described on their pages. Prices are competitive and you can order online for delivery within 10 days at a fixed p&p fee of £4.95.

www.hilltoy.co.uk

House of Toys

If you're interested in old toys, tin soldiers and the like, visit this site. It not only offers old toys for sale, but also includes a history of various toys and toy manufacturers, tin toy art, books and magazines on toys and links to other toy and collectibles sites. If you have a question related to old toys, you can ask Mr Bighead.

www.houseoftoys.com

Playbug

This site is aimed at the younger child – up to age six – and includes mostly educational toys and those that are suitable for playing in groups. It is a well designed site with a good range of products that you can sort by age, price or type: you can order online and delivery costs just £3.75 within the UK, or is free if your order exceeds £75.

www.playbug.com

Puzzles and Toys

This simple, clearly laid out site offers a wide selection of traditional and modern jigsaw puzzles and educational games, all made from top quality non-toxic EVA foam, a material both durable and safe for children of all ages. You can order all goods online.

www.server2puzzlesandtoys.com

Toys R Us

This site is the online equivalent of the superstores where Geoffrey the Giraffe reigns supreme. You can order all their product lines here, from toys and games to computers, babywear and even pushchairs.

www.toyrus.co.uk

Toy Town

This site is part of the massive Shoppers Universe, based in Manchester. It groups toys into categories according to the age, ability or sex of the child and you can also arrange them by price. Each is fully described and most can be delivered world-wide. There isn't a huge selection in some categories but those that are on offer are the current chart-toppers, so if your local store has run out of that must-have favourite before Christmas, this is worth a try.

www.toytown.co.uk

TRAVEL AND HOLIDAYS

Wherever you want to go, you can find out about it on the web, and often also find a good deal on how to get there and where to stay. The sites below include tour operators, travel offer sites, and useful guides. You might also find useful information under *Entertainment, Geography* and *Museums, Galleries and Historical Sites*.

1001 Villa Holiday Lets

This site is well organised and easy to use as you can search for villas and apartments around the world by the use of keywords or by location. Each listing includes plenty of information and a number of colour photos to help you make your choice. To save time at the site, you can also request the adverts by e-mail.

www.1001-villa-holidaylets.com

A2b Travel

Here you will find everything you need to know about travelling into, around and out of the UK. This comprehensive online travel resource includes flight booking, flight arrival and departure times, a huge hotel finder, car-hire details, traffic reports, plus bus, ferry and train timetables. There are also lots of travel tips to help you on your way.

www.a2btravel.com

Airport guide

With maps, directions and full details of all the airports in the UK, this is a highly valuable site for the regular traveller or holidaymaker. Add it to your Favourites!

www.a2bairports.com

Airport Rental Cars in the US

Do you want to travel in the USA? If so, you will find that this site will steer you in the right direction as it has an interactive guide that enables you to find the best rental rates. Over 90 major airport auto rental companies and franchises at over 100 airports are listed here. Even if you are not going to the States, the tips are relevant for car rental anywhere in the world.

www.bnm.com

Air Tickets Direct

This 24-hour travel agent offers bookable discounted air fares online, with a good search facility.

www.airtickets.co.uk

Association of British Travel Agents

'Look before you book' at possibly the best index of UK travel sites you can find – and it gives information on reputable agents only! This site includes a full listing of ABTA members.

www.abtanet.com

British Foreign Office Travel Advice

The consular division of the Foreign and Commonwealth Office produces a range of material intended to advise and inform British citizens travelling abroad. This includes advice to help British travellers avoid trouble, especially threats to their personal safety arising from political unrest, lawlessness, violence, natural disasters, epidemics, anti-British demonstrations and aircraft safety. Get access to the full range of travel advice notices, and a selection of consular information material. In certain circumstances the site may recommend that you contact the local consul.

www.fco.gov.uk

Cats' Eyes Europe

Through this site tickets can be booked for events and exhibitions throughout Europe, along with rooms and flights. A mailing list service is also available.

www.thecatseyes.com

Chester-le-Track

If you are thinking of making a journey by rail, check this site out first. It gives helpful information not only on train timetables but also on routes, ticket types, performance, the various train operating companies, the current political influences on rail travel, and so on. It claims to be the online equivalent of your local station – personally we think it's far better although we miss the bacon butties!

www.chester-le-track.co.uk

Dangerous Places

The travel guide with a difference! Fielding's Dangerous Places claims to take you to the areas that you simply would not come back from alive. Each country has a synopsis of why it is so dangerous to visit. The guide is also divided into topics such as forbidden places and criminal places to make it easier for you to see exactly where NOT to go on your next holiday.

www.comebackalive.com/df/index.htm

Driving in Europe

If during your holiday break or day trip you wish to hire a car to drive in Europe, then this site is just for you. Here you will be able to familiarise yourself with the wordless road signs you will encounter. As well as explaining signs, this site will also tell you about safe travel in Europe and information on the fines you would receive if you were to break the law.

www.travlang.com/signs

Ebookers

The aim of this site is to be Europe's best travel portal and preferred travel retailer on the web. There's lots here to explore and purchase 24 hours a day, seven days a week, including two million discounted flights to destinations throughout the world on over 75 airlines, world-wide hotel booking, car hire and travel insurance, package holidays, special-interest destinations and lots more.

www.ebookers.com

easyJet

This flight operator has been very successful offering no-frills, good-value flights. If you access its web site, you can find news and information on all its services and you can also buy tickets online.

www.easyjet.com

English Tourist Board

The gateway to the Visit Britain site, which covers England, Scotland, Wales and Northern Ireland, this site offers views of England and general travel and tourism information.

www.travelengland.org.uk

European Tourist Information Centre

A comprehensive travel database containing just about everything you will need to know. You will find that in addition to country-specific sections, there are general links to sites providing accommodation, rail, underground, airline, weather, currency, language, electricity, telephone, TV and map information.

www.iol.ie/~discover/europe.htm

Eurotrip

This comprehensive site contains everything you need to know about backpacking your way around Europe. It has useful links, advice and gives tips on cost-effective travel.

www.eurotrip.com

Flyer information

If you are a frequent flyer, you may be interested in the travel listings, events, features and weather information on this site.

www.flyer.co.uk

Fodor's Travel Online

This incredibly large travel resource from the established guide book company includes comprehensive, customised hotel and restaurant searches, online phrase books, a guide to sports and adventure holidays, as well as region-specific notice boards. However, the highlight of this site is the customised mini-guide facility where you specify your holiday preferences, and it creates an appropriate guide.

www.fodors.com

Foreign Languages for Travellers

This very useful site enables you to read and listen to handy phrases in over 70 different languages. It also translates between any two languages and not just English. For convenience, the languages have been alphabetically organised. Simply select the language you speak and then select the language you want to learn.

www.travlang.com/languages

Great Outdoor Recreation Pages

Primarily for US travellers, this site that 'offers the freshest and most unique travel destinations and inspires viewer participation in everything from an afternoon hike to a week-long biking adventure. GORP visitors recount their own experiences and share information through a sophisticated menu of online forums, contests, discussions and cross-marketing initiatives'.

www.gorp.com

The Guide

This site is an online guide to a few of the major cities in England and Wales. It is very easy to use and contains good graphics. Most importantly, though, the guide is updated regularly with the latest information. Currently the cities covered are Bath, Bournemouth, Brighton, Bristol, Cambridge, Canterbury, Cardiff, Carlisle, Chester, Edinburgh, Harrogate, Kendal, London, Newcastle, Nottingham, Oxford, Plymouth, Stratford, Windsor and York. The guide points out all the places to eat, sleep, shop and visit. Worthwhile if you are planning a holiday or even a day trip to any of these places.

www.theguide-uk.com

HolidayDeals

Exactly that! Bargain holidays and cheap flights, especially for last-minute holidays.

www.holidaydeal.co.uk

Holiday Rentals

This online brochure is UK-based but has over 3,500 private homes to rent in over 42 countries around the world. You can browse the site by country, for listings with colour photos and prices. There are also special sections for ski chalets and golf properties. You can check availability online, but reservations must currently be made directly with the owners.

www.holiday-rentals.co.uk

Holiday Tales

This travel library collates individual stories of people's trips. If you do not want to rely solely on the guide books and brochures, get a more personal description of a trip here and relive the experiences of others. The trips are organised by continent, then by country.

www.travel-library.com

Hostelling International

With 4,500 hostels in more than 60 countries, Hostelling International helps provide cheap, practical accommodation for budget travellers around the world. Look up the addresses and telephone numbers of hostels here and find out more by clicking through to their individual web sites.

www.iyhf.org

Irish Tourist Board

The official web site to tell you everything you need to know about a holiday in Ireland, from views to information on how to get there, hotels and an interactive route finder.

www.irlenad.travel.ie/home

Leisure and Living Caravanning

Here you can find listings of park home estates, caravan sites, caravan holiday homes, manufacturers of caravans, caravan dealers, resorts, caravanning supplies and services and much more.

www.martex.co.uk/leisure-and-living

LeisureHunt

Leisurehunt is a world-wide accommodation search that lets you select the type of establishment you require. It includes hostels, campsites and B&Bs as well as hotels, and you can select your preferred price range and facilities. Once you have found a place to stay you can make your reservation online.

www.leisurehunt.com

LondonTown

The official web site for London, this offers you maps, lists of events, a directory of places to go, and information on pubs, restaurants and accommodation. Request an Essential London e-mail guide and find out all the latest to maximise your visit.

www.londontown.com

Lonely Planet

Lonely Planet publishes some of the world's best guide books for independent travellers. Their books are known world-wide for reliable, insightful travel information, maps, photos and background historical and cultural information. On their site they have every continent covered with an ever-increasing list of travel guides, atlases, phrase books and travel literature. Everything that is listed in their guidebooks is here for you to view on the web site and there are even hints and tips from other travellers. The important section on healthy travelling includes all you need to know about 'pills, ills and bellyaches'.

www.lonelyplanet.com

Maiden Voyages

More than ever, intrepid women travellers are circling the globe and this site has been written by women travellers to give practical advice and stories of interest to fellow women travellers. If you do not want to go it alone and you need a partner to share expenses and help you enjoy the view, you can post your request here too.

www.maiden-voyages.com

Paris

This site is 'a collection of everything regarding the City of Light'. Go on a virtual tour of Paris and see the sights.

www.paris.org

Paris Anglophone

Parisians have long endured a reputation for being rude and unwelcoming to English speakers. As a method of rectification, the Paris Anglophone has been set up to enable you to plan all that you need to do before you leave for the city. It is an all-in English guide that covers everything from what to do on a weekend break to renting an apartment on a short-term lease, to relocation. The site also lists thousands of English-friendly businesses.

www.paris-anglo.com

Planet Rider

Having read, rated and reviewed thousands of sites, and keeping only the most informative and useful ones to create this unique system, Planet Rider allows you to make your travel decisions quickly and effectively. A lot of countries are covered here, so you are bound to find something to suit you. Go on some of the 10-minute vacations, compact tours of the world's most popular destinations which contain lots of relevant links.

www.planetrider.com

RailWatch

Rail Watch is a non-profit American organisation which is supported by local officials, victims of railroad accidents, other concerned citizens and shippers from around the country. It is dedicated to educating the public about rail safety issues and to holding the nation's railroads accountable for their actions.

www.railwatch.org/home.htm

Scottish Tourist Board

The official site of the Scottish Tourist Board, containing all kinds of information related to holidays in Scotland, from accommodation to travel and details of the regions.

www.visitscotland.com

Signpost Premier Hotel Guide

Signpost publishes an annual directory of premier hotels in the UK, with full information on location, services and quality levels. This is their online service where you can find out about all the very best hotels in the UK, whether for business or pleasure.

www.signpost.co.uk

Small Luxury Hotels of the World

This site is aimed at millionaires who can afford to pay hotel bills that resemble an average monthly mortgage repayment! If you want to see how the other half lives, search through the top-class luxury hotels on offer here, either by exotic location or by holiday theme. For dreamers and lottery winners.

www.slh.com/slh

The Subway Page

At this site you can download maps of the subway systems in use in many major cities in the world. The site also contains links to many subway information sites around the world. A particularly useful part of the site is the city and area transit guides.

www.reed.edu/~reyn/transport.html

Theme Parks

These sites have information on theme parks and thrill rides throughout the world.

www.thrillride.com

www.screamscape.com

Timeshare

Timeshare properties can either be a good investment or a risky one. The Timeshare Users Group (TUG) provides some advice to prospective buyers and current owners. The site rates timeshares, runs a chat room and provides a forum to buy and sell timeshare accommodation.

www.tug2.net

Travel Companies and Agents

There are many different travel companies offering a vast array of holidays. Like the companies themselves, the respective web sites seem to offer a huge range of facilities. Some only offer holiday details or information and do not have online booking facilities, while other sites offer a complete service that enables you to spot bargains and snap them up. Here is a list of some of the reputable travel companies that you can find on the net.

www.airtours.co.uk

www.bathtravel.com

www.firstchoice.co.uk

www.kuoni.co.uk

www.lunnpoly.com

www.sunsail.com

www.thomascook.co.uk

www.thomson-holidays.com

www.trailfinders.co.uk

TravelSelect

From this easy-to-use site, you can book airline flights, rental cars, Eurostar and hotels with a bonded travel agent.

www.travelselect.com

UCL Hospital for Tropical Diseases

For information on the in-patient and out-patient services offered by the tropical diseases specialists at UCL, look up this site. You will also find that the consultants offer both pre-travel and post-travel advice.

www.uclh.org/services/htd/advice.shtml

US Travel Warnings

Travel warnings are issued when the State Department decides, based on all relevant information, to recommend that Americans avoid travel to a certain country. It is essential that you check out a potential hot-spot before you visit it and this is one of the best places to carry out your research. However, it is still advisable then to seek a second opinion (from the British Foreign Office Travel Advice site, for example, see page 414) before you decide whether or not to go on your travels.

travel.state.gov/travel_warnings.html

Virtual Tour of Jerusalem

Tour through the old city of Jerusalem and see the holy sites, visit the gates and take a look at the Chagall windows.

www.md.huji.ac.il/vjt

The Virtual Tourist

This site contains thousands of links grouped together by geography and category and quality rated by tourists. One of the biggest travel-related directories in the web, you find services such as online booking of flights/hotels/cars, currency converters and time zones, driving directions service, dictionaries/languages, weather data and more.

www.vtourist.com

Walt Disney World

For anything to do with Walt Disney World in Florida, visit these sites.

www.wdwinfo.com

www.wdwinfo.co.uk

Welsh Tourist Board

The official site of the Welsh Tourist Board, providing information on Wales with scenic tours and all kinds of holidays.

www.tourism.wales.gov.uk

World Executive Hotel Directory

Aimed at the business traveller, this site provides a guide to luxury hotels around the world together with news of available discounts. In addition, it includes information on tipping and dress codes, as well as invaluable guides to getting from the airport to the centre of town.

www.worldexecutive.com/index.html

World of Holidays

With its own search facilities, this is a good place to find last-minute and other holiday deals.

www.worldof.net/holidays

WEATHER

BBC Weather Service

The BBC web site is huge and contains a lot of information, much more than material just related to their own TV programmes. The weather pages include both a UK and world weather forecast, as well as shipping forecasts and pollen forecasts.

www.bbc.co.uk/weather

Dan's Wild Weather Page

An interactive site for children, where they can learn all about all kinds of weather conditions. Created in the US, it does have an American bias but is interesting and educational nonetheless.

www.whnt.live.advance.net/kidwx/

Hurricane and Cyclone Names

Ever wondered how those storms we see on the news get their names? Find out here. It is part of a much larger site operated by the Tropical Prediction Centre in the US, which provides a huge amount of information on hurricanes, cyclones and other tropical storms.

www.nhc.noaa.gov/aboutnames.html

Online Weather.com

A site covering the UK and Ireland which aims to provide local weather forecasts, the twice-daily updates mean that you can rely on the information, although it is presented in a rather basic format.

www.onlineweather.com

El Niño Theme Page

El Niño means 'the little one' in Spanish and is a disruption of the ocean-atmosphere system in the tropical Pacific. It affects the weather all around the world, causing a marked increase in rainfall in the US and devastating bush fires in Australia. For an in-depth understanding of this phenomenon, look up this site.

www.pmel.noaa.gov/toga-tao/el-nino

The Met Office

This site predictably covers every aspect of meteorology for those looking for information and forecasts.

www.meto.govt.uk

The Very Useful UK Weather Page

This concise site contains links to other weather sites that provide coverage of the UK. It is particularly targeted at those who participate in outdoor activities, so they can check the weather prospects before proceeding, but it is a useful reference for anyone needing to know weather conditions, tide times or even avalanche prospects before taking a trip.

www.uk-weather.co.uk

Weather Photography

This site features some stunning pictures of all kinds of weather, and tips on how to photograph such phenomena yourself. The images were all taken by Dutch photographer Harald Edens, and are updated regularly: there is also a guest page where he displays the best photos sent to him by other weather photographers. If you particularly like any of his own pictures, you can buy them online.

www.weather-photography.com

Weathervine

Ever wanted to chase a storm? Well here's your chance. The Weathervine Storm Intercept team have put all their archived storm-chasing footage online for you to view from the comparative calm of your own home. There are also hundreds of links to other sites. Some of the information is a bit technical, but the footage is excellent.

www.weathervine.com

Weather.Com

At this site you can get a 10-day forecast for your local area, plus details of previous averages and records, and view the satellite weather map for the current conditions. There is a lot of other information here, but most of it is limited to coverage of the United States.

www.weather.com

Wild Weather

This site specialises in bringing you reports on the worst weather from around the world. Ideal for storm-chasers! It also offers wild weather clothing, a feature on 'meteorologist of the month' (usually American forecasters), and special features on previous weather events.

www.wildweather.com

WorldClimate

This site has been designed for anyone interested in the general historical weather patterns around the world. You will find a range of climate data in an easy-to-use form, with links to other similar sites. The site does not contain weather forecasts or reports. The data is also not suitable for professional or research use.

www.worldclimate.com

World Meteorological Organisation

This is the official site of the WMO, the United Nation's specialist agency on weather, water, climate and atmosphere. The site includes everything from weather prediction to air pollution research, climate change activities, ozone layer depletion studies and tropical storm forecasting. The site also catalogues all WMO publications and has links to other UN organisations.

www.wmo.ch

Yahooligans Weather

A great site for school projects or for anyone who wants to understand weather conditions but can't get to grips with the meteorologists' jargon. Here it is all explained simply and clearly.

www.yahooligans.com/Science_and_Nature/The_Earth/Weather

WEDDINGS AND MARRIAGE

Weddings seem to take an awful lot of planning and involve a lot of different purchases, so it's handy to know that there are sites that specialise in helping you to arrange things. Some of those below offer planning services, others have links to wedding resources of all kinds, while still others offer unusual or one-off wedding items. There are also some sites on marriage – mostly giving advice and guidance on how to make it work after that first big day. After all, as one of these sites puts it, 'A wedding is a day...a marriage is a lifetime.' For details of marriage ceremonies in faiths other than those included here, consult the sites listed under *Religion*.

2-in-2-1

This American site gives information on shaping and maintaining your marriage, as well as offering the usual wedding services. Its marriage clinic covers all sorts of marital problems and issues, and it also has links to many other marriage research sites.

www.2-in-2-1.com

Confetti

This internet service has been designed to make your wedding experience enjoyable and stress free by giving you all the information and advice you want, when you want it. It aims to meet the needs of everyone involved in the wedding and not just the bride and groom.

www.confetti.co.uk

Hindi Weddings

If you are invited to, or are participating in, a Hindi marriage ceremony, it is wise to know what to expect beforehand. This simple one-page guide will help.

www.lalwani.demon.co.uk/sonney/wedding.htm

Hitched

Another all-encompassing site, with sections for everyone involved and an enviable selection of suitable jokes and tips for speeches. It has links to hundreds of wedding and reception venues throughout the UK, plus a handy diary planner facility to make sure you get everything done on time. You can even buy stag and hen night 'accessories' in its online shop.

www.hitched.co.uk

Jewish Weddings

This simple text-only guide to Jewish weddings and marriage will tell you all you need to know. It is part of a huge site giving information on all aspects of Judaism, but has the most comprehensive guide to Jewish weddings that we could find.

www.jewish.org.pl/english/edu/JewFAQ/marriage.htm

Marriage Care

This site gives information on marriage in the UK, marriage preparation classes run by the Catholic church, and gives advice on how to maintain a healthy, happy marriage. You can download their marriage preparation guide, or find details of courses in your area at this site.

www.marriagecare.org.uk

Marriage Encounter

This service, offered by the Anglican church, helps married couples to get the most out of their marriage, their commitment to one another and learn to improve their relationship. It is open to all married couples, whatever their faith, and consists of a weekend learning break in which you can explore and share your feelings, hopes, joys, fears and disappointments while learning to improve communication and deepen your relationship. Apart from a registration fee of £10, there is no charge and accommodation and food are provided. It is not recommended as an alternative to counselling for couples with serious problems.

www.marriage-encounter.freeserve.co.uk

Register Office Weddings

If you don't want to marry in church, you can have your ceremony in the local register office. Use this site to locate the one closest to you, and find all the information you need on procedures including how to book, how much notice is required, how much it will cost, and so on. There is also a handy search facility allowing you to locate wedding services in your area, but this does not yet cover all areas of the UK.

www.registerofficeweddings.com

Web Wedding

If you want ideas for your wedding, this is the place to come and browse. It has an impressive database of over 10,000 wedding suppliers – for everything from the dress to the honeymoon – with some special offers and competitions as well. There are also links to online wedding stores.

www.webwedding.co.uk

Weddings Abroad

If you fancy getting away from it all for your wedding, rather than just for the honeymoon, visit this site. The company that runs it arranges in excess of 4,000 weddings each year for couples wishing to marry outside their country of residence, and boasts some of the most beautiful and exquisite places to marry in the world.

www.weddings-abroad.com

Weddingbells

This is the web site of the American magazine with the same name. It is published twice a year, with many of the articles being free for you to browse on the web site. Here you can find out information for the best man, parents of the bride and groom, guidance on stag and hen parties and lots more. Also available are lots of different speeches and information about the wedding ceremony.

www.weddingbells.com

Wedding Rings UK

This Birmingham-based company offers discounted handmade wedding rings in a range of styles and price ranges. You can purchase over the net, and if you don't know your size they will send you a gadget to tell you before despatching your order. All items are delivered by secure courier, usually within 72 hours.

www.wedding-ringsuk.com

Weddings and Brides UK

Weddings and Brides UK have pulled together all essential wedding information and put it into one place. You will even find out what the potential pitfalls are at this site. For example, is your wedding car reliable and is there a back-up available if your car breaks down? It also has details of products and services for weddings and honeymoons. This site is a must for anyone planning a wedding.

www.weddings-and-brides.co.uk

WeddingChannel.com

Weddings are often one of the most stressful, complex and expensive endeavours people undertake. Wedding Channel is aimed at helping both men and women through the process of planning a wedding and starting a new home. This is a comprehensive and useful wedding-related site.

www.weddingchannel.com

Wedding Guide UK

This site offers information and advice to anyone planning a wedding. It has a comprehensive product and service section, giving details of hen and stag activities, marquee hire and wedding insurance – right through to where you can buy all your bridal wear.

www.weddingguide.co.uk

WOMEN'S INTERESTS

It seems a little unfair to have a section for women without one for men! Most sites are, of course, suitable for anyone. But these offer information specifically for women, on everything from career advancement to childcare, sports to socialising. See also *Business and E-Business, Children, Employment and Careers* and *Parenting*.

Advancing Women

More of a 'webazine' for women filled with articles on the business, careers, the workplace, international women, personal finances and current affairs.

www.advancingwomen.com

Cabinet Office Women's Unit

Find out what the government is doing for women, and review statistics on women in the workplace, childcare, women's health and so on. You can download a selection of useful factsheets and read up on the latest initiatives.

www.womens-unit.gov.uk

Center for Reproductive Law and Policy

The CRLP is a 'non-profit legal and policy advocacy organisation dedicated to promoting women's reproductive rights'. The site, a review of these rights for women all around the world, is presented as a series of to-the-point statistics. It provides a valuable information resource on the status of women across the globe.

www.crlp.org

Emancipation of Women

For those studying women or the history of women's lib, this site (part of the Spartacus Schoolnet resource) gives lots of information, including biographies, key dates, strategies and influential groups.

www.spartacus.schoolnet.co.uk/resource.htm

E-Mum.com

This is a great site for any woman trying to juggle a career with a growing family. It has articles on health, childcare and other subjects of interest to the modern working mother and a number of forums on which you can exchange information and advertise items you no longer need.

www.e-mum.com

Everywoman

There are a number of sections in this site, including health, cooking, gardening, travel, finance and law, all designed to cater for the interests of women in the UK.

www.everywoman.co.uk

Femail

If this seems familiar, it's probably because it is advertised a lot on other sites. It is a women's online community site, offering information on everything from careers to shopping, plus the latest news.

www.femail.co.uk

The Feminist Majority

This massive resource is not militant. It avoids stridency and instead provides daily news, articles on women in sports and in the arts, information on breast cancer and violence against women. It contains links to a variety of feminist journals and an online feminist store. Included is information on a number of ongoing campaigns to end injustice to women around the world.

www.feminist.org

Handbag

This site is trying to offer the most useful place on the internet for British women. Handbag includes expert features, advice, questions and answers, combined with a multitude of online services edited and customised for women in the UK, as well as free web access, e-mail, news, information, interactivity and online shopping. Handbag has its own editors and a range of expert writers covering topics from arts and education to relationships and travel. Visitors can have their questions answered and take part in online discussions.

www.handbag.com

iVillage

A women's network which claims to be 'a place where women don't just read about how they can get the most out of life, but can help each other do it'. The site offers interactive tools, resident experts, feature articles and says it can answer any problem you're facing.

www.ivillage.com

National Federation of Women's Institutes

The Women's Institute (WI), reaching further into urban areas from its traditional rural roots, claims to be an organisation that is changing. Educational and physical-activity courses are now offered, and the WI campaigns on a number of national and international issues. However, you will still find plenty of references to home economics and crafts!

www.womens-institute.co.uk

New Woman

This fun-filled and informative magazine site for women is one of the best on the web. There are fashion pages that tell you about the latest bargains and give lots of practical tips, and pages on all aspects of beauty care, including a virtual beautician who can help you improve on the looks nature gave you!

www.newwomanonline.co.uk

Security for Women Travellers

This is a web page rather than a site, but contains such useful information for women travellers (particularly backpackers) that we couldn't leave it out. Find out what to take and where to avoid, how best to protect yourself and what to do if anything untoward happens. Part of a very informative site for all backpackers.

ease.com/~randyj/secure5.htm

Townswomen

The Townswomen's Guilds might sound a bit fuddy-duddy but they certainly are not – and they're very popular. They run thousands of groups across the country, co-ordinating all sorts of activities (not just jam-making!) and often canvass opinions from their membership on political issues. Find out more at this, their national site.

www.townswomen.org.uk

Walking Women

A site for women who like to walk! Not for the faint-hearted or stiletto-heeled, this organisation arranges hikes, trails and other group walks exclusively for women.

www.walkingwomen.com

Women–Networking.com

This site is from a professional internet company and it is a great resource for the everyday busy working woman. Here they try to help women sort out all the useless sites and replace them with sites that they need. The site is dedicated to helping busy working women get ahead and through the day in a practical way. Includes money and job advice, menus and shopping.

www.women–networking.com

Women's Aid

This federation exists to help women and children who suffer emotional, physical or sexual abuse in the home. Their site offers advice not only to sufferers but to those around them, including anyone who suspects that someone they know is undergoing abuse. It gives details of their refuges, appeals and initiatives and is a good source of general information on this most disturbing form of victimisation.

www.womensaid.org.uk

Women's Rugby

Fancy a sport that is distinctly unladylike? Mud, bruises and brute strength? Then try women's rugby, becoming more and more popular on the muddy fields of Britain today. Find out more at this site, which includes match reports and articles by some of the top female internationals.

www.scrum.com/women

Women's Sports Foundation

This organisation is dedicated to the promotion and enhancement of women's and girls' sport across the UK. It gives information on sports by region and has links to other sites promoting sport for women.

www.wsf.org.uk

Women's Wire

Whatever you want to do, you can probably do it here. Whether it is checking on your stocks and shares, decorating your home, looking for a job or starting a business, this American-based site can provide light-hearted articles and quizzes to help you. There are also resident experts ready and waiting to consult you about any aspect of your life.

www.womenswire.com

Glossary

The following terms are either used in this book, or are in common use in email or internet discussions. If you are unsure of other terms, try checking one of the online dictionaries listed in the section *Computers: Terminology and Problem-Solving*.

Access provider Another name for *internet service provider (ISP)*.

Account Your account with a service provider may comprise one or more e-mail addresses and other information that allows you to access the internet.

Acrobat This is a browser plug-in that allows you to read files written in PDF (portable data format), which often includes government and commercial documents. You can download the Acrobat Reader software free from www.adobe.com

ASDL Asynchronous Digital Subscriber Line: the technology used by some telephone companies for faster web access via a traditional phone line. Likely to be overtaken by *broadband* access.

Attachment A file that is sent with an email.

Bandwidth The speed of an internet connection via a modem, usually specified in kilobits per second (Kbps).

Banner An advertisement provided on a web page – usually graphical – that advertises another site or service. Banners usually contain *hyperlinks* to the site advertised; some change their content depending on what you have asked to look at.

Beta software The pre-release version of software, often provided free but without guarantees that it will work as described. Companies often release beta versions of a product to the public to gauge their reaction to various functions before making the final adjustments.

Bookmarks A browser function that allows you to store details of the pages on the web that you like and want to return to (some applications, including Internet Explorer, call these Favourites).

Boolean operators A set of qualifiers, such as AND, OR or NOT, used to restrict the results of a search performed by a search engine. See *Chapter 6* for more information.

Broadband A high-speed internet connection – often 10 or more times faster than a modem – which is now available from some cable operators. One advantage is that the service is always 'on' – no dialling in is required, and it does not tie up your phone line.

Browser The software that allows you to surf, or browse, the web. Examples include Microsoft's Internet Explorer and Netscape Navigator.

Bulletin board or BBS An internet 'meeting place', where you can post messages and read messages from others on a specific topic. Similar to a newsgroup but less interactive.

Cable modem The method used to access *broadband* services via a cable operator, in place of a traditional modem.

Channels Another term for various web services incorporated into web browsers, portals and search engines.

Chat room A facility that allows you to 'talk' (in typed words) with other internet users via a web site. You usually need to download certain software before you can use this facility, but there should be no extra charge. It is wise to monitor your children's use of chat rooms. See *Chapter 9: Protect yourself from internet problems*.

Click through The process of accessing one site from another via a hyperlink, often a banner advertisement.

Client A term sometimes used by 'techies' to describe software used by an internet user, such as a browser or e-mail package.

Compression Reducing the size of a file through the use of a zip or compression utility program. This helps to speed the file through the network, and makes it quicker to upload and download.

Cookie A text file used by web sites to keep a record of visitors. When you visit a site a cookie is stored on your hard drive so the site recognises you when you return, saving you the need to retype. The cookie also tells a site the names of the last few sites you visited and what type of browser you are using. It can result in unwanted email (*spam*). If it worries you, you can instruct your browser not to accept cookies. Check your manual for the procedure.

Corrupted file A file that has been damaged. Corruption may occur through splitting, virus attack, or incompatibility with software. There are some utilities on offer to fix corrupted files, but not all forms of corruption are fixable: it is usually best to request the file again.

Crash The name usually given to a software failure that results in one or more computers being shut down. If you use a computer, you are probably familiar with the signs: your keyboard or mouse no longer respond to commands, and the screen appears to be locked up. The same occurs with servers, and in most cases, it is caused by an overload of information on the system. Web servers often crash if they get an excessive amount of people trying to access them at once. Generally the only way to resolve a crash is to shut down the machine and restart it.

Cybercafé A public facility, usually a coffee shop or wine bar, where computers (usually PCs) are provided for anyone to access the internet. There is usually a small fee to cover costs, and you may need to book in advance, particularly for live netcasts of popular events.

Dial-up connection The most common way to connect to the internet, by linking from your modem via a standard phone line to a service provider's server.

Digital certificate A security device that allows two people to exchange email in a relatively secure manner and which is recognised as the legal equivalent of a written signature in many parts of the world. This function is not supported by all software, so consult your manual or online help for details.

Discussion group A facility by which users of a web site can send messages to a group of other users: the message is sent to the site and then distributed to anyone who has signed up for the discussion.

Domain name Another term for URL, the address of a web site (for example, www.webopedia.com).

Download The process of transferring a file (whether program, text, image, sound or video clip) from the internet to your own computer.

E-commerce The trading and promotion of goods and services on the internet: basically, commerce on the web.

E-mail Messages between internet users that are delivered electronically. They can include text, images, sound and video clips, and are usually read with software such as Outlook Express or Netscape Mail, although there are some web sites that will allow you to read mail. See *Chapter 7: Email* for more information.

Encryption The coding of a file or message to prevent interception by non-authorised persons. Encryption generally follows a cipher-style format, with both parties having the relevant decoding mechanism.

Electronic signature Personal details, usually in plain text form, which you can attach to your e-mail messages.

E-zine A term sometimes used for a magazine-style web site, which is updated regularly to include the latest news.

FAQ Frequently Asked Questions: a section often included on a web site to save the owners from having to repeatedly answer the same questions posed by its users.

Firewall A secure 'layer' around a company's intranet or other network that prevents unauthorised persons from outside the company, such as hackers, from gaining access to company information. It may also be used to prevent information from leaving the company's network from the inside.

Flaming The sending of rude or ill-considered messages to a newsgroup or within any e-mail message. See the section *Netiquette* in *Chapter 7: Email* for more information.

Flash Another browser plug-in, this time one that allows you to view animated graphics. Download it free from www.macromedia.com

Folder Sometimes called *mailbox*, and used to store messages outside the Inbox.

Forum/fora A discussion group, often technical, that is operated by a newsgroup, BBS or list. Members air their views on topics and questions submitted by other members of the forum.

Frame One or more panels, or panes, within a displayed web page. Sometimes individual panes can be scrolled separately, other times the borders of the frames are invisible.

Freeware Programs or other software that is made available by its owners free of charge, for anyone to use for as long as they like. Utility programs and graphics are often available as freeware on the internet.

FTP File Transfer Protocol: the method by which files are transported across and downloaded from the internet.

Gateway A server at the entry or exit point for a company or service provider. When an email message is routed from one country or company to another, it passes through several gateways, each of which analyses the address information and routes the message accordingly.

Gb/gigabyte A measurement of computer disk storage, roughly one billion bytes.

GIF Graphics Interchange Format: a format used for graphics files (pictures) on the web.

Global village The term often used to describe the effect of the internet, and electronic communication in general, on social and business communication. In effect, with the advent of free or cheap e-mail, you can talk to anyone as if they lived next door, rather than halfway around the world. Time zones permitting, of course.

Hacker A person who invades computer systems to obtain information, often of a personal or confidential nature. Some large companies employ 'professional' hackers to establish the security of their systems. Hackers are often responsible for the leaking of security information to the media, and usually operate from home using sophisticated telephony and computer equipment: they dial into systems and automatically generate user name and password information until they get the right combination and the system allows them access. For this reason, you should never use obvious passwords, such as your name, date of birth or address, or those of your partner or children. Use something like your favourite colour, that others are less able to find out.

Hit A term used to indicate an internet user's visit to a web site. Measuring the number of 'hits' tells the web site owner how many visitors their site has attracted.

Homepage The main page – or sometimes the only page – of a web site. The term is also used in some browsers to indicate the web page that you have identified as your 'home', that is, the page that you want to display when you first open the browser and whenever you select the 'Home' button.

HTML HyperText Mark-up Language. A system of codes that produces formatted text and graphics, which is used to generate documents for the internet and can be used to format email messages. Most email software now allows you to write messages in HTML without requiring any knowledge of the codes, but some email software on older systems is unable to display HTML and will show it only as plain text.

HTTP Hypertext transfer protocol: the standard methods used to transfer HTML documents across the web. URLs always start with the letters http; those with https indicate a *secure server*.

Hyperlink A highlighted word, phrase or image in an internet or e-mail document that, when clicked on, takes you directly to the document it references.

Internet The world-wide network of computers that you link into and 'surf' when you connect to the world-wide web. See *Chapter 1: A beginner's guide to the internet* for a fuller description of the internet and its various components.

Intranet An internet-like structure that is available only to certain users; usually within a company or other organisation. Items are accessed and stored as if they were on the internet, but the general public cannot gain access to them.

IRC Internet Relay Chat: software used for discussions in *chat rooms*.

ISDN Integrated Services Digital Network: a digital telephone line that provides faster-than-modem connection to the internet and can transfer large amounts of data quickly.

ISP Internet Service Provider: if you connect to the internet via a modem, this is the company that provides the link – it is their server that you dial to access the web.

Java/JavaScript These are programming languages that are used to produce documents and programs for the web.

JPG A file format often used for photographic images on the web.

Link A connection between web pages or parts of a web page. Full name is *hyperlink*.

Log in If working on an *intranet*, this refers to the point at which you have to supply your user name and password to connect to the network (login, without the space, often indicates the actual name or password you use). If working from home or a non-networked computer, it refers to the point at which you dial in to the ISP to connect to the internet or send and receive messages. It usually requires you to enter your user name or e-mail address and a password.

Log out or log off The point at which you end connection to the network; for an intranet, when you select the option to exit or disconnect; for a non-networked computer, when you select Disconnect to end the phone connection.

Mailing list Another name for a *discussion group*.

Mb/megabyte A measurement of computer disk storage, roughly one million bytes.

Meta-search engine A type of *search engine* that searches not only its own database, but those of other search engines to provide a greater scope of results.

Modem The device used to convert computer signals for transmission down a telephone line. See the section *Modems* in *Chapter 2: Getting connected* for more information on how this works.

MP3 A file format for digital music, used to transfer music files across the web.

Multimedia A term that describes integrated text, images, sound and video communications.

Net An abbreviated name for the internet.
Netcast A broadcast made over the internet: online TV, if you like. Often used for live broadcast of sporting and political events.

Netiquette A set of 'rules' for internet users, particularly participants in newsgroups or discussion lists, regarding acceptable conduct and message content. See the section *Netiquette* in *Chapter 7: E-mail* for details.

Newsgroup A forum for discussion among internet users on a particular topic. See *Chapter 8: Newsgroups* for more details.

Newsreader The software required to participate in Usenet newsgroups.

Nickname A name you specify when adding a person to your address book, which allows you to send mail to them simply by typing this name. This saves the need to remember all or part of an e-mail address.

Online/offline You are *online* while you are connected to the internet via a telephone connection; *offline* when the line is disconnected. If you have a large document to read from the internet, it is often sensible to *download* it so you can read it offline, to save telephone costs.

Online service provider/OSP A service provider that operates from an internet web site, allowing you to connect and send or receive mail from any internet-enabled computer; also used to describe web sites that offer multiple services including e-mail. MSN Hotmail is an example of the former; Yahoo of the latter.

PDF See *Acrobat*.

Plug-in A piece of software, usually supplied free from the manufacturer's web site, that allows you to view, listen to or read specific types of file.

POP A protocol used by, and giving its name to, a server that allows you to pick up your e-mail from any location using the web (for example, pop3 or APOP).

Portal A web site that offers services, for example, matching jobs to qualified experts or sellers to buyers. Revenue usually comes from advertising on the site: you should not be charged for an entry.

Posting A message, or the process of sending a message, to a newsgroup or discussion list.

Properties The settings used by your software, or the settings and characteristics of a message. The former are sometimes called Preferences or Options.

RAM Random access memory: the short-term memory store used by your computer to hold details of files and programs you are currently using. The more RAM you have, the more efficiently your computer will work – subject to the limitations of its processor, of course.

Rules Values you set that identify messages and perform a set task on them, such as redirecting messages to a particular folder or returning them to the sender. Sometimes called *Filters*.

Search engine A set of programs that allows you to search the web for information using specific keywords. For further details, see *Chapter 6: Searching for information*.

Secure message An e-mail message that has been encoded and encrypted, often with a digital certificate, to avoid interference from hackers.

Secure site A web site that has been protected to avoid interference from hackers. It is generally safe to submit credit card details etc. to a secure site, but not to an insecure site. Many browsers show a padlock symbol to indicate whether or not the site you are viewing is secure.

Server A computer on which files are stored or through which files and e-mail are transmitted. Your ISP operates a server for your incoming and outgoing mail, and one or more to host (store) web site pages and search engines. All your internet and e-mail activities are routed through a server.

Shareware Programs and products that are made available free on the basis of trust: once you have become familiar with them, you are required to pay to continue using them. Contrast with *freeware*.

Signature file See *Electronic signature*.

Sign on Another term for *log in*.

SMTP Simple Mail Transfer Protocol: the set of instructions your computer uses to send e-mail from your computer to your service provider's server. It is a standard method used across the internet.

Software A collection of programs, built from individual instructions that tell a computer how to perform tasks.

Spam Unwanted or junk email. Like most junk mail, you are left wondering how the sender got hold of your name. The answer, as shown above, is through cookies; some spam results from other sources, in much the same way as junk mail, fax or telephone calls, but this is generally less common.

SSL Secure Sockets Layer: a system of encrypting online payment details for added security.

Streaming When you listen to or watch a live broadcast over the internet, data is 'streamed' to your computer, allowing you to listen to it as it downloads, rather than having to wait for it all to arrive on your hard drive first.

Surfing Using the internet, or, to be exact, the world-wide web. It is called 'surfing' because it is supposed to be quick and effortless – anyone who has tried to learn to surf in the real world knows this is not always the case! It is another term for *browsing*.

TCP/IP The standard way in which computers 'talk' to each other across the internet – basically a common set of commands, language and interactions.

Threading Grouping messages by topic or conversation. This is often used when viewing newsgroups and other multi-user information, to sort the relevant from the irrelevant. See also the section *Netiquette* in *Chapter 7: E-mail*.

Upload The process of sending files from your computer to another on the internet. The most common form of upload is the sending of an e-mail message: you also upload when you update your own web site and make it available to others.

URL Uniform Resource Locator: the official name for an internet address. For example, the URL of Webopedia is www.webopedia.com.

Usenet A world-wide network of *newsgroups*.

Virus A destructive command or program that causes damage to the software on your computer, usually by changing or deleting files or causing commands to repeat indefinitely.

WAP Wireless Application Protocol. A technology that allows access to the internet from portable, non-wired equipment such as WAP telephones.

WAV A type of sound file (having the extension .WAV) that can be played on your computer.

Web host An organisation that stores and maintains web sites on its own servers, registers and sells domain names, and offers other internet-related services. If you run your own site from home, your ISP may be your web host; for more commercial sites a dedicated web hosting company is often used.

Webmail A term sometimes used to describe e-mail accounts provided by *online service providers* such as Hotmail, which are accessed via a web site rather than using dedicated e-mail software such as Outlook Express.

Webmaster The person responsible for the smooth running and updating of a web site. The address of the webmaster is usually shown at the foot of the page in case you need to contact them. Sometimes called a webspinner.

Web page One online page of a web site. The main web page is called the homepage.

Web ring A collection of related web pages or sites, often produced by several people or organisations, which link to each other and concern the same topic.

Web site A collection of web pages that provide information, usually regarding the person or company that owns the web site, and may allow online trading (e-commerce), enquiries, or other facilities.

Webspinner Another term for a *webmaster*.

World-wide web (www) The international network of computers providing information to others via the internet. It is called a web because each item, or page, generally provides links to other pages provided by other companies or individuals, and in theory, it should be possible to find almost any web site purely by following enough links (although of course it is quicker to use a search facility!).

Worm A particularly damaging type of *virus*.

Zip file See *compression*.

Index

Note: page numbers in **bold** indicate that the topic is described in the explanatory part of the book; all other entries are for web site listings.